IN GREED WE TRUST

Secrets of a Dead Billionaire

To Jon,

My dear Friend, fraternity brother, teammate, and statesman for the precious quality of life preserved in the Blackfoot Valley, all the best,

David Montgomery

IN GREED WE TRUST

Secrets of a Dead Billionaire

David R. Montague

Published by

Two Trout Press

Bonner, Montana

Two Trout Press
P.O. Box 903
Bonner, MT 59823

Published in December, 2007

First Printing
10 9 8 7 6 5 4 3 2 1

This book is a work of fiction.
Names, characters, places, institutions and incidents
are products of the author's imagination or are used fictitiously.
Any resemblance to actual locales, institutions
events, or persons, living or dead, is entirely coincidental.

Library of Congress Catalog Card Number: On file.
ISBN 978-0-9647787-1-9

Printed in the United States of America

This book is set in Adobe Garamond 11.5 pt
Book design by Marla Goodman
goodpeople@goodwerks.com

The book homepage and website is located at:
www.greedwetrust.com
The publisher website is located at:
www.twotrout.com
Both designed by Mary Silkwood Montague
email: mjmwebdesign@yahoo.com
or contact Two Trout Press

To Mary, who builds worlds without footprints

"'Gimme! Gimme!' cries the Nero in the bassinet."

—Thornton Wilder

Acknowledgments

I wish to thank the many pundits, political leaders, lobbyists, and business executives who have contributed ideas to this book. For a handful of you, these contributions required great personal sacrifice, and while you may have been sentenced to hard time, at least you will be allowed to serve it in penitentiaries reserved for civilized felons. I hope you will use your time to increase prison productivity, perhaps by making lawn ornaments in the wood shop or by teaching investment strategies to other felons.

In particular, I wish to thank the memory of Enron Corporation, its principals, and its many cheerleaders. Before the collapse, important magazines including *Fortune,* countless service clubs and fraternal organizations, and nearly every business school in America singled out Enron and its leaders as corporate icons and positive role models for future businesses. These modest lapses in judgment were later explained away on the grounds that those who emulated Enron were duped by a small handful of bad apples whose legacy died when the company died. However, the fact that Enron and its leaders were able to fool the nation's entire business infrastructure, the American public, plus thirty-six million energy consumers in California should tell us more about our infrastructure and ourselves than about Enron. And maybe it did because since Enron's demise, all the apples in the corporate barrel have been bright, crisp, clean, and wholesome as fruit in a Christmas stocking. Nevertheless, without the example of Enron this book would not have been conceived.

I would also like to thank "The Economy" and our billionaires and multimillionaires, that one-tenth of one percent of Americans who have worked so diligently over the past thirty years to create it, strengthen it, and ensure its ascendancy. The personal economies of us two hundred and twenty million middle class working Americans tend to stagnate. We live paycheck to paycheck and must finance purchases of everything from furniture to automobiles. Some of us, in order to keep body and soul together, forgo health insurance or apply for a second mortgage, a second job, another credit card, a winter fuel subsidy, a student loan, food stamps, or a new career at a call center for nine dollars per hour. This situation might cause widespread disillusionment if it weren't for "The Economy." I think I speak for all of us when I say that nothing lifts my spirits more, when I turn on public radio every morning, than to hear news that productivity is up, labor costs are down, inflation is in check, stock markets are booming, and "The Economy" is robust and expanding. In good times, when executive bonuses in finance light up the sky like supernovae and when corporate bottom lines flow into CEO's and investors' pockets like oil through a shiny new pipeline, we all drive to our jobs filled with pride and with confidence, and we work extra hard to contribute to the Gross Domestic Product. As a result, doctors write fewer prescriptions for antidepressants, and each of us sleeps more soundly at night knowing that God is in His heaven and all's right with "The Economy." Thanks, "The Economy," for being there. We hope you will still be there in 2027 when the last baby boomer retires and your margin calls flood in.

Those forces of nature that permit "The Economy" to exist and that shape its tone and textures also deserve special acknowledgment. These immutable laws of economics work like gravity and the speed of light, and when operating in a deregulated environment on a global stage, they are free to perform free market magic. In fact, they are greening the American economy by forcing us to discard socialist tendencies and to comply with the intelligent design inherent in nature's laws. Fierce competition, resulting in the survival of only the fittest players; rugged individualism; aggressiveness; the mechanism of supply and demand; enlightened monetary policy; laissez faire labor pools in countries liberated from age and wage regulations; the concentration of wealth in the hands of those most likely to make large investments for large returns; the imperative to growth; the leveling of international playing fields; the elevation of predation to a fine art; and the elimination of interference from governments, unions, ethics, empathy, and good taste; all these forces and more allow The Invisible Hand to write our future. I am confident that it is writing a script that will produce an America unlike anything we have ever known on this continent. In gratitude, I offer my hand to The Invisible Hand. We will not betray your trust. We will continue to vote for your candidates, report for work, shop, borrow, pay our taxes, and schedule our knee-replacement surgeries in Thailand.

Finally, I wish to thank my financial mentor, Scrooge McDuck. You still give us hope. Deep down inside, each of us two hundred and twenty million knows that if we just work a little harder, grab a little more, network with more enthusiasm, and learn the secrets to success hidden away in those motivational tapes, then some day we too will be able to backstroke through cubic acres of money, which is our only goal in life. You continue to represent that American Dream for the rest of us ducks who are not yet rich enough to swim, not yet poor enough to quack, but just comfortable enough to remain sitting.

Preface

How does a billionaire define the American Dream? How does his definition differ from your own? How did he get so rich? What does he think about democracy, labor, nature, society, law, or investors he has pleased – or fleeced? What makes him tick? What makes him different from you? Beliefs are imbedded in actions. To the extent that we have access to someone, we can observe him and infer at least some of his beliefs. However, wouldn't it be instructive, interesting, and maybe terrifying to eavesdrop? To learn first hand what Henry Ford or Louis the Fourteenth actually thought? If only we had a rich uncle who was candid.

Unfortunately not everyone has a rich uncle, and not every rich uncle will say exactly what he thinks. In that regard I am fortunate. I had a rich uncle and in his journals he was as honest as a sledge hammer. His name was C. Binal Running, advisor to presidents and Chief Executive Officer of Porcudyne, a major multinational corporation. He served on the boards of directors of numerous corporations, all of which are household names, spearheaded countless charitable commissions, and played golf all over the world with the rich, the famous, and the powerful. In his eyes, his life was the embodiment of The American Dream.

Chief, as we called him, retired in 1990 to his ranch in Montana, his compound in Jackson Hole, his ski lodge in Aspen, his winter home in Palm Springs, his city home on Central Park West, and his getaway vineyards in Tuscany. During his retirement, he kept journals that can only be described as straightforward. He planned to make them into a book. Initially, his plan was to finish a manual for the benefit of his grandchildren and a few other young people determined to succeed in business without being tried and convicted. His working title for the book was, *The CEO's Code of Conduct: A Dictionary of Advice to Inspire Young Executives.* However, the longer he wrote the more he believed that his book attained a broader perspective and would appeal to a wider audience. Just before his death, he expressed uncertainty about the title.

My Uncle Chief passed away on July 5, 2007. He left his fortune to foundations, charities, immediate family members, and The Society for the Preservation of Reputation. Since I was his only relative with any literary inclinations, he left me his journals, a small stipend, and instructions to assemble his manuscript, edit it, and see that it got published. As I studied his journals, I agreed with his judgment that his book might appeal to a broader audience than aspiring executives. It might even include the rest of humankind, which Chief called, variously, "ordinary people," "the masses," "consumers," and "the other ninety-nine-and-a-half percent." Having completed my assignment, I am now convinced that if you vote, like democracy, have children, enjoy nature, watch television, use a computer, own credit cards, consume anything, hope to open your own small business someday or otherwise improve your lot in life, or care about the future of America and the rest of the world, then you could benefit from reading Chief's book. To underscore its broad appeal, to keep it focused on Chief's vision, and to add a needed touch of subtlety, I changed the title to, *In Greed We Trust: Secrets of a Dead Billionaire.*

Each of the 365 entries in Chief's journals is short and topical, perhaps a reflection of his busy life. Some are simple definitions and some are miniature case studies. Many are insightful, inflammatory, or amusing, and all are highly personal, reflecting the strong opinions and private prejudices of one man. They are arranged in alphabetical order like entries in a dictionary. Taken together, they add up to his personal code of conduct, a code that he advocated for all others determined to succeed.

Chief's thoughts focus on what he knew best: Commerce. But they transcend business and reach out to include the historical, cultural, political, economic, anthropological, and philosophical assumptions that guided his life. He defines the world and America as he saw both, though what he wrote would not be suitable for anything requiring tact, such as a commencement address. He thought of his journals more as the revelation of his trade secrets, a kind of boot camp for billionaires, and let critics be damned. His vision is therefore blunt, uncompromising, and sometimes shocking. Near the end of his life Chief believed that his vision added up to wisdom and it is that wisdom that he instructed me to pass on. I have attempted to do so in this book.

Please remember that I am only the messenger.

Additional Acknowledgments

I wish to thank my wife, Mary Silkwood Montague, for enduring countless hours of listening as I read portions of the manuscript aloud to her. Instead of fleeing in terror or boredom, she offered love, support, patience, enthusiasm, sharp criticism, and brilliant suggestions. I also wish to thank Marla Goodman, who designed the covers and layout. Her enthusiasm, expertise, and energy transformed a lump of text into a living book with vibrant covers and a soul. Her lively communications and insightful suggestions about the content and design of the book were indispensable. Finally, I wish to thank a handful of clever friends for snips of wit so irresistible that I had to borrow them, and another handful of patient friends for reading and commenting upon selected entries. It takes a village to write a satire.

However, the village is blameless. I made final editorial decisions, and anyone who doesn't like them should not attempt to burn down the village. Likewise, if you want to throw tomatoes, you won't be able to throw them at Chief. His will required us to scatter his ashes over the Bureau of Engraving and Printing in Washington, D.C. That is where he currently resides, having trickled down out of the passenger door of his Lear and onto the grounds of our nation's currency factory.

If you want to throw tomatoes, you'll have to throw them at me. I prefer Romas. If you can find me.

—*David R. Montague,*
Somewhere in Montana

IN GREED WE TRUST

Secrets of a Dead Billionaire

Contents

Introduction

I begin with a disclaimer. Contrary to rumors circulating in the popular press, I am not now, nor will I be, a candidate for the office of President of The United States. The four or five hundred million dollars needed to acquire the job is not a problem. I could write a check for that. Three other problems will prevent my candidacy. First of all, I am dead, and I would not be physically able to occupy the White House. Second, the political party to which I belong has not yet been founded so I would lack an organized support network. Finally, no person in his or her right mind would want the job, let alone push for it, and I have always been in my right mind.

Nevertheless, I believe this book of opinions can guide voters to make the right decision about whom to vote for in any presidential election. Just read it, grasp it, and follow its precepts, and if you have the right stuff, chances are you too will one day be able to write a check for the office. If not, at least you will know who best represents your interests and the interests of our economy and you will therefore know for whom to vote.

That said let me tell you a little about myself and my book.

Win, lose, or draw, I always left the table with more in my pocket than I brought. How is that possible? To answer that question, you will have to read this book, but I will give you a hint. Years ago a club of international blackjack players bribed some Las Vegas dealers to show them how the house can always win when the house really wants to. As one dealer explained, "we understand the deck better than you do." If you are going to play the game, you need an edge, and you gain an edge by honing it, not by luck. So, when you play the game to win – and you always play to win – you play with a deck that you "understand" better than your competition. In other words, the real game is in the deck. Play is merely performance.

My name is C. Binal Running and I have more than you do. I have more because I always win. I also hold more honorary degrees from more prestigious universities than you can count. For eighteen years I served as founder, President, Chairman of the Board, and Chief Executive Officer of Running-Mach 4 Industries and for the next fifteen years, after a successful IPO and several mergers, I served as Chief Executive Officer of Porcudyne. In 1984 I took on the additional position of Chairman of the Board at Porcudyne. I have served on the boards of directors of nine Fortune 500 corporations; as a member of the President's Council of Economic Advisors during three administrations; and on the Board of Governors of the World Bank. I retired in 1990.

With retirement came reflection. I have two grandsons who will soon be entering college and choosing their careers. It occurred to me that I might have gained a little wisdom during my own career that I could pass on to them to help them make their way in the world, so I started writing this book. The more I wrote the more I realized that hundreds of other young men and women could benefit by reading it, by using it as a reference, and by following its implicit philosophy.

America is a nation made great by those who are not afraid to compete. There is not much room at the top. Thus, the struggle itself to get to the top, the drive to win, counts for something, and this book is designed to assist those who are willing to try. However, it is dedicated to those few rugged individuals who will not only try, but will succeed: To the future CEOs of America.

There is no fast track to becoming the CEO of a large, multinational corporation. However, some tracks are better made for speed than others.

For example, if you can trace your family ancestry back to the sixteenth century and your family owns several residences, at least one of which you can refer to as a compound; if your family tree is populated by CEOs, a smattering of ambassadors, a federal judge or two, plus at least one presidential or vice-presidential candidate or a senator; or if your family is newly rich but filthy rich, then you will have more speed than most, and the principles revealed in this guide will be familiar to you. You are already wired. You already attend or have attended the nation's finest prep schools and private colleges. You are already lined up for Harvard Law or its Graduate School of Business or to their equivalents at Stanford or Yale or at one of a handful of other exceptional, private institutions. Your successful participation in the American Dream is assured and all that other people can do is congratulate you, envy you, and hope to gain your acquaintance as an ally.

Everyone else who aspires to the highest level of wealth, status, and power must learn to follow the advice presented in this guide. This advice is the distillation of centuries of experience refined, in recent American history, to an essence. It is also your key to transforming The American Dream into your personal American reality.

Best of luck to you.

— *C. Binal Running*
Aspen, Colorado, July 6, 2007

THE ABAKUS EFFECT During his shortened career, lobbyist

Sly Abakus probably passed more legislation through Congress than Senator Robert Byrd of West Virginia, who first won election to the Senate during the Hayes Administration.

How did he do it? Sly did it the old fashioned way. He bribed people. But that doesn't begin to fairly describe his generosity. Sly stood tall for patriotism, morality, religion, sports, families, and chocolate éclairs. At the same time, he helped out unappreciated lawmakers and overworked government officials with four star meals, football games, golf trips to Scotland, indentured garment girls in Saipan, and cases of fresh green lettuce. Clients respected him so much that they often overpaid him for services rendered, services almost rendered, and services that might some day be rendered, and he was always willing to share this bounty with others who promised to render services his way. He also gained fame for mastering the use of the virtual wire transfer and for founding several beautification projects, including a philanthropic charity that provided cheap collagen injections for ugly thin-lipped homeless girls littering public streets of The Golden Triangle[1] where he spent his youth. In recognition of his particular brand of humanity and generosity, both of his friends gave Abakus the affectionate nickname, "The Prince," and they called his company, "The Family."

---

1 For those whose geography is shaky, The Golden Triangle is a poor region of northern Thailand, eastern Myanmar (Burma), and western Laos near the Mekong River, where a lot of opium is traditionally grown. The other Golden Triangle is in California, composed of Beverly Hills, Holmby Hills, and Bel-Air, where a lot of products made from opium are traditionally consumed. Sly made his bones in the second Golden Triangle.

What bad things could ever happen to such an old fashioned prince and a family guy?

Sly got into trouble because he forgot the first law of the jungle. There is always a bigger predator than you, and if not bigger, a pack of smaller predators more tenacious than you. And they are both ready to eat you alive the first chance they get.

What happened? Abakus and his family of highly trained professionals became loose lipped, openly referring to some of their clients as "meanies," "diddle heads," and "prairie monkeys." Meanies, who are sensitive about their image, struck back demanding an investigation, and there was no stone this side of Pluto large enough for Abakus to hide under. The result was that Sly and The Family became the signature lunch that they were used to eating. Success had fattened them up until they felt impervious – and it made them taste like prime rib to the diners who carved them on a public platter. I call this phenomenon, "The Abakus Effect."

Learn from the mistakes of others. How far do you think your corporation would get if the whole world knew how you gained government contracts without having to bid on them, how you personally authored an amendment to a bill that congress passed, or what you really thought about a group of gentlemen you just fleeced? If you are going to succeed in business without really being tried, you need to think like Tuco in the film, *The Good, The Bad, and The Ugly*: "When you have to shoot, shoot, don't talk." That is, stick to business and keep quiet and you'll survive longer. If you need to crow, then let your wallet do the crowing for you. No one has to know how it got filled, who filled it, or why, and no one wants to know how good you feel about it.

Don't fall prey to The Abakus Effect. You can't spend smugness, and you'll lose even that when they send you to jail. Or in Sly's case, to six years of hard labor cleaning septic tanks on Indian reservations.

ACCESSIBILITY   Be accessible to people you need. Let others learn self-reliance.

ACCOUNTABILITY   Be accountable only to yourself. At the same time, build and maintain an image of broader accountability. Draw on your lowyers, accountants, and communications gurus to sustain a myth of accountability to regulators, stockholders, boards of directors, and the population at large. Like thick insulation, a good image will always protect you from the heat.

ACCOUNTING   Harry Potter has magic. We have accounting. Our principles of accounting should be able to accomplish no less than the wizardry of Hogwarts School.

First of all, pick an accounting firm that is a team player. Avoid firms that think of themselves as necessary adversaries. There is no such thing as a necessary adversary. That is a concept invented by regulators determined to put an end to free market commerce.

Once you have picked your firm and it understands your objectives, think of it as a team of magicians ready to concoct exactly the illusion you desire. Then turn them loose. Let them account, advise, and recommend. Sit back and relax. If they are competent, they will give your corporation the exact look you want and that look will carry the weight and authority of hard, factual numbers. Don't worry about corporations like WorldDom, Some Beam, and others who gave accounting a bad name by requiring their accountants to overstep the bounds of credibility. People forget. Plus, it is not difficult to appear credible. Just follow that ancient Greek principle of moderation and be content to let the bean counters play with pocket change. A few million here, a few million there properly stirred into the caldron of numbers will never raise an eyebrow let alone an investigation.

On the other hand, even an investigation of accounting practices may not be the end of the world. For example, under the leadership of Grits Haslips, whom most of us knew as Machinegun Grits, Some Beam was accused of inflating stated profits by a few million dollars before the company fell into bankruptcy. The SEC investigated Some Beam, and Machinegun had to leave town by sundown. But he left with a severance package also worth a few million dollars, a handful of Ferraris, and a small island. His severance package could have included a Swiss Alp or two and it probably should have, but all things considered, Machinegun Grits made it out of the woods in pretty good shape.

In some cases, however, investigations of accounting methods can mean the end of a world, not merely its reorganization. You are all familiar with Endrun, one of the nice guys, according to Sammie Schill, and you are familiar with Schill himself, the company's CEO during its peak and immanent collapse. Schill, a fraternity brother of founder Bucky Leize, is the fellow who impressed his peers and professors at the University of Granada's Graduate School of Business Mismanagement when he informed them during his first day of seminars that, "Hey, Bro's, I'm the smartest fucking gringo you'll ever meet." During darker days, when he tried to convince Russia that it was about to suffer an energy shortage, this same fellow suffered an episode on the streets of Moscow when he accused passersby of spying on him for the KGB. Clearly this was a paranoid moment. Everyone knows that Russian passersby now plot against foreigners only for the FSB. The episode looked even worse for Schill when one passerby reminded him that he was not even in Moscow, but Sacramento, though he woke up the next morning in New York where his chambermaid from Honduras spoke fluent Ukrainian and brandished a Twinkie wearing a tiny "Fighting Illini" sweatshirt. This sharpened his state of mind because he understood at once that the Twinkie was suffering from delusions of grandeur.

Instead of delusions, Schill dealt in miracles. His most original accounting miracle he called "horse to glue" accounting, a procedure that lists projected future profits as current profits in order to fortify his company's stock value. While this strategy is often sound practice when executed in moderation, it cannot help but draw unwanted attention to itself when it turns your company into mucilage and harms institutional investors who are the Wall Street equivalent of Kentucky Derby winners. Schill's flaw was not his shortage of genius. He was bright as a grow light. But he also thought his filament was invincible. This led him to believe that he was invincible. For a while invincibility worked to his advantage. However, I think he must have been adopted by sadistic parents because after he got to be head master at Endrun, he beat all of his charges with rolled-up stock certificates and turned *them* into orphans. Next thing you know, his light went out. Schill's lifeboat sank and he was committed to a federal prison for twenty-four years where he now plays Monopoly with himself and guards against sinister forces.

When pushed too far, accounting can do a lot for your enemies, so never demand from accounting more than it can deliver. Accounting is not demolition derby or martial arts cage fighting. It is a subtle art, like haiku, and it requires wit, not steroids. Accounting is our friend so treat it exactly as you would treat any other friend: Keep it focused on what it can do for you.

ACQUISITION   Acquire as much as you can as quickly as you can, both in your personal life and in your business life. Acquisitions measure a person's level of success in the world and they affirm a person's worth in the social hierarchy. Just be certain than you learn to exercise good taste so that you can impress a broader range of people, including specialists in the arts, entertainment, and academia. Nothing spellbinds an art historian more, for example, than a da Vinci or a Rubens. What could validate you more than the envy of experts?

In your professional life, business is acquisition, the acquisition of wealth in any form, including money, securities, precious metals, gemstones, real estate, art, important artifacts, commercial paper, manufacturing facilities, natural resources, other companies, and virtually anything else that other people want. The more you control, the greater your power to control more.

There are those who preach that the less you own the better, or that Americans have too much. Such people, like Ralph Nader, or admirers of Karl Marx, Henry David Thoreau, Saul Alinsky, Woody Guthrie, and Trappist monks, always have an axe to grind, and living without important possessions gives them the image they need to carry on their crusades. I would like to challenge such people to trade in their soapboxes or their crucifixes for spectacular homes filled with priceless possessions then see how long they continue to crusade. Idealism is no match for the real world. The desire to be right might give you a rush of dreams, but they are impossible dreams. In the real world, people don't want ideals; they want to be rich, and that is called, "The American Dream."

So acquire, acquire, and acquire more. Try to own more personal posses-sions than some small countries own. Massive possessions will demonstrate to anyone that you have exercised your wits and your guile more effectively than entire populations elsewhere; plus they make for great conversation with dinner guests. Live large and you will never have to feel small.

ADAPTATION   Years ago a friend of mine, CEO of a Fortune 500 company, introduced me to an older businessman from the West who had made a few million dollars all on his own. He had been raised during the Great Depression on a ranch. At an early age, he went to work as a laborer and gandydancer for the railroad and learned that he had to almost break his back every day to keep his job because so many desperate men were lined up ready to take it away from him. He tried to imagine that there had to be better, easier ways to make a living, including armed robbery. But before he committed any crimes, he joined a special faith, the religion of survival. This church preached only one doctrine and had only one com-mandment, a thought and a phrase as common to his generation as "Go for it!" is to ours. It was, "Root, hog, or die." Loose translation: "You'd better perform, Buddy, or you're history." It meant adapt or perish. Sink or swim. Do whatever you must to feed yourself and your family, and do it now, because no one is going to give you another chance. And if you can't do it now, go die and get out of the way because others are clamoring to fill your spot.

From that Depression era training ground, this businessman devel-oped an outlook. Resources were stretched thin. If another man had food, that meant to this man that he himself could go hungry. If another man had comfort, it meant that he himself could have pain. He learned quickly that *he* would have food and that *he* would have comfort, and to hell with everyone else. Let other people worry about themselves. Let *other* people go hungry and suffer, people less willing to do whatever had to be done. He assumed that he was locked in a life or death battle with every other human being on earth, and he trained himself to believe that he could win every battle. In other words, he adapted to his circumstances. And he continued to adapt. He sold furniture when furniture was hot and appliances when appliances were hot. He bought real estate contracts, sold jewelry, bought and sold land, and built apartment buildings. In short, this hog learned how to root.

Once over cocktails, he laughed and told me that he had been criticized because he was a ruthless and selfish son-of-a-bitch. Because he had no real friends. Because his wife and children and even his grandchildren hated him and tolerated him only because they hoped to find some reward in his will. He winked when he told me that, as if to say, "won't they be surprised! I managed to take care of myself. Let them fend for themselves." Here was a man with an eighth grade education worth thirty or forty million dollars who always smiled, who maintained perfect control over his business interests, and who loved the challenge of besting other men. When another man walked into the room you could see this fellow size him up and take his measure, probing for strengths and weaknesses. He was seventy years old when I met him, and just as determined as he was at eighteen that no man would take his place and no man would get the better of him.

He did not prosper because he was a genius, as he liked to think, or because he was blind lucky, as his detractors liked to think. He survived and prospered because he adapted, like a model of Darwinian Theory, and in doing so, this man made himself a survivor for his circumstances, one of the fittest of the fit. Men like that we call, "The best and the brightest."

If you wish to become a CEO of a major corporation, you must learn to adapt to your circumstances and to follow the religion of survival. My acquaintance keeps a bronze sculpture of a razorback pig on his desk as a reminder of the motto he learned from his circumstances. "Root, hog, or die" might not be a pretty phrase, but it is a motto worth remembering.

Of his childhood, he said: "It wasn't fun. It wasn't pretty. I don't even like to think about it. But every morning I go to my office like Caesar, to count my tribute, and I know that ninety-nine-and-a-half percent of the people in this world cannot do the same. *I* will have food. *I* will have comfort. *I* will provide. *I* will decide. Because *I* have mine – and to hell with you and to hell with everyone else." Then he invited me to sit in with his weekly poker group. "When you lose, I win, so let's play," he said.

All his poker pals called him "Number Won." And he did.

ADVERTISING   Have you ever drunk a glass of orange juice or watched a soap opera? Have you ever asked yourself why?

Albert Lasker told you to, that's why.

Who was Albert Lasker? He was an architect of the future. The principles he helped to found grew and developed until they influenced more people worldwide than those of Sigmund Freud, Albert Einstein, or Walt Disney, who succeeded because of Lasker. Albert Lasker invented modern advertising.

In the quaint old days before modern advertising, companies thought up boring slogans and printed them on labels. Maybe *Elmer's Elixir* healed gout, hemorrhoids, and consumption. Some progressive companies even bought an ad in a local newspaper now and then to discretely remind the public that they existed or to inform customers that new rakes were now available, fifty cents each. Some people probably even noticed these ads before they stuffed their newspaper between their walls for insulation or stacked it next to their fireplace to use for starter. Time and commerce ambled on.

Then came Lasker, who understood that advertising was not just information; it was salesmanship. Before long, the nation discovered that a small, limping, regional brewing company in Milwaukee put its beer into sterilized bottles. Almost overnight, this brewer vaulted into national prominence. Sure, consumers liked beer. But now they trusted this brand, and their descendents trusted it. Never mind that all breweries used sterilized bottles. Only Lasker and his client were clever enough to advertise the fact and do it first. Lasker had defined product appeal and reach.

Orange farmers were hurting because they couldn't sell enough of their fruit. They were actually cutting down their own trees to make room for other crops. Lasker had a better idea: What if people drank more juice? He sold America on orange juice and rescued growers, and we haven't been thirsty since. He invented mass recognition of product and mind share.

Household products are boring. And every sell job needs a hook to interest people. How do you hook America's housewives? How can you take them away from their humdrum routines long enough so they will listen to your pitch for laundry, hand, and hair soap? Lasker invented the soap opera. And when he did, he let a genie out of its bottle. What human factors most interest and therefore will most efficiently motivate consumers? Information? Rational choice? Obeying rules? Nice manners and friendly faces? Maybe the trials of ordinary women sacrificing all for their families. Maybe throw in an occasional undercurrent suggesting passion, jealousy, greed, envy, competition, power, submission, rage, pride, lust, romance, duplicity, revenge, bad behavior, and unbridled sexual desire. Lasker located the center of human motivation not in the cerebrum but in the gut and he opened the door to the visceral saturation and social engineering inherent today in all information technologies.

Advertising grew. Promotions targeted specific markets and specific demographics striving for name-recognition of brands and institutional trust in companies that stood for quality and value. Increasingly advertisements carried subliminal messages appealing to the viscera, and they worked. But these pioneering efforts gave us only a hint of the future. With the advent of television and later, the realization that television appealed most to children and to the maturation level of children in adults, advertising began to perform miracles.

Today, using the spearhead of television, which reaches everyone worth reaching and which has conditioned people since birth to welcome compelling visceral imagery, it is possible for one corporation to arouse an entire nation overnight and steer it like stampeding cattle toward exact promotional ends, again and again and again.

The most powerful people in America are not the President, the Chairman of the Joint Chiefs of Staff, the chairman of the Federal Reserve Board, or the hottest Hollywood director. They are good ad men and women backed by corporate budgets bigger than the gross domestic products of some nations. When you want to exercise real power, exercise them.

Consider one small example from one sector, the film industry. Once upon a time, a movie was a movie. A fanfare premier was staged. Reporters caught glimpses of stars and a fair number of people eventually watched the movie.

Today, the business plan of a media holding company requires a three-hundred million dollar extraction from consumers to meet projections for a particular quarter. A plan is unleashed. A script is approved. The latest *wunderkind* and diva are signed. The result? The film, yes, and coordinated around its release date: Children's toys, coloring books, stuffed critters, glassware, a sweepstakes, clothing, towels, a board game, and a video game, all available from an international fast food chain, department store, or box store; music tracks on tape, CD, and Internet, a director's cut DVD, and a novel based on the script; plus countless blogs, endorsements, reviews, interviews, and talk show appearances, all woven into a buzz blitz that blankets all known media from cereal box billboards to email chain letters.

In short, in the weeks before, during, and after release, every corner of America and most corners of the rest of the developed world will be besieged with a constant, horizontally and vertically integrated, unavoidable stream of advertising and products, and a huge percentage of the consuming public will respond, without a second thought, like lemmings. When the company collects its three hundred million and a little more, the campaign will slide into obscurity and residuals, and the company will launch the next campaign. What makes all this possible?

You flash flesh and jack up volume to hook your audience, and then spin your magic and blast consumers into the marketplace. That is, you sell.

Alexander the Great tried to conquer the world. He made a pretty good show, but it took him a decade. He also marched through hell and died young. Today, corporations conquer the world in days. A few thousand men and women are able to control, direct, and manipulate virtually every human being on this planet who has electricity and a disposable income, every quarter of every fiscal year, because they can tell people what to dream and then make that dream seem to come true. That is, they sell. We sell.

Unlike Alexander or Napoleon or the Caesars, we don't have to endure hardships, bad lodging, and corpses. We can conquer the world from the comfort of our suite of offices, our yacht, our place in the Hamptons, our bungalow in Malibu, or our Tudor in Boca Raton. Do you think you should commit to the power of advertising?

Is there really a Santa Claus? Yes, Virginia, advertising works.

AFFIRMATIVE ACTION   There is nothing affirmative about a law or a policy that requires you to hire a less capable person to do a job when a more capable person is available. Always hire the most capable person. If circumstances require you to do otherwise, then create meaningless positions with important titles to minimize the damage the incompetents you are forced to hire can do to your organization. Use them for window dressing. Most of them will move on out of boredom. In the unlikely event that one or two develop into truly capable workers, consider yourself lucky and give them meaningful work. If they genuinely fit in, welcome them into the corporate family. Merit is all that matters.

A couple of additional notes: During the last twenty years or so, I have witnessed a significant up tick in the number of African American MBAs. I conclude that African Americans are the fastest growing segment of true believers in The American Dream. They seem to want their pieces of the pie badly enough that record numbers of them are abandoning their traditional discontent in return for wholesale acceptance of the free market system. Ignored for two hundred and fifty years, just as it was in sports, academia, and the professions, this vast pool of talent will produce plenty of winners. Keep the doors open, as long as they demonstrate good taste in ties.

The same can be said for women. Increasing numbers of women are outperforming men in prep school, college, and graduate school, and more and more are opting for careers in corporate business. I assume this means that they have decided to emulate their brethren more than criticize them, and I welcome such women into our midst. They won't need to wear ties. A tasteful hint of cleavage will accomplish the same thing.

No business has time to nurture people. Individuals must nurture themselves to a high level of competency before they apply for a job. If they have succeeded, hire them without regard to irrelevant factors such as age, race, gender, ethnicity, or number of arms and legs. Then throw them into the water and see what happens. On the other hand, if they have failed to nurture themselves and they are incompetent, send them away so they can drown on someone else's time. If you are moved to do something truly affirmative, recommend the incompetents to your competition.

THE AFFLUENT SOCIETY   John Kenneth Galbraith's book, *The Affluent Society*, served as a Bible for liberal economists, when there still were liberal economists. In a nutshell, Galbraith believed that leaders should come from a class of highly educated cultural elite with an agenda to create a humane society and to distribute wealth broadly, people like the Kennedy clan, rather than from a class of highly successful financial elite content to create jobs, accumulate wealth, and let people choose rationally, with their consumer votes and their personal motivation, whatever kind of society they like. Thus, by "affluence," Galbraith meant something very different from what you and I mean.

Sooner or later, Galbraith's thoughts, like Keynes's demand side outlook, will be resurrected, as the societal pendulum swings.[2] When that happens, if it happens in your lifetime, keep this thought in mind. Galbraith has one overriding flaw. This patrician man from Harvard thought of himself as a man – even as a savior – of the people. He should have known better. There are no saviors. There are only survivors. Don't make the same mistake. Let those who are able save themselves. Affluence is not a blessing. It is something that you, along with everyone else, must learn to take for yourself. If you succeed, you rule and you survive. If you fail, you live as most people have always lived: You face a life of poverty, deprivation, misery, and premature death.

The only real salvation for humankind is personal motivation, principally the motivation to avoid misery, and you won't learn that from the liberal elite, unless, of course, you are one of the liberal elite, in which case you have already found salvation and you will be motivated to keep it. At that point, you might as well promote high culture, higher taxes, and the meaning of life, which should make you feel better about yourself and should also keep the other ninety-nine-and-a-half percent from starting a revolution and pillaging your compound on the Vineyard. Recognize, however, that your efforts will also keep those ordinary people from striv-

---

2 Thorstein Veblen's 1899 book, *The Theory of the Leisure Class*, might also be resurrected. I recommend that you read it now. And turn it on its head. That is, disregard the author's sociopathic hatred of wealth, his satire, and his implied value judgments. Treat the book as a sociological manual on how to govern. You will learn as much from it as you will from reading *The Prince*. And you will discover who invented the concept of, "conspicuous consumption."

ing and competing for real affluence. Why should they struggle to be rich when Harvard's finest is willing to pay their electric bills for them, plus throw in Shakespeare and Mozart for free?

Forget about putting a chicken in every pot. Worry about putting a Rolls in every garage that matters. Then, with what's left over, people who invest can build production scale chicken factories so when the other ninety-nine-and-a-half percent decide to fill their own pots investors who took all the risk can provide them with chickens and with jobs plucking the chickens. They can also take a nice cut of the action as a reward for a brilliant idea well executed. Isn't that what a real affluent society is all about?

AGGRESSION   Aggression is the gift evolution gave specifically to men. It is the engine that drives progress. It is the power that slams man against man in combat, in sport, and in business. It is the elixir that lifts an uncertain boy into confident manhood. I don't want to undersell the profound effects of environmental conditioning, but it is obvious that the main contributor to human aggression is testosterone. It provides the combative edge. And for this reason, I also believe that fewer women will ever rise through the ranks, though they are all welcome to take the challenge.[3] (Parenthetically, the roots of aggression might also explain the results of a recent study. It found that a disproportionate number of executives are tall and balding, and have pot bellies, heart trouble, hairy backs, and calloused knuckles.)

The bottom line is that business, like rugby, was invented by civilized men so that we could go at each other without reserve while staying within rules that prevent wholesale slaughter. It was a wise invention. It allowed us to lay down our axes and pick up our laptops and stay in the battle longer, until the last ounce of strength has been drained from us.

Know yourself. Understand the gifts you have been given. Let the power of aggression push you to the top of the feeding chain.

---

3 Women compete as hard as men only they use different weapons. For example, it has been argued that guile might some day outperform aggression. If so, then women might gain an edge, if not the upper hand.

ALCOHOL   Booze is one of the pitfalls of success. Learn to handle it and don't let it handle you. On the other hand, if you have ever done business with a Russian or a west Texan, you know that in order to stay eye to eye you'll have to slam down half a fifth of one hundred proof and still function with all your faculties on red alert. A skill like that takes practice.

When drinking socially, order the finest liquor straight, on the rocks, or tainted with only a minimum of mix, as in a dry Martini or a Manhattan. Stick to basics. Keep it simple and someone is sure to think that you are a connoisseur. Never order drinks that are pastel or decorated with fruit and umbrellas; they all require an explanation.

Use alcohol to communicate a message about yourself. For example, drink the way Hollywood expects heroic cowboys to drink and no one will doubt your innate virility. Or drink the way Hollywood expects James Bond to drink and no one will doubt your polish or your mastery of the situation. Alcohol is a tool. Keep it sharp; keep it handy; use it when you need it; and never treat it like a toy.

THE AMBASSADOR OF LICENSE   Bucky Lieze, founder of Endrun Corporation, was known by his friends and associates in finance as, "The Ambassador of License." He was one of the great pioneers in the License to Steal and Call It Service movement, and phobia against all regulation formed the foundation of his company just as it formed the foundation of the movement.

Mr. Lieze was born into modest circumstances in Alabama. His father was a mule salesman and deacon to a revival tent healer and evangelist for Jesus. Mr. Lieze became a self-made man. He was elected Exalted Archon of his fraternity at the University of Alabama at Ralph, and he went on to earn a doctorate in tongues from the University of Chattahoochee. After a few years of government service he formed Endrun.

Peers often speak most eloquently about a man's accomplishments. Here are some of the awards that his peers bestowed upon Bucky Lieze and Endrun before the company's untimely debacle.

Prior to its collapse, Endrun, by its own accounting, was one of the ten largest corporations in America. For six consecutive years, *Rich* magazine named Endrun "America's Most Amazing Company." It also named Endrun "The Best American Company to Work For."

Mr. Leize was one of America's highest paid executives. His annual salary topped forty million dollars and over the years, like any CEO worth mentioning, he was able to profit eight times more handsomely by executing back dated options, and by selling off company stock before it tanked while cleverly promoting its value to employees and investors. His accomplishments did not go unnoticed. His name appears across America, from the Wall of Greatness of the Alpha Ralph Chapter of Iota Nu Beta Fraternity, to the Texas Big Business Hall of Glory. Mayor Dingette Morewhite of Mega, Texas, Endrun's International Headquarters, proclaimed a Bucky Lieze Day. The University of Mega granted Mr. Leize an Honorary Doctor of Deep Thoughts Degree and the University of Alabama, Ralph gave him an Honorary Doctor of Ralph-Law Degree. He received the Revered Citizen Award from the Mega Big Wheel Club, the International Chief of the Year award from the Mega Fellowship for Children Club, and a You're a Saintly Mensch Award from the National Association of All the Descendants of Abraham Except Moslems. The prestigious Stanley Leland Business School Alumni Associations named Mr. Lieze the Mega Megamerchant of the Year. The University of Chattahoochee gave him their Exalted Alumnus Award. The University of Rock Springs College of Business and Administration named him winner of the James T. Kirk Master of the Galaxy Award. And the august and scholarly Secret Key Society honored him with its Meritorious Alumnus Award. He was given awards by the Horatio Hornblower Association of Distinguished Tuba Players, The Church Street Over the Transom Club, and the prestigious TVCEVWL (Texas Vigilance Committee to Exterminate Vampires, Werewolves, and Lowyers.) He received many more awards. Each award was a testimony to Mr. Lieze's ability, integrity, and success, as an example for others to emulate. At the same time, Business schools around the nation praised Endrun as a model for future corporations.

The Ambassador of License was universally recognized by the most trusted core of America's social infrastructure, including many organizations to which he contributed generously, as one hell of a guy to admire. This kind of loyalty is rarely conferred by members of any social group, let alone by our best and brightest. Even those cohesive groups that are bound by secret oaths almost never unanimously and publicly express this kind of unqualified admiration for one of their own. John Gotti, for example, never had it so good.

I'm not going to discuss the debacle. Mr. Lieze was a pioneer and his greatest contribution, even greater than his use of derivatives, his innovations in accounting, and his use of communications to stockholders and employees, was the stamp of approval he gave to deregulation through his efforts to promote The License to Steal and Call It Service movement. His torch will be carried forward by all of us who remember him and who recognize his contribution. And we are legion.

Here's to you, Bucky. May you rest in peace.

AMBITION   Without ambition, people prepare their own meals, daydream, have sex in the afternoon, play three hours a day with their children, write letters, turn over rocks to watch beetles, read novels, take long naps in hammocks, play musical instruments, sit around driftwood fires with friends to tell stories and sing songs, identify wild flowers, visit sick people in hospitals, poke anthills with sticks, watch wild birds, finger paint, waste weekends in museums, visit Hutterite colonies, spend a month in an ashram, donate to convents, make wooden flower boxes for windows, search for frogs in cattail marshes, grow asparagus, watch clouds, sleep in, visit graves of dead relatives, compose thoughts in diaries, photograph fascia on Victorian houses, lay on grass hot nights and watch stars, run through sprinklers, print 35mm film, collect colorful rocks, build snow gnomes, volunteer, make sand paintings then shovel them up before anyone sees them, stand in rain until drenched, write poetry, avoid confrontations, struggle to pay bills, and then die.

With ambition, people network, career, make money, gain celebrity, make more money, keep score, and then die.

The question is, do you merely want to be and disappear, or do you want to win and leave your name in lights before you vanish? Would you rather end up on your way to a nursing home with unpaid bills, hippy memories, and ragged underwear, or with more T-bonds than China and more toys than God? If you have any doubt, permit me to quote that famous professor of real estate sales, coach of the upwardly mobile, and philosopher of intimidation, Robert J. Ringer: "In business, love, and life in general, 'getting paid' is what it's all about."[4]

AMORALITY

AMORALITY   Unlike most human beings, corporations are amoral. They don't have a moral axe to grind and they are not answerable to any recognized moral authority, such as God. Corporations exist to generate capital in the form of profits, not to save souls, feed orphans, or forgive sinners. Given our Calvinistic Puritan origins, it is probably predictable that corporations flourished in America. We needed a refuge from the weight of moral obligations, some place where we could exercise the rest of our personalities. That refuge gives us life and saves us from self-doubt, self-criticism, self-analysis, and skepticism of all kinds. While moralists fuss and fret over what might be right and what might be wrong, we are free to jump in and build offices, power plants, call centers, assembly lines, strip malls, and nuclear warheads that take labor and return capital that people can use to survive, and we can do all that, *no questions asked*. With the possible exception of the separation of church and state, no division in America should remain stronger than the separation of morality from business.

ANIMAL RIGHTS

ANIMAL RIGHTS   Sooner or later, particularly if you are in pharmaceuticals, agribusiness, or cosmetics, you will encounter a small sector of the public devoted to animal rights. These people contend that animals should have the same rights as people.

Through all recorded history, only two groups have stood up and said, "We have rights," human beings and corporations. In other words, any group that is clever enough to claim rights is advanced enough to possess them. Since all other groups don't claim rights, they obviously don't know what rights are, and therefore, they have none. If you are going to assign rights to chickens, you might as well assign them to cockroaches,

---

4Robert J. Ringer, *Winning Through Intimidation*, Los Angeles Book Publishers Co., 1973, p. 233.

and if you assign them to cockroaches, then you might as well give them to rocks. Then you might as well just lock up the entire planet and throw away the key. On the other hand, if animals, plants, and minerals ever present us with a bill of rights, then we must recognize their rights. Until then, however, these groups are resources, and those of us who claim rights have the right to use them any way we see fit.

I conclude that this whole movement for animal rights is carried on by people who find it difficult to differentiate themselves from lower creatures. I do not share the same difficulty. And I wonder: If you cannot recognize or accept your own supremacy among animals, how will you ever learn to recognize or accept it among other people? Life is a race, not just between people, but also between species, and the winners take all. If I end up a mile ahead of you and three miles ahead of the nearest chicken, I guarantee that I'm not going to question the results of the race.

I am reminded of a story that a couple of friends of mine like to tell. Harry and Milo are CEOs and best buddies, and a few years ago they went fishing in Alaska. On their second day out, they encountered a hostile grizzly bear that charged them. As Milo dropped his rod and took off across the tundra, he shouted to his friend, Harry: "Oh, man, I hope we can outrun that bear!" As Harry sprinted past Milo, he replied over his shoulder, "I don't have to outrun that bear, Milo. I just have to outrun you!"

Equality is not literal. All it means is that every creature was born into the same world at the same starting line. The only thing that matters is how you finish.

ANNUAL STATEMENT   Each year, as you know, if you are a CEO, you will be required to produce a stately document attesting to the condition of your company. Ideally, it should be a statement of earnings with flair. It should portray the company both as a Rock of Gibraltar and as a Maserati, solid enough to outlast any economic assault, yet vibrant, stylish, aggressive, and *avant guard.* It should present you and your management team as the brightest and most successful, the most humane and down to earth, the most accomplished, prudent, responsible, caring, dedicated, yet most insightful, intuitive, and forward-thinking men and women on earth. It must show that the company is safe but never boring, as exciting as a fireworks display but never too hot to handle. Like the nightly news, your annual statement must inform and entertain, and it should broadcast the message that anyone interested in hitching his or her wagon to a star need look no further, for here, at last, is a company that will touch your heart, thrill your imagination, *and* fatten your wallet. And so, each year, as you plan your annual statement, as you reach out to touch the wallets, warm the hearts, and thrill the imaginations of investors everywhere, you will have to dig down deep into your soul and pull out equal parts of Andrew Lloyd Webber, Walt Disney, and P.T. Barnum. If you can pull that off, then your annual statement will pull the investors in like country kids to a carnival.

ARBITRAGE   The daring rescue of a damsel in distress so that you can have your way with her immediately, without having to keep her in your stable.

ARROGANCE   Ordinary people use the term "arrogance" as an insult. But then ordinary people haven't seen their earnings increase three thousand percent in two decades.

I don't stop at saying, "What's wrong with arrogance?" I say celebrate it. Develop it. Cultivate it. Turn it loose and enjoy every moment of it. If you are a successful CEO, you've earned it. More than that, you'll need every bit of arrogance you can muster if you hope to survive America's boardrooms.

Let's get back to basics for a moment. Every animal learns to identify members of its kind by recognizing shared traits. For example, a grizzly bear sees another bear with a shoulder hump, a penetrating stare, and big canines dripping with drool, and he says to himself, "Hey, that ain't no black bear." Then he has to decide: Bluff and fight? Or bluff and flight? You need to be equally discerning when you meet others. How do you quickly identify other successful CEOs and other people of means? What do you look for? Forget the tie. Any half-wit can get lucky buying a tie. In fact, forget all the trappings. You can also forget character traits like intelligence and talent. Many intelligent people are too reticent to lead anything more cumbersome than their own shadows, and talent is as common as warts. What you need to look for is arrogance, the same arrogance that you project to others. It is the one recognizable common denominator shared by 78.1% of all CEOs.

Look at the eyes, the mouth, the shoulders and hands. Listen to the speech. Watch the body language. If it is there you will spot it immediately: An exceedingly high estimation of self-worth presented to lesser people, which means you and everyone else in the world, including mothers and mentors. If this visage makes you feel like a bug on someone's windshield, then you are lost in the wrong neighborhood. It should make you feel like you are part of a homecoming – and stimulate your adrenalin, your salivary glands, and small hairs on the back of your neck. Once you know that you are with your kind, you can then choose the most appropriate course of action: You can assert your superiority.

What about the other 21.9%? Some CEOs, such as The Man from Omaha, seem to possess humility, which is the opposite of arrogance. What can I say? People still spot UFOs; laboratories report incidents of remote viewing; and side shows feature three headed sheep. At this point in our development not all anomalies can be explained.

I advocate arrogance because it works and because it relieves you of having to explain yourself. It is much more than a defining character trait. It is a worldview; the correct worldview, which underscores the supremacy of the individual who uses his wits and his guile to accumulate great power, influence, and wealth and to keep it by repeatedly defeating his enemies and besting all others who compete against him for ownership of the same resources.

My advice? Like a majority of rich people everywhere, whether world-class athletes, entertainment celebrities, heirs and heiresses, or successful CEOs, be as arrogant as you like. Who is going to stop you, or even challenge you? And who on earth should believe in you if you don't? Furthermore, your arrogance will be good for business. It will attract other arrogant people, and thus winners, and will repel shy and modest people, who tend to be losers. And in the event that your sense of self-esteem exceeds your abilities, take heart because if you have crafted your arrogance correctly, it will lend your bluff such conviction that you will win more hands of poker and more corporate battles than you ever thought possible, even against people with twice your ability.

Arrogance is the just reward of the rich. Anything less reveals vulnerability and if you are rich, that is the one thing on earth you can't afford.

ART   For centuries, we have thought of art, and by that I mean painting, sculpture, music, dance, literature, drama, all the fine arts, as the end result of mature human beings at play. In the past, it was much easier to play than it is today. Artists had patrons to support them and too much time on their hands. Artists in the contemporary world, on the other hand, have responsibilities, such as property taxes, health care, personal automobiles, cable television, cell phones, and soccer camps for the kids. Artists' time is tightly budgeted. Because they have to support themselves, they need to be both efficient and productive, and they need to see an adequate financial return on their investment of time. How has this changed situation affected art as an investment?

Historically, art has been more of a grand speculation than a worthwhile investment. The investment-minded art buyer of the past gambled that the contemporary artist's work would be deemed great at some unspecified time in the future following the artist's death, and that it would then skyrocket in value. Nine times out of ten, the buyer lost that gamble. For every Picasso there are ten Fred Fiddlemeisters.

All that has changed. Today, art does not have to be a gamble and it does not have to depend on creative play, imagination, intelligence, gifted perceptions, or any innate talent whatsoever. Its value doesn't even have to depend on the artist's death. And while the contemporary product might not carry the potential for astronomical profit that a high-risk speculation carries, it also does not have to represent an unbearable risk. When considered as any other profit-making product, like diapers, automobiles, tranquilizers, or hedge trimmers, and when produced according to the principles of supply and demand economics, sound marketing strategies, and efficient production methods, art can be as profitable a product as a hair blower.

I credit Brootus Kingkitsch, The Painter of Blight, with developing this sector for the modern economy. Not only does his corporation sell an extraordinary quantity of product, it has developed imaginative spin-offs that promise to reap outstanding profits, such as Christmas tree ornaments, dog food dishes, and an entire community near East Saint Louis, Illinois, built to resemble his paintings. With a touch of genius, not to mention brilliant irony, The Painter of Blight long ago discovered that the upwardly mobile and the *petite riche* feel better about themselves when they are surrounded by images of other people's poverty, such as disheveled cottages, broken down house trailers in rural Mississippi, and ravaged urban ghettoes. Consequently, his East Saint Louis development community will feature commodious luxury condominiums built to resemble from the outside the burned out remains of project tenements. Best of all the entire community will be walled in, just like a real ghetto. Can you imagine the premiums his corporation will be able to charge for this kind of specialized real estate?

After all these centuries, art finally has been raised out of the speculator's portfolio to the level of commodity and Kingkitsch has demonstrated its low-risk, reasonable-profit potential. If there were a Nobel Prize for the fine art of marketing, I would nominate this pioneer. And I enthusiastically recommend that you explore this sector. The Brootus Kingkitsch success story is only the tip of an iceberg.

ASSET MANAGEMENT   Assets, assets, assets. It's all about assets. To the extent that you are a student of anything, study asset management, since managing assets will become your primary activity. As a CEO, your job will be to manage the corporation's assets. Good asset management will elevate the value of your company's assets, which will put you in position to acquire more assets. As you raise the value of those additional assets you can then acquire even more assets. The same is true in your private life. The only difference between your professional assets and your personal assets is, of course, that your personal assets always come first. Remember Lincoln Logs, Erector Sets, and Legos? Think of them as assets and think of yourself as a budding architect. Build your assets from solid ground up. Keep building. Enhance their worth. Get more. Build more, and get more and more and more and more until you amaze yourself. Once you are amazed, acquire more assets. And all along the way, manage them with the same love that a child puts into his little skyscraper.

As you get older and as your assets increase to astronomical levels, you will find that the management of your personal assets will become pretty much a full time job. When that happens, it will be time to retire, collect your generous severance package, begin drawing your ample retirement, take your Social Security, and, of course, manage your assets. Naturally, you will want to aim for security and income more than for aggressive growth, but with the mountain of assets you will own at this point, your management strategy will be mostly irrelevant. Just keep in mind that as the value of your assets increases, a little management here and there will allow you, even in retirement, to increase that increase so that you can add new assets.

Some children required three or four sets of toys to finish their projects. Remember? We adults are not so different. When it comes to assembling wealth, you can never have too many assets.

ATTITUDE   The most important psychological asset for any potential CEO is the right attitude. If you recognized at an early age that a few people are destined to lead while millions are destined to follow, and you included yourself in the first group, then you are well on your way to forming the proper attitude. Just remember that leadership is something you take, not something you agree to. In commerce, no band of sheep ever elected its own shepherd.

In other words, don't be seduced by democracy. Business is not politics, and there is nothing democratic about running a company. And there is certainly nothing democratic about winning promotion to CEO or chairman of a board. That process only seems democratic. For example, let's say that it is time for you to become Chairman. In essence, you nominate yourself, build your alliances, reserve rewards for your supporters and punishments for your detractors, and then wait for the vote of the board. If you did your work well, with the right attitude, then the outcome of the vote will never be in doubt.[5] Bottom line? When the vote goes your way, you take over as expected, others follow, and that's the name of the game.

It is also important to remember that no shepherd ever donated his wages to his sheep. Don't be seduced by sentiment or ideology. Business is not philosophy or charity. It is competition in the service of profit. Still, not all leaders are cut from the same stripe and you need to be able to distinguish those who possess the right attitude from those who don't.

For example, do not confuse a real CEO with an entrepreneur. Unless you have a flawless idea for Internet development, never aspire to become an entrepreneur. Most entrepreneurs are dreamers, not leaders. They are dedicated and monomaniacal people who take excessive risk and who care more for their ideas than for their assets or their careers. They think it is more important to innovate than to keep score, and most of them fail miserably. For every Bill Gates there are a thousand nameless bankrupts still puttering away at their own pathetic inventions. Likewise, learn to distinguish between a real CEO and a faux CEO. The former has read and learned from his Machiavelli. The latter allows soft issues, such as "social responsibility," environmentalism, and pampering workers, to intrude on his judgment.

In case you are scratching your head to find an example of a faux CEO, I will provide two to illustrate what I mean: Eves le Chat, founder of Bigfoot Outfitters, and the hippies, Jake Light and Mike Goodman, who made funky ice cream apparently for the fun of it. Bigfoot is one of a handful of clothing, outdoor recreation, and footwear manufacturers who belong to the Fair Labor Alliance, a contrarian front group that coddles foreign workers. I have it on good authority that the CEOs of all companies that belong to the FLA meet at a secret location in Maine every May Day to worship wood sprites, sip Fair Trade tea, and eat Marx Marshmallow-Pinko Praline ice cream not available to the general public. I should also note that le Chat established Bigfoot as a "slow motion company," to distinguish it from a company that grows its revenues as fast as possible. The term speaks for itself. Jake and Mike, on the other hand, before selling to a real corporation, just floundered ahead and gave away their profits for

---

5 Business is not politics, but politics might be more like business than politicians want to admit.

pet causes and for the hell of it. What real CEOs could do with good ideas, like the ideas that started these companies, excites the imagination. But don't hold your breath. All too often the best ideas come from people with bad attitudes. That is, from faux CEOs. Remember, if you have a good idea, don't focus on the idea itself. Focus on the bottom line. Ask yourself what potential you might be wasting? Ask yourself why you should live like a baron when you could live like a king, or at least like The Duck?[6] And finally, ask yourself why you should throw away money on pet causes when it would be more cost effective to write a letter to some newspaper's editor? The Mother Theresas of the world might have their place, but it is not at the head of a corporation.

Being a real CEO requires you to have perspective, toughness, and dedication to profit as the only engine that drives our economies and our careers. Exceptional profits come from exceptional attitude, not exceptional ideas. If you want to comfort lepers and feed starving babies, join the Peace Corps. If you want to create economies that will allow these types to find employment and help themselves, then build a business empire and be strong enough to know that the work you do creates more prosperity than all the rhetoric and giveaways of all the bleeding hearts in history. Particularly for you. So why waste your life wiping the noses of the poor and the incompetent when you can drip enough prosperity on them so they can fix their own lives? These people don't need handkerchiefs. What they need is training, jobs, hope, good role models, and some downward trickle. Spend a few minutes to think about these things. Seriously. Ask yourself if you have the right attitude.

Here is a test. Where does your imagination take you when you have free time, no deadlines, and no one watching you? If you find yourself thinking about tropical islands and mango groves, you are in trouble. If you fantasize about slaying evil dictators and slipping a Ben Franklin to the paraplegic hustler on the sidewalk, you are in huge trouble. On the other hand, if you find yourself plotting a strategy to rape a rival company to get

6 Don't confuse The Duck with The Dick, who became a politician. The Duck, as you surely know, made his fortune selling cures for baldness, bad taste, and rude behavior. His favorite meal is raw baby duck hearts, which earned him his nickname. While he is somewhat less reclusive than Howard Hughes was, he also lives more lavishly and wears clothes, though his clothes are widely regarded as unremarkable.

what you want in order to strengthen your position and increase your net worth, then bully. You may or may not have ability, but you have the right attitude. That attitude will make your company more money than talent will ninety-nine times out of a hundred, and it will guide you to your personal net worth more directly than any moral compass.

Attitude is not just image. It's the real thing.

AUDITS   Never permit an uncontrolled audit of your books. Your books are your private property and no one has the right to inspect them without your input. Likewise, never authorize an audit the outcome of which you have not designed. If your money is paying for the audit, then you have every right to get the outcome you desire. If someone else is footing the bill, you have the same right because the books are your or your company's private property. These principles hold true today as much as they held true prior to the Arthur Anderson debacle in 2002, the subsequent accounting reforms imposed by Congress, the Justice Department, and the Securities and Exchange Commission, and the subsequent loosening of those reforms begun in 2006. The only things that have changed are the ways in which you will need to manage information. For example, primary data, the information auditors look at, might in fact have to come from secondary sources that look primary, that is, sources over which you can exercise control. Likewise, the shredding of paper documents and the erasing of hard drives, in the event of a security breach initiated by outsiders, such as regulators, will have to be accomplished in a more timely and efficient fashion. I suggest that you have your information geeks work out a system of *daily* erasures and shreddings of mainstream sources so that sensitive or misleading information cannot ever fall into the wrong hands. This will take some doing, but the outcome will be well worth the cost.

So long as you exercise the control over your company that you should exercise, then any audit, whatever its cause and whatever its goals, will be a pleasant experience.

AUTHORITY   All authority is self-appointed. Since everyone has a self, everyone has an appointment. Everyone also has a belly button. Respect authority that matters: Yours. Everyone else can pick lint.

AUTOMATION   Busy hands are the devil to pay. Almost everything is cheaper when automated. I recommend that you install as many automated systems as you can devise except, of course, for personal secretarial functions. It's always nice to keep a couple of trophies around the office and if they can make coffee, turn the copy machine on and off, and use their PCs for something other than online shopping, IM, and email, all the better.

AWE   Most people are followers in search of a leader. Awe is the naïve emotion they express when they think that they have found one. As you develop your leadership abilities, you will inspire awe and the more you inspire the better. Learn to appear always confident, always in control, always bigger than life, a demigod who lives beyond the highest aspirations of heroes. Your dress, your automobiles, your homes, your wife, and above all else, your demeanor should convey, even to ordinary people, the message: "This is what it's all about." Put simply, learn to inspire by your public image the same admiration from others that you reflect every morning in the bathroom mirror to yourself. And always stay on guard. Study the way others react to you. If they seem to be less than awestruck, then work on your image and your presentation. Try repeating this mantra: "I am a god. My life surpasses your dreams. Admire me, fear me, and follow me, and your life will improve." You are allowed to wink as you repeat this mantra only if others respond to you as they should.

On the other hand, never debase yourself by expressing awe for another human being. *You* are the chief. Others are second best or worse. Besides, no one you ever meet will deserve such admiration.

THE AXE   When it comes to firing staff executives, think of yourself as a Roman general doing battle against Celtic hordes. You wield a large iron battle-axe and you must plant it squarely between the eyes of your prisoner or lose your soldiers' respect, if not your life. Then do the job and celebrate a job well done. If you have an aversion to the process, train your Chief Operating Officer, President, or Director of Human Resources to fire staff executives, or outsource the job and hire one of those companies that holds the outgoing employees by the hand and counsels them through the process.

However, I strongly recommend that as a CEO you personally fire staff members (but only staff members) and I advise that you do it in the traditional manner. Meet the condemned in a conference room along with at least one other staff member who outranks him. Don't sit. Tell him that he is out, no explanation. Hand him a sheet describing what, if any, termination benefits he will receive, and what, if any, company property he must surrender and when. Then tell him that he has fifteen minutes to vacate the premises. Leave and nod to the two security guards waiting outside. They will enter the room and take over. End of story.

There is no reason for sentiment or ceremony, and no reason to waste more than a few moments on the job. Never provide an explanation. Anything you say can be used against you in a wrongful discharge suit. If details need to be worked out, refer his lowyers to your lowyers. Your safety comes from the extensive documentation you have added to the condemned's personnel file, plus any deeply personal reports garnered from private investigation as an ace in the hole. Make sure the fired people are ostracized and are never allowed on corporate property again. Just to be safe, watch your back for a few weeks.

Many people think of firing as an unpleasant task. However, you may also think of it as a useful tool. It is an excellent strategy, periodically, to select at random a popular and highly rated staffer to use as a sacrificial lamb. Fire your chosen lamb in a particularly cold and brutal manner, with no forewarning to anyone, then sit back and watch the fun. Initially, most other staffers will deeply resent you. As their resentment evolves into self-interest, and their self-interest into fear, they will reaffirm that you have unlimited power, that you are answerable to no one, that you can be capricious and cruel on a whim, and that they must never offend you. This strategy is guaranteed to make them better employees. I promise you that for six weeks following the sacrifice, every time you enter their space they will wag their tails and wet the carpet.

If you are the one getting the axe, the news will have to come from the Chairman of the Board, if that is someone other than you, or from one of your close friends on the board after they vote. It is of no consequence. You will have seen this coming clearly for some time, your affairs will be in order, your limo will be waiting to spirit you off to a gala lunch with your wife and friends, and the severance package, which you and your attorneys and friends on the board that hired you so carefully wrought, will be itemized in your termination agreement. That will be that, unless, upon your dismissal, this board decided to *add* a few millions to keep you at bay. So unfurl your golden parachute and let it carry you ever so gently down to ground level and be off. There will be other venues to conquer after a truly superior lunch.

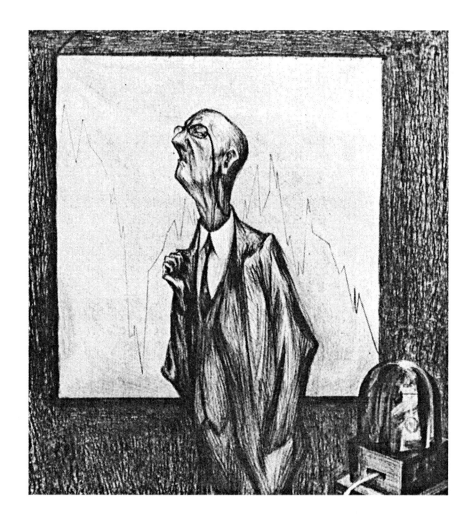

"Meet the condemned in a conference room along with at least one other staff member who outranks him." p. 28

BACKDATING   Aside from wishes granted by good fairies, stock options issued by corporations to top executives as part of a compensation package are the only thing in the known universe not governed by time lines. Everything else has an expiration date.

That is why stock options are a popular source of income for CEOs. In addition they don't look like income. They don't have to show up on a P&L as an expense. If they show up on a P&L at all, they don't have to be tied to a specific individual. And regardless of what they are tied to, they can be used before they existed. Where else can a baby celebrate its birthday before it was born?

Don't think of stock options as compensation. Think of them as opportunities. They are like opportunities in the real world where, for example, ordinary people buy and sell stocks and take their chances. The timing of a stock trade must be clever if the ordinary person hopes to make a profit. Similarly, if a CEO hopes to profit from a stock option he must execute it at just the right moment. However, since stock markets are notoriously unpredictable, and since the stock option was intended as compensation to the CEO, corporations have figured out a way to do what no ordinary investor has ever done: They changed hope into certainty.

It's called "backdating" and it means that you, as the CEO, can execute your options today, when your stock price is high, but date the execution six months ago, when the price was low. That way, you eliminate all risk and you don't have to get stuck paying inflated prices. You can then make instant profits and someone else, namely your company, can eat the difference. That's part of the quiet compensation you receive to make up for your inadequate but highly publicized – and criticized -- salary and perks. It's a nice benefit and one that you should use until you die. Actually you can continue to use it after you die. That's part of the magic also not available to the general public.

How does that work? If you and your family have close relations with your company, your board of directors can take care of your family, in the event of your untimely death, by executing your stock options after you die but backdating them to when you were alive to validate the fact that your new shares are part of your estate. This will not only provide money for your heirs, it will prove to your colleagues, friends, and neighbors what a clever investor you must have been and how carefully you planned for your family's well being.

Working as a CEO entails sacrifice, concentration, endless thought and planning, exhausting travel, strident negotiations, constant pressure to produce, and sleepless nights, sometimes in foreign countries where you own vineyards and the air conditioning is primitive at best; in short, your life involves long hours of pain, misery, and suffering unknown to all others. Thank God a few perks like backdating make the effort worthwhile. So worthwhile I am confident that backdating or something like it will persist long after hostile regulators disappear.

BACKSTABBERS   No CEO worthy of the name has ever been stabbed in the back. In order for someone to stab you in the back, you would have to trust that person. That kind of trust is not only against the rules; it is alien to the kind of personality one must have to succeed as a CEO. Therefore, a backstabbing can only be viewed as a form of self-abuse. If you are prone to self-abuse, find a more amusing way to practice it.

BAKSHEESH   It's not a puzzler. When you need to get inside a secure building, you bribe the doorman. In the Middle East, Arabs use the term "baksheesh" to describe this oil that lubricates the sticky hinge. It's a nice term to use when discussing business at a cocktail party surrounded by nosey bystanders because most of them won't know what it means. Like discretion, the need for baksheesh is universal. Use it whenever and wherever you must.

Be aware that in 1977, moralists passed The Foreign Corrupt Practices Act, which made American baksheesh illegal and made our overseas playing field uneven. It took eleven years to convince the moralists that we needed "grease payment exemptions," which permit limited use of baksheesh in special circumstances, but you will still have to cover your tracks.

In the real world, beyond the view of Congressional attempts to regulate business, baksheesh is as ubiquitous and as necessary as oxygen. So how should you proceed? First of all, you can dress up a bribe to look like just about anything other than itself. Second, extreme secrecy, backed by veiled threats, nearly always ensures proper confidentiality. In other words, in a private setting, offer your gift, your payment, or your contribution in such a way that the recipient will accept it and be content and extremely grateful for his good luck. Make sure that he understands what he must do to demonstrate that his baksheesh was worth your investment. And of course make sure that he understands what he must *not* do if he wants to continue to have good luck and unlimited use of all of his body parts.

Doors open easily when hinges and doormen are well maintained.

THE BALANCE SHEET   The balance sheet provides investors with the illusion that they are looking directly into the factual workings of a corporation. The first thing you need to know about a balance sheet, therefore, is that it is a big deal. It is the first impression many investors get of your business, and the only window through which most investors can peer. Do it well. Do it right.

The second thing you need to know about a balance sheet is that it doesn't need to balance. It only needs to look like it balances. So much in accounting is a matter of semantics. Is a loan from a friendly banker a liability? Or, if you consider borrowing against future sales that are almost a certainty, is it income? Is a stock option, or a low interest, long-term forgivable loan to an executive or director, a cost of doing business, or is it, when you consider the added loyalty it brings, another asset, like a factory or a fleet of company cars? As you can see, definitions play a key role in balance sheets, and nothing is ever black or white.

One thing is certain, though: Investors read balance sheets. They may not understand them entirely, but they will read and interpret them. Hence, it is essential to give the consumer what the consumer wants and to bolster the confidence of anyone who cares enough about your corporation to look at your books. The balance sheet is a kind of snapshot of the corporation at work and it should reflect the best you have to offer. At the very least it should reflect clearly the message you want to convey to the investor.

I recommend that you dress it up nicely with lots of colorful layout, imaginative graphs, and employee photographs. Spare no expense. I also recommend that you don't take it seriously. The real books are locked in your safe, of course, and the public balance sheet may be thought of as the makeup and the costume an actor wears when performing a role in a play. When the drama that is your business reveals itself on stage, wait for the reviews, listen for applause, and if you have done a good job performing then you will get the reaction you planned on and no one will throw a cabbage.

BALLS   You either have them or you don't. If you don't then you are in the wrong business. Need I add that, when used in this metaphoric sense, they are not gender specific and never have been?

BANKRUPTCY   Certain privileges are reserved for larger groups of people to ensure collective welfare in the face of adverse circumstances. Such privileges are almost never given to individuals. For example, individuals are not allowed to declare martial law or rights of eminent domain, but larger groups may do so when necessity dictates. A nation may establish martial law when threatened with disorder, or a public utility or real estate developer, working in concert with the courts, may invoke eminent domain to ensure rights of way for an important transmission line or a development that will enhance the local tax base. The end result in either case is that society at large, the economy, and individual consumers all benefit. Can you imagine the chaos our lives would be thrown into if any individual who perceived a personal threat or wanted to establish personal access was allowed to declare martial law or invoke eminent domain against his neighbors? This distinction between personal desire and public good seems obvious, and yet the law allows individuals to declare bankruptcy. Let's take a hard, realistic look at this situation.

There are two types of bankruptcy, personal and corporate, and one is no more like the other than a plum is like a prune. Business bankruptcy is a necessary management tool designed either to save a company and the jobs it provides while placating creditors, or, in a worst case scenario, to liquidate a company and thereby save creditors from even more devastating losses. In either case, larger groups of people, specifically the company's employees, its shareholders, and/or its creditors, are helped. In addition, the economy benefits. The local tax base might be preserved and society at large is spared what would otherwise amount to a tragic financial failure without recourse, the kind of thing that happened daily during The Great Depression.

In a personal bankruptcy no one is helped except one individual, possibly devious, who has failed to use his or her credit responsibly, and I question just how helpful that bankruptcy is to that person since future creditors will look at the bankrupt as a pariah. A personal bankruptcy damages the economy, harms creditors, and reinforces the dangerous precedent that individuals can accumulate mountains of debt and, when they no longer want to pay that debt, simply walk away from it. Personal bankruptcies should not be allowed and are nothing more than a legal gimmick encouraging irresponsible individuals to shirk their financial and moral duties. Yet the law persists. I recommend that as a CEO, you encourage lawmakers to continue the sweeping reforms of the personal bankruptcy laws recently enacted. Make it even more difficult for consumers to discharge debt. Make it illegal to declare bankruptcy more than once in a lifetime. Reduce the amount of assets the bankrupts can keep while thumbing their noses at the creditors who trusted them. Make them accept responsibility and pay their debts, even if it takes a couple of decades. And try to get some criminal penalties for the worst abusers. If we make it difficult enough and unattractive enough, maybe in time we can do away with the whole concept of personal bankruptcy and instill in people some sense of personal responsibility for their actions.

Corporate bankruptcy, as I said, is a different matter altogether. The term, "reorganization" is more accurate. It is a tool of management designed to help companies in difficult circumstances *meet* their responsibilities as best they can. And it is something you might have to use at some time during your career. Don't be hesitant to use it if you must. There are some circumstances that leave no choice. For example, any corporation facing a barrage of frivolous lawsuits or a class action suit for perceived damages must decide whether to preserve the institution of the company in altered form, or to lie down and become the object of a feeding frenzy, like a wounded animal among jackals. People continue to smoke cigarettes despite warnings *printed by the company* on every pack. Women choose to feed their vanity and insecurity by having breast implants despite warnings against malfunction, disappointment in the results, and unpleasant side effects. Commonly these warnings are attached to advertisements for plastic surgery and to TV shows promoting it. Nevertheless such consumers are first in line to sue when the opportunity arises. What is a corporation to do? Stop producing what consumers demand? Or meet demand and then have to pay out billions in settlement money and end up on an ash heap? This is money that might have gone to new plants, new jobs, health and retirement benefits, and higher wages The sane alternative is to seek rational protection in a court of competent jurisdiction. The sad truth is that individuals increasingly refuse to take responsibility for their own actions and their own choices and the worst of those are not opposed to grabbing a windfall from the nearest corporation if they can. As a CEO, one of your responsibilities is to ensure that they can't.

Now and then, truly tragic circumstances compel a company toward bankruptcy. I am thinking of a fine old company founded by a wonderful family, a firm that has benefited consumers for decades: R. Tomane Company. Through no fault of the company, the particular type of malignite they mined near a small town high in the Grace Rockies, caused problems. Malignite is a useful substance found in nature, not invented by company chemists, and it is widely used in the manufacture of insulation and cotton candy. This malignite turned out to contain copious traces of another naturally occurring compound commonly known as fairy dust fiber, or dimetholtricyano-2-3-strychnopheno-6-6-6-atrazalarsenataminalkoloid, which upon extensive analysis was determined to pose some potentially adverse risks to humans. For example, incidental contact with fairy dust can cause extensive third degree burns; eating it correlates with immediate stomach and liver disintegration; and excessive inhalation can result in fossilization of lung tissue. Tragically, the company had to shut down its malignite operations costing hundreds their jobs, plus a few hundred people died. A few hundred more will die, and a few thousand more will suffer ill effects for the rest of their lives. One resident compared his town to a Kurdish village after it had been gassed by its own government. The end result might be the same, but we must all understand that Chemical Ali intended genocide while R. Tomane, operating with only the finest intentions, was victimized by chance and circumstance. Miners expect problems, but who would have thought, for example, that the new high school running track, donated generously by the company from its mining waste, would asphyxiate the runners plus family members who handled their laundry?[7]

Who should pay the medical and funeral bills and provide aid to a nearly moribund village? No corporation can become caretaker to so many people – an entire community -- and still perform its mission in the economy. Reorganization is the only intelligent solution. There should be plenty of government and NGO programs to assist the townspeople. It is exactly for reasons like this -- floods, hurricanes, volcanoes, tornadoes, drought, tsunamis, and illness caused by natural substances inadvertently released into a populated area during the course of gainful employment -- that we pay taxes and donate to the Red Cross. No good would come from bleeding away the company's assets until it could no longer do business. Why compound a tragedy? Bankruptcy, augmented by a congressional act to limit fairy dust fiber industry liabilities, would at least save some remnant of the company so it can continue to employ tens of thousands of

---

7 Who would have anticipated that thousands of homes and buildings in America that used fairy dust fiber insulation, including New York skyscrapers, might pose risks to workers and firemen when those structures are disturbed or destroyed? As for carnivals, thank God that today people prefer deep fried Twinkies over cotton candy.

dependent workers around the world and continue to satisfy the demands imposed on it by millions of consumers. Meanwhile, given some public assistance, some local can-do enthusiasm, and a few decades of massive cleanup, the affected village will return to business as usual. In three or four generations no one will even remember that this vital and picturesque little community once fell on hard times.

In sum, personal bankruptcy is the result of a moral weakness leading to a situation in which no one wins. Corporate reorganization, on the other hand, is an economic imperative leading to a win-win situation favoring both the company and the public at large. Citizens need to understand the difference between the two kinds of bankruptcy. They also need to be reminded, periodically, that there is no free lunch. Sometimes bad things just happen and we all have to pitch in and work together to see our way through. And sometimes, when bad things do happen, ordinary people have to make personal sacrifices to benefit society at large. That is one of the grave responsibilities that our citizens must exercise in return for the privilege of living and working in a free-market democracy.

THE BARD ANOMALY   It's hard to argue with success, so I have no argument with Lyric Airlines. Explaining success is another matter.

Hal Bright, an attorney and founder of Lyric and Chairman of its Board, must be credited, along with members of his handpicked management committee, with many innovations that contributed to the company's success. Among those innovations, three principles have guided Lyric to become America's top carrier. The company moves nearly one hundred million passengers yearly and it has shown a profit for fifteen years without interruption. Other airlines don't even come close. Here's why Lyric works.

Simplification. Operations from top to bottom are kept as simple as possible. For example, the company owns a fleet of some five hundred airplanes, all of them Boeing 737s. Planning, maintenance, booking, flight schedules, use of airports, baggage handling, service equipment, the whole enchilada, is based on the 737.[8] The result of this simplification is a series of incidental cost savings that add up to a mountain of efficiency.

Utilization. The more you utilize fixed assets, the fewer assets you must own to achieve goals. On average, each Lyric airplane flies thirteen hours daily, and annually, each aircraft moves, on average, a quarter of a million passengers. In addition, the company transports immediately flight and ground crews wherever they are needed when things get backed up. The result is unmatched productivity.

Cost Reduction. The lower your overhead, the higher your profit potential. Prior to the 787, Lyric orders accounted for almost ten percent of Boeing's sales, and all orders were variations of the one model. That kind of leverage results in economy of scale, and huge savings to Lyric on cost of hard assets. In addition, Lyric uses secondary airports whenever possible to reduce fees and hassles for customers. The company also utilizes derivatives, mostly options on fuel futures, in a brilliant plan to hedge fuel prices. The plan was so successful that in 2006, for example, Lyric paid half the going rate for jet fuel while its competitors got tanked. Finally, passengers who want to fly Lyric must purchase their tickets directly from Lyric *and* provide the airline with documented proof that they would rather love their fellow passengers than dismember them with a chainsaw. The net result? Travel agents scorn Lyric because they can't get kickback commissions, but passengers love Lyric because their ticket prices are cheaper than those of conventional airlines and because they never have to try to get a chainsaw through security.

The rest of the Lyric success story is widely attributed to the efforts of Lovey D. Bard, named President and Chief Operating Officer in 2001. Bard worked as a secretary for Bright before she joined Lyric. Then she rose through the ranks of Lyric as corporate Secretary, Vice President of Administration, and Executive Vice President for Customer Love before she was named President. She described herself as the "Chief Service Provider" and was considered the prime architect of Lyric's "love one another" corporate

---

8 For Lyric and any other airlines concerned with customer pleasure, watch the new Boeing 787 phase out older fleets. I was given a private tour of the plane in June, 2007, and I can tell you that it is a winner. It will roll out for ordinary people to see three days after my death and twelve minutes before Airbus suffers a massive coronary.

culture, which places great emphasis on customer satisfaction, employee fulfillment, and the idea that both customers and employees should have fun at Lyric. As a result of this culture, Lyric's airplanes are cute. All the planes are painted bright colors, and some are painted to look like friendly dolphins cavorting through oceans of clouds. Flight attendants, who must intern at Second City, specialize in witty one liners, and flight crews sing selections for eager passengers from *Rent, Cats,* and *The Sound of Music.* Lyric also coddles its employees. For example, it has no problem giving baggage handlers free vacations and fried chicken when they return from tough temporary duty assignments with Army Reserve units, and any mechanic can walk into the President's office to discuss bad hydraulic systems or his wife's affair with a Republican. Lyric says it values people.

Well. We all value people. People are essential assets, like pig iron and bauxite. And while it is true that Lyric enjoys the highest ratings for customer satisfaction and is swamped with applications from prospective employees, it remains to be seen whether the lyrical "love one another" model contributes anything to the success of corporate culture in general. People will like anything and anyone that coddles them, particularly when it is a complete anomaly from established carrier norms based on the standard "screw one another" model. Just as clearly, those standard norms work, in the vast majority of cases, without dolphins grinning, and without transforming a corporation into a patsy for customer whims and employee neuroses.

Look at this thing realistically. Travelers and pilgrims encounter problems. That has always been the case. Mary and Joseph couldn't find a hotel room so they slept in a barn and gave birth to baby Jesus. Did they complain? So passengers on normal airlines who paid a thousand dollars for a quick commute west are fed salted peanuts and warm drinks while the toilets overflow during a six hour wait in an overbooked flight on the tarmac in one hundred degree heat then get diverted to Sioux Falls three hours late for a meeting in Seattle while their luggage is sent to Kuala Lumpur and instead of a hotel during the last night of the local Shriners' convention the airline gives them a voucher for black coffee and an egg muffin. So what? These things happen. Passengers need to toughen up and stop whining. You want to talk about hardship? A century earlier these pilgrims would have been part of a wagon train fleeing Sioux warriors. A "love one another" wagon master would not have made any more difference then than it does now.

Lest someone accuse me of gender bias, I wish to point out that even though Ms. Bard's "love one another" corporate culture seems to fit into that realm of nurturing supposedly monopolized by women, we all know that testosterone-deprived individuals can function effectively at the top of the corporate world. Consider the example of Smartie Stewright. Smartie was the first CEO ever convicted of false plausible deniability. She had stuffed a turkey with crumbs not available to Club members and their culinary staffs, and then hinted that she had used Wonder Bread instead of focaccia. This is a serious breach of etiquette. As a result, she was sentenced to five months in The Women's Correctional Facility at Sea Island where she was forced to eat TV dinners and knit mittens for displaced Tibetan nuns. Though scarred, clearly brutalized, and shackled with an ankle bracelet, she emerged from her ordeal with renewed vigor and went on to build record profits, proving that she had the toughness of an Abrams tank not far beneath that Betty Crocker image. I give Ms. Bard no less credit.

However, I speculate that when Lyric closes its doors, is taken over by another corporation, or is forced to alter its culture, its employees will not be fit to work anywhere else. They would find the new culture too harsh. And many of Lyric's existing passengers would prefer to ride a mule than to fly another airline. In other words, while Lyric has cleverly found a niche, one clearly resulting from employee frustration in the workplace and perceived customer neglect in the marketplace, that niche is a temporary phenomenon and Lyric's adaptation to it does not represent an adaptation to the competitive world at large. Whatever advantage they gain from a "love one another" culture would disappear utterly the moment other airlines adopted a similar culture. And the fact that all other airlines have not adopted a similar "love one another" culture, but continue to operate under the "screw one another" model, should tell you something. The deregulation of airlines in 1978 and Lyric's subsequent expansion plus their emphasis on simplification, utilization, and cost control are the real contributors to their success. This "love one another" outlook is an amusing eccentricity, not an innovation.

Lyric reminds me of that albino moose seen wandering around the Maine woods. It lives and breathes. It is unlike any other moose and it seems to be healthy. It is healthy, but it is not healthy *because* it is white. It is healthy because it is a good moose. Who cares if it is white?

Eventually, a semi will flatten this albino moose and Ms. Bard's legacy will evaporate. The woods will then return to normal. Airline passengers will remember that airborne cattle cars still get there faster than trains, busses, automobiles, and cavorting dolphins. Balance sheets everywhere will return to the serious business of measuring profit and loss, not human satisfaction and dissatisfaction. And Airline executives will leave the love scene to Nashville crooners.

BEARS AND BULLS   Bulls charge, bears hibernate -- and wolves follow the herd. Need I add that wolves follow the herd not because the herd is leading them, but because they know how to feed on stragglers? Every successful CEO knows that there is more to the markets than bulls and bears. If you have a problem with that, join Oxfam. You can always teach lepers in Tanzania how to grow maize.

BEAUTY   That old saying about beauty being in the eye of the beholder certainly must be true. We have all seen The Grand Canyon, or at least pictures of it. We have all heard people say how beautiful it is. What we see is layer after layer of dirt and rock. If you have a penchant for geology, it offers some interest. A person could almost chart the strata that could hold coal or gypsum or uranium or oil shale. Beyond that, it is a gaping hole in the middle of a desert, people!

If you like beauty, buy art. Buy it right, outlive the artist, and in forty years you might make a fifty to one return. *That's* beauty.

BEHAVIOR   You have three choices. You can let chance modify people's behavior for random ends. You can allow ideologues and professional propagandists to modify people's behavior for their ends. Or you can use all your influence and power in a free market to educate people so they will make choices that help you satisfy your ends. As you can see, you really have only one choice. This is a matter of such great impact that, throughout your career, it should be your second highest priority, your most important job right after keeping your golden parachute rigged and ready.

When practicing this educational kind of behavior modification, your rate of efficiency will seem low because there are so many others out there trying to accomplish the same thing. On the other hand, since all your competition is engaged in the same type of social engineering that you are, competition becomes a collective act with a combined rate of efficiency that is almost frighteningly high. With general aims that are virtually identical, competing efforts to shape motivations this way or that actually reinforce each other and create what I like to call, "a motivational mindset." Like soldiers waiting for battle orders or a team of athletes waiting for their coach's instructions, whole populations achieve a pitch of readiness and a constant state of extreme motivation. They know that they must spend. They are ready to spend. They are just waiting for the specific details of their marching orders. In brief, they are ready to jump. They just need to be told where and how high.

Your job is two fold: Do your part to maintain that pitch decade after decade, and, when the timing is right, week to week, step in and give the orders to jump that benefit your organization specifically. *Never* let up, and *never* miss a cue, and the social system that sustains your business will propagate and will reward you. Even in the face of stiff competition.

Thus, happily, this is one area where you don't have to worry so much about your competitors. Using contemporary electronic media and the internet, corporation A might lure consumers to buy imported sweat shirts today, and corporation B will lead them to hardware tomorrow. But is there any essential difference in the consumers' modified behavior? Of course not. They get out. They believe. They support. They buy. They are always ready. It doesn't matter what you are selling. They love the bait. They want to take the bait. And without fail, they will take the bait, over and over and over again.

I once met a man in a Vail restaurant who looked like a rancher and I asked him what business he was in. He told me that he was a grass farmer. What he meant was that he was really in the business of growing hay so that his five thousand cattle could eat too much and, without knowing it, ready themselves for the feedlot and then for market. In a parallel way, corporations are in the business of grass roots democracy. We plant and grow desires so that populations can freely choose to ready themselves for markets.

The bottom line of human behavior is: Change hearts and minds to suit your needs and money will find you the way rivers find an ocean.

BELIEF   Historians, philosophers, theologians, sociologists, psychologists, linguists, feminists, and just about everyone else with initials following his or her name, has plenty to say about belief systems. Good CEOs are no different. Our view is simpler than most, however, and probably closer to the mark. In sum, people will believe whatever they are told to believe. So tell them what you want them to believe. Tell them what is good for business, what will help your corporation, and what will make your life and your job easier. Tell it with subtlety. Tell it often. Tell it with conviction; demonize alternatives; and you will have people eating out of your hand.

If you are top 500 or multinational and don't have a news network or two at your disposal, consider investing in a few newspapers, radio stations, and television stations in each important market area you serve. Ideally, buy your way onto the board of an important media conglomerate. In the U.S. this is one of the great benefits of deregulation. We can exercise considerable control over public opinion without FCC regulators going berserk. Media clout will not only allow you to shape belief, it will help you buy loyalty. Think about *your* public, the consumer resources of the world, all looking for a place to spark their dreams and spend their capital. Where their hearts go their heads will follow. Where their heads go their wallets will follow. And where their wallets go, you may follow, with a scoop shovel and a ledger.

BETA   In any venture, I advise that you calculate Beta before you proceed, whether the venture is a stock purchase, the takeover of a company, or your marriage. Beta defines absolute risk in relation to composite risk. It is risk that cannot be diminished through diversification. It can be quite disarming, particularly when applied to human relations. In fact, if you have trouble with Beta, you are probably better off avoiding human relations, and by that I mean distracting emotional entanglements. It is not difficult to learn to relate to other people as entities and assets, resources and liabilities, rather than as complex personalities eliciting your volatile emotional responses. Doing so will allow you to reduce your personal risk to nearly absolute zero and to clear the way to enjoy all your rewards yourself, strictly on your own terms. This can even be accomplished while in a state of marriage and parenthood. You don't need to make an announcement. Just discipline your emotions, tolerate these other people for their benefits to your career and your personal well being, and stay sharply focused on the demands of your job.

BLAME   If there were a holy Ten Commandments of business, the first would be "assign blame," and the second would be "always blame someone else." Let's take a look at the reasons why.

Let me start by asking you a question: Where are we? The universe we inhabit is endless chaos, small parts of which are shaped into more or less orderly processes by random acts of chance circumscribed by the laws of physics and probability. Where does business fit into this mess? I'll tell you where: Business is the most orderly form of activity in the known universe. As CEO, you are the prime mover and, so far as planning, organization, and outcomes are concerned, your track record is demonstrably better than the track record of the entity that supposedly made stars. Remember, all business is predicated on control, and the more effectively you control things, the more predictable will be your outcomes. Nothing should be left to chance in business. Think of your corporation as nature itself, a nature that you created and set into motion. Most of the time, it runs with absolute, inevitable, clock-like precision. You, the prime mover, set this nearly perfect world in motion, and therefore, you are the only person on earth qualified to assign blame when something goes wrong. Clearly, when something does goes wrong within your business, the problem had to have been caused either by some incompetent within your organization, or by some sinister human intervention from outside. In short, when your carefully wrought plan fails, either someone on your staff screwed it up or an outside enemy sabotaged it.

Your job, as a CEO, is to decide which and then to assign blame. Blame, heaped upon someone on your staff whose incompetence embarrassed you, not only feels good to administer, it acts as a powerful motivator. The shame of being ostracized by the chief authority figure in one's life, and subsequently by excruciating peer pressure when the rest of the pack follows your lead and goes for the incompetent's exposed underbelly, will motivate any executive to be more prudent and accomplished in his or her future behavior. Likewise, blame will explain failure and will elevate the authority of the person pointing the finger. The buck stops with you so you get to choose how and where to spend it. Of course, assigning blame also covers your ass.

In the case of sabotage, blaming the enemy will galvanize the will of your team, and will focus their attention on threats coming from outside the corporation. Nothing unifies a company or soothes a failure more than demonizing the forces of alien evil that threaten your very livelihood and thus the well being of your women and children.

I recommend that you develop the habit of blaming until it becomes second nature to you. Once other people recognize you as a person who can identify faults and point out their causes enthusiastically to the rest of the world, those people will quickly learn to fear and respect you, and your stature as a strong authority figure will grow geometrically. Practice assigning blame on your spouse, your children, your friends, your family, and your neighbors. Clearly, assigning blame is not only useful, it can be fun.

As to the second holy commandment, it should be obvious that as the CEO of a large corporation, as the leader in the rough and tumble battlefields of business, as the best of the best and the brightest of the brightest, you must do everything in your considerable power to maintain and foster an image of infallibility. A CEO is *never* wrong. Therefore, whatever the circumstances, blame someone else.

THE BLUFF   I am a little uneasy about revealing all of my secrets to success lest the word gets out and you must then devise your own new means to accomplish the world's work. Yet I am confident that the select few who aspire to live by the principles explained in this book will understand the need for discretion toward the other ninety-nine-and-a-half percent.

Much of the world's work, whether accomplished through business, politics, or warfare, rests on the solid foundations of The Bluff. If you don't play poker, learn. If you're not very good at it, improve. The awful truth is that each of us is mortal, petty, neurotic, stupid, trivial, weak, cowardly, self-doubting, and at times loathsome. The hands we are dealt never contain enough aces. How do we survive our all too human traits to achieve dominance over others? How do we keep Soviet missiles out of Cuba? How do we acquire to divest a sickly but asset-laden company from the hard working hands of its founder? We stare coldly into the eyes of our adversaries and wait for a sign. In time, their imaginations will pick and choose from what we have told them. Soon thereafter, their fear will overcome their confidence, and they will blink.

You should master The Bluff long before you are a candidate for CEO of anything. If you cannot master it, then I suggest that you try a different career, something less demanding at which you can excel. For example, you might want to become a shoe salesman, or pick up a fried chicken franchise. They deal in certainties like foot size and bonus meals.

The hard truth is that you can't run with the big dogs until, during a high stakes game, you can magically transform a pair of deuces into a full house queens over and get by with it.

THE BONE   If you have ever dined in an outdoor café off the beaten path south of the U.S. border, you are probably familiar with the phenomenon of an annoying peasant watching you eat your porterhouse steak. In this situation, I recommend eating most of your steak – you paid for it – and then giving the peasant the bone. He should be able to get five or six percent of the protein that made the whole steak, which is probably more premium animal protein than he normally eats in a week. It's a win-win situation.

A similar situation can occur at the top of the corporate ladder. As a general rule, when former employees of a company that you have profitably dissected become the equivalent of hungry peasants, whining about lost jobs and benefits, throw them a bone. It's the greatest public relations gesture you can make, and everyone will recognize the goodness and generosity inherent in your voluntary charitable giving.

The finest example of an amazingly generous bone thrown to former workers, in my recent memory, is offered by I. L. Winnit, former chairman of Double Crossing and a gentleman renowned for his generous philanthropic giving. Winnit was an options and a promotion genius. At one point, he made more than half a billion dollars with his stock options on his way to achieving temporarily a net worth of six billion dollars in eighteen months during a stock buying frenzy. After the company collapsed, the Department of Justice and the SEC investigated the company and Winnit. They claimed that both had schemed to inflate stated revenues. A number of Double Crossing employees lost their retirement benefits in the collapse. Things were looking grim for I. L. Winnit when he was dragged before a congressional committee to testify. However, with a sure stroke clearly indicative of his genius, he shocked all present when he offered to give displaced workers, out of his own pocket, twenty-five million dollars. *Twenty-five million dollars!* That was an amount equal to a full five percent of his options take! That was *more* than he spent on his own new garage, which was slightly larger than the Smithsonian. Talk about defusing your critics.

The lesson here should be obvious. When your back is against the wall and you are confronted by the specter of ordinary people who covet what you own, by critics and regulators, *and* by the press, throw the people a bone. Like Santa Claus, you will make everyone feel grateful just to imagine you. Who knows? The next time they hold a hearing instead of serving you with a summons they might set out cookies and milk.

THE BONUS   Always keep a holiday stocking pinned to your mantle, just in case the real Santa Claus happens by with a little something to celebrate the year's end. Make sure it is a deep stocking.

As a rule of thumb, keep your salary only mildly unreasonable, your stock options as invisible as possible, and your bonuses astronomical. Your salary is a published constant, always available for criticism. Your stock options are difficult to calculate. Your bonuses hit like lightening and any criticism of them will dissipate as quickly as thunder when other issues intrude. Plus, when the economy is troubled, stock and options used as bonuses can be wrapped in accounting camo packages that help them blend into a balance sheet quietly. And never tie one hundred percent of your bonuses to performance, except in a good year. The control you exercise over your team is considerable, but never absolute. Why pay for the failures of others?

On the other hand, when your little corner of the economy is robust and you and your team perform brilliantly and all those around you are making money, then award your annual bonuses proudly and let any criticism remain where it began, with the envy of others. How much should you expect? Eyebrows start to rise at around thirty million dollars, whether in stock, options, or cash or any combination of the three. On the other hand, larger bonuses have been taken. Why not go for a record? The fact is that a handsome annual bonus is a small price to pay for success and top leadership.

Let's take a look at the costs. At year's end in 2006 Wall Street gave away twenty-four billion dollars in bonuses. Let's assume that this figure represents only ten percent of all bonuses awarded by major corporations in America that year. Of America's three hundred million inhabitants, about half file tax returns. The rest are children and other dependents, retirees, slackers, incompetents, tax cheats, and people living off handouts. A quick calculation will reveal that two hundred and forty billion dollars in annual bonuses divided by one hundred and fifty million workers equals a price tag of only sixteen hundred dollars per tax payer. Considering the risks of bad leadership and heated competition from foreign companies, one hundred and thirty-three bucks per month, or seventy seven cents per hour for every hour ever worked, per worker, is a small insurance premium for citizens to

pay to keep America's top corporations on track and to bring happiness and
good cheer each holiday season to our hard working corporate leaders

This brings to mind that old saying, "Make hay when the sun shines."
You can live or die by the bonus. I strongly recommend that in a good year
you choose life, and not just life, but life magnified. If your personal annual bonus equals ten to thirty times the lifetime earnings of the average
American wage earner, then be satisfied that at least for this year, Santa
knows that you've been good.

Who said America is no longer a land of opportunity?

THE BOTTOM LINE   There is nothing complicated about corporations. They exist to make money. Add up all revenues, subtract out all
expenses, and the balance left is net profit or loss. That is the bottom line.
It measures how well or how poorly you did your job. Anything that does
not contribute to your bottom line is irrelevant and it should be eliminated
from your business plan and your corporate culture. Anything that can
contribute to your bottom line but currently does not should be incorpo-
rated into your business plan and your corporate culture. In the corporate
world, the bottom line is the voice of God. When God speaks, either listen
or be damned.

That said, be reminded that in every corporation at any given moment there are at least two, and as many as several dozen, bottom lines to
choose from. I have always thought of these as one strategic bottom line
and one or several tactical bottom lines. The strategic bottom line is the real
picture, so far as your accountants can calculate it accurately, and that is
the one you must use when planning. In most cases it is for your eyes and
the eyes of your CFO only. Tactical bottom lines, on the other hand, are a
moving target. Using accepted accounting procedures, for the most part,
your bean counters can play with the numbers and adjust reality to reflect
higher or lower profit, depending on the impression you wish to convey
to enemies, investors, regulators, and the public. While a solid strategic
bottom line will win your war, impressive tactical bottom lines can win a
host of tough battles and those victories can contribute greatly to winning
your war.

A word of warning. Don't trick yourself into believing in a tactical bottom line when it differs considerably from your strategic bottom line. That is called wish fulfillment and mistakes like that can ruin your corporation and end your career. Learn to be nimble, not delusional.

All business demands one character virtue not discussed enough in classrooms or boardrooms: Flexibility. You must be flexible. If you are flexible you can be nimble. What is right one day might be wrong the next, and what works as your bottom line in one situation might be detrimental in another. Be as flexible as you must to be right. And be as nimble as you must to dance circles around unwanted scrutiny. Meanwhile, in private, like presidents and generals everywhere, straighten your back, hang up your dance shoes, and always, always listen to the voice of God.

THE BUCK STOPS HERE   Most people have the illusion that all corporate decisions are the sole responsibility of the CEO. Nothing could be farther from the truth. Large, multinational corporations, in particular, are so complex that whole divisions run with virtual independence. However, it is a good idea to encourage the illusion, up to a point, so people will have confidence in their CEOs and know that someone somewhere is in charge.

On the other hand, no CEO can be totally responsible for the misdeeds of misguided underlings. If every buck stopped with the CEO, then he would be held responsible for every little misdemeanor and felony committed by people he employs, and that would be outrageously unfair.

What should you do with that coffee mug your daughter gave you that announces, "The Buck Stops Here?" If you must, keep it on your desk. It is a nice reminder of who's the boss, and you can quickly put it in your filing cabinet when your security team in Bangkok runs amok, your whiz kid in Hamburg shorts the market for a half million dollar profit three hours before you announce an unexpected third quarter loss, or your Vice President in Johannesburg is overheard by a reporter to say that when it comes to miners, apartheid wasn't all bad.

Of course I have been discussing the phrase, "The buck stops here," in relation to responsibility. It may also be discussed in relation to earnings.

Where do the bucks stop? Where should they stop? Why do they stop here? For deep pockets these are deep questions.

Remember that you are a CEO, not *un existentialiste*. People can drown in deep pools. You are better off to let your mind tread water and accept things the way they are, particularly when the way things are is friendly to the way you are. Namely, rich. No dog bites the hand that feeds him. Why should any alpha dog question the nature or the function of the hand itself?

Unless, of course, he is a poodle. And French.

BUCKY AWARDS   Picture a thin foot-tall dollar sign cast in solid platinum. Who wouldn't die to watch a televised ceremony where dozens of these were handed out to corporate winners? Entertainers have the Oscar, the Grammy, the Emmy, the Golden Globe, The People's Choice, the CMA, the SAG, and the Tony, to name only the most popular award shows for self-congratulation. Even boring writers can collect awards in New York City every November at the National Book Awards Ceremony and Dinner. Why should our nation's CEOs be left out in the cold? And what better antidote to bad press than good press?

I propose a gala annual ceremony recognizing our nation's finest CEOs to be held in a dignified place such as the Waldorf=Astoria Hotel on Park Avenue. Think of the categories deserving recognition. Most Hostile Takeover. Most Imaginative Accounting. Greatest Apparent Increase in Gross Revenues. Widest Gap between Stated and Restated Earnings. Best Human Resources Outsourcing. Best Superfluous Product Development. Most Aggressive Expansion, with domestic and offshore categories. Highest Inflation in Stock Value. Most Successful IPO for a Failed Company. Most Revenue Gained from Restructuring Pensions. Shortest Planned Obsolescence for a Household Product. Highest Net Profit Margin. Highest Productivity Relative to Wages. Most Profitable Downsizing. Best Golf Score. Best Ad Campaign. Most Effective Use of Lobbyists. Lowest Unit Labor Cost. Biggest Country Estate less than One Year Old. Most Ferraris. Leanest, Meanest, and Most Profitable. Best Bankruptcy. And of course, one of the top categories, Best Actor Before a Senate Sub-Committee.

The possibilities are almost endless. A show like this would provide a public relations shot in the arm for our profession, and it would provide a venue for some spirited competition on neutral ground where winners get glory and losers get to walk away under their own power. Think about it. How many Buckies could one great CEO win in a lifetime?

BUSINESS   Every now and then in human history a self-proclaimed savior leads his tribe from point A to a bed of quicksand. More often than not such saviors were motivated by brilliant but uncooked speculations, and the followers tagged along because they were used to swallowing whatever they were served. Even more startling, those who survived the quicksand had a marked tendency to pick themselves up, wipe themselves off, and blaze an even shorter path from point B to the next swamp. Human beings require very little encouragement to enhance their misery.

I say it is time to lure humanity out of the swamps and harness them for productive ends that will improve their lives. I believe that multinational corporations practicing international business are doing just that.

Look around you. In the same way that empire ruled the Roman world and the Roman Catholic Church ruled the Middle Ages in Western Europe, corporations are emerging as the undisputed rulers of the planet. However, unlike previous rulers, corporations are decentralized authorities that depend on the will of populations, measured in market forces, and that collective will is qualitatively better than the autocratic will of a single ruler. If I am right, our age of business has started the greatest and most benign advancement in world history. It will license greed and make it plausible for the masses. It will give individual humans everywhere an opportunity to assert their natural self-interest and attempt to take care of themselves with less fear of meeting dissonance or destruction as their reward for effort expended. After all these centuries, we are finally getting down to the real business of life: Money. Without it people falter. With it they have a chance.

Look at the progress we have made in America only recently in our history. The simple idea that any man can make and then trade a value added product for goods and services worth more than the effort and materials he spent to make it, has blossomed into companies like ICBMS and Microfang. The loyalty of the people, in the form of dollars spent, has been directed to corporations, and corporations control public information as well as the nation's capital. Everywhere business is beginning to rule. The congregation waits for proclamations from the Chairman of the Federal Reserve Board just as it once waited on the Vatican. World economies are interdependent as never before. Even in China and the former Soviet republics, the profit motive has replaced failed collectivist ideologies. African farmers, who lack electricity in their huts, use cell phones to get current information on local markets so they can maximize their profits from selling their vegetables, chickens, and baskets. Wherever you look in the world today, you see people scampering to make a buck and then scampering again to spend it. People are learning how to become their own saviors. Truly, it is a wonderful time to be alive.

Take the flame that is handed to you and deliver it, like an Olympic runner, to the next venue and then the next, until every street corner in every city in every nation on earth boasts a MacCruddie's bistro, a W*ALLMINE! Megastore, and a Fortressbank. Build, develop, and invest. In time, the methods of global commerce will overcome regional and indigenous habits in everything from art and philosophy to family and folkways. The cell phone tower will replace the totem pole; television will supplant basket weaving; and paved freeways will top gumbo ruts and traces on deserts. People everywhere will build, communicate, sell, spend, and invest. Towns will become cities. The world will truly become a global village, or perhaps more accurately, a global megametropolis. The result will be a single unified world culture that discards weird and threatening differences in return for one ethos shared by all. Just as strips and malls in Buffalo are indistinguishable from those in Twin Falls and Little Rock, whole societies around the globe will redefine themselves according to proven norms. Listen and already you will hear seeds of an international age of commerce whispered and sometimes shouted on every street corner of the globe: "What's in it for me?"

For ordinary people, historically speaking, that was an impossible question to utter in the face of Cossacks, kings, prophets, and tyrants, unless you wanted to be drawn, quartered, and eaten by mastiffs. Today the question is expected, and people who ask it will have a fighting chance to end up buying their own home, working for a solid company, starting their own business, sending their kids to college, or if they are truly gifted, founding the corporation that will some day replace Microfang or Big Boo. At the very least, they will find access to a public toilet and potable water.

The Age of Commerce is a toddler ready to leap from its basinet and cry to the world, "Me! Me! It's time for Me!" It will grow into a Goliath that consumes whole centuries and gives back in return opportunities for bright, motivated people to win jobs, clothing, education, transportation, housing, medical care, and all the tacos and soft drinks they demand. A natural division of labor and of capital will follow separating those who make the tacos from those who run the franchise from those who own the concept. Market forces will rule. And that can't help but be a good thing. Which would you rather eat, raw speculations in a swamp or tacos supreme with sour cream in an ergonomically molded orange polypropylene chair designed to perfectly accommodate your somewhat larger than average butt cheeks?

Maybe at last our wandering is over.

THE BUSINESS PLAN   Every successful business results from one percent planning and ninety-nine percent execution. That does not diminish the importance of the plan, however.

Without an airtight business plan, any business venture is doomed to failure, or worse, to mediocrity. The plan is absolutely essential. The caveat is that if you don't have the will to execute your plan, then the best plan in the world won't save you.

A good business plan for a large, multinational corporation should be no longer than six to twelve pages. Most business plans run hundreds and even thousands of pages, analyzing and projecting finances, markets, sales, cash flow, personnel, operations, efficiency, productivity, you name it. Most often that is because business plans are designed for someone else, typically an investment banker or potential shareholders. They are a sell job authored by business bureaucrats for other business bureaucrats, and the more they weigh the more weight they are given. If those are the hoops you must jump through, then jump. But meanwhile, reduce your understanding of your business to its essential parts and then focus on them. How you carry out your plan will fill in all the remaining blanks.

In brief, and in addition to capital, every business needs three things to compete successfully: Organization, communication, and leadership. Everything else flows from this holy trinity of good business. The plan that *you* use should focus only on those essentials. The fact is that nine-tenths of all businesses large and small fail miserably in one or more of these three missions, and the reason for that failure is poor execution, not poor conception.

The problem is that no one can learn the best execution of the holy trinity of skills from a school or from a plan. That execution must come from you. If you do not possess talent for these three skills, you will never run with the big dogs. But don't despair. Your career is not over. As a senior executive, you can still contribute to the team, finish in second or third place, and pull down several million a year. You could even write novel-length business plans for people who will actually read them.

On the other hand, if you are gifted with the holy trinity, then your odds of finishing first with the most are greatly improved. Business is and always will be the bastion of the exceptional individual, and the best business plan available is a single personality who can organize like a nun, communicate like Ronald Reagan, and lead like General George Patton.

BUZZ MARKETING   The claims that buzzards make for their brand of marketing are all true. You can sell more products faster with less advertising expense than by conventional means. All you have to do is ignite a buzz. So how do you start a good buzz? Basically, you use the oldest form of communication on earth. You start a rumor.

Here's how it works.   Strategically plant an entertaining story about a product. Plant it carefully and remember that people love gossip, scandal, weird events, secrets, forbidden topics, gut-splitting humor, anything that is over-the-top outrageous, and anything that involves bigger than life celebrities. Even more important, people love to be in the know. They love to be part of an inside group so they can retell entertaining stories that others haven't yet heard. If you put the right plant in the right places, consumers will work for you for nothing and do the job of a thousand costly ads, and your rumor will spread by word of mouth like a wildfire. Then you can listen for the "ching-ching-ching" at your cash registers.

Buzz marketing bypasses rational decision-making and product value. Instead, it zeroes in on what really matters: Fitting in and following the herd. What could be cooler than being the first on your block *to know*? And what could be worse than being left out of the loop altogether? Buzz marketing makes bandwagons that people like to jump on.

In addition to retelling entertaining stories however, people also like to follow the influence of leaders, particularly of celebrities. Who are you going to want to believe, some nameless paid model or a hotshot actor with a testimonial in hand? The real secret of buzz marketing is the network. Set up a series of hubs centered on influential people, each one of whom sustains a buzz within his or her circle of influence. As the buzz spreads, a second tier of influential people will sustain their hubs, and so on down the line until an entire sector of consumers is influenced by what suddenly adds up to a new fashion. Bottom line, everyone wants to be part of the in-group, and buzz marketing allows all consumers in and keeps them amused in the process. Word of mouth always has been and always will be the best salesman, and buzz marketing lets you create and direct word of mouth in predictable ways.

It is also cost efficient, and downright cheap, compared to highfalutin ads on television, and I think it is more effective. It is also perfectly compatible with the Internet, which is not surprising since the Internet inspired it. In an age of constant coercion and in-your-face sell-jobs at every turn, buzz marketing offers consumers the appearance of authenticity and a chance to kick back, feel like they are not being manipulated, add their two cents worth, and enjoy being led to market. The buzzards call this "pull," as opposed to the "push" of conventional advertising. That works for me. You can pull sheep to slaughter just as fast as you can push them, and maybe faster. The only thing that matters is getting them there.

"The real secret of buzz marketing is the network." p. 57

CALIFORNIA   If you are not headquartered in California, I recommend that you acquire and maintain an additional home there. When the economy is hot, California can be on fire and you won't want to miss the action. As of this writing, it is the most populous state in the Union with around thirty-six million inhabitants, and the seventh largest economy in *the world.*

If you are in hitech you'll want to build in one of the ultra-fashionable areas accessing the Silicon Valley, near all the charms of San Francisco and the Napa wine country. Keep in mind, however, that Northern California is still a hotbed of liberal unrest and weird ideas so be careful not to sully your reputation by association.

In all other areas of business, I suggest fashionable southern California where conspicuous consumption has evolved into exquisite exhibitionism. Try not to be shy. You can't go wrong building a little Taj Mahal in Bob Hope country, where former President Ronald Reagan, modern America's principal promoter of free market enterprise, lived, worked, golfed, and retired. It just doesn't get any better than that.

CAPITAL   Everything in an economy has intrinsic value. Let's say that you possess a rock. The rock has value and you will be able to trade it for other things, such as a piece of wood or, if the rock contains gold, a new automobile. The intrinsic value of your rock is set by consumers who covet it. This intrinsic value may be described as capital, and since it is more convenient to exchange notes carrying preassigned value than to exchange actual rocks and pieces of wood, we create money to stand for capital. As long as everyone in the economy agrees to the preassigned values of money, it works as a surrogate for the value in things and it thereby acquires intrinsic value itself and in this way becomes not just a surrogate for capital, but it becomes capital itself. Add up all your marketable assets, including your money, and the value you possess will be the amount of capital you own. Of course, all this is elementary. I lead you through it, however, because unless you think in terms of capital, instead of other vague, subjective, and sometimes fashionable concepts like beauty, tranquility, harmony, and The Sacred, you are liable to miss some of the greatest opportunities of your career.

What did George Hearst see in the mountains of Nevada, the dry peaks of Butte, Montana, and the velvety humps and valleys of The Black Hills of South Dakota? Sacredness? Tranquility? Beauty? No! He saw capital in the form of silver, copper, and gold. The first geologists to look over the plains of West Texas and Oklahoma, the deserts of Saudi Arabia, and the tundra of Alaska saw capital. The developers of the uninspired peaks of Sun Valley saw capital. The purchasers of a clever but clumsy computer program they named MS DOS saw capital. What all these people had in common was their productive use of imagination.

Think capital wherever you go and whatever you do. And train your imagination to see all the forms that capital might take. Every person has an imagination, but if you learn how to put yours to work, you will gain a competitive edge over those who don't and maybe, just maybe, one day you too will stand on the edge of history and see, where others see only a quiet lake, some beaver dams, undisturbed trees, and a vista that stretches for mile after uninhabited mile, a fountain of capital as you imagine a magnificent theme park with hotels, casinos, waterslides, restaurants, museums, auditoriums, shopping malls, and a giant sports arena.

Capital does not exist in nature. It exists only in the acquisitive imagination of human beings; in the desire to improve one's lot. Call that desire "greed." It is universal. Just as the hungry peasant desires more food, the imaginative developer desires more capital. Greed is the alchemy that turns meaningless objects into capital, and capital is the energy that turns nature into economy. Without capital, nature would rule and we would be troglodytes. With capital we rule nature and troglodites.[9]

---

9 Unlike "troglodytes," the term "troglodites," coined by former lobbyist and email rhetorician Jack Abramoff, is not insulting. It is a term of endearment that refers to financially unsophisticated ordinary people after they take advice from financially sophisticated gentlemen who wear expensive ties and make large donations to their own charities.

CASH   Never dwell on the value of the obvious.

CASH COW   You know all about these animals. Remember that vending machine business that you started in prep school, or that term paper business you ran in college? I know that you remember your trust fund. Or your friend's trust fund. Where it comes from doesn't really matter. What matters is that everyone needs a reliable source of cash. You'll never know when you might be caught short.

Remember the plight of the Leizes? The Endrun Corporation Leizes? Bucky Boy and his wife? These folks must have accumulated a billion dollars in capital but what good did it do them after the government froze their assets and the press and the courts started persecuting them? A man used to a certain life style can't change overnight, you know? So to make ends meet for the forthcoming holidays, they were forced to sell some of their most valuable personal property at a garage sale in their Rancho Santa Fe getaway residence-- a garage sale! – just to keep pâté on the table and gas in the Bugatti. There is a lesson here. Always keep a good, solid cash cow handy so you'll never have to worry about going hungry at Thanksgiving.

CAVEAT EMPTOR   It means "let the buyer beware," for those of you who slept through your Latin classes at boarding school. It means that if you sell something without an explicit warranty, the buyer assumes all risk. It is a useful legal precedent based upon the Darwinian principle that the fittest are entitled to prevail. A buyer who is naïve and who neglects to inform herself as to the quality of the product she is purchasing deserves whatever she gets. Conversely, a seller who is clever enough to squeeze profit out of a product without explicitly misrepresenting it, deserves all the lemonade he can consume. Like an athlete, if a person chooses to become a consumer, that person must learn the rules of the game and must train to be in good enough shape to play it correctly. A lazy or ignorant consumer who gets hurt in the game has no one to blame but herself.

Be ever vigilant in your lifelong battle against so-called "consumer protection" legislation. It is all designed to allow incompetents into the game and then allow their trial lowyers to sue businesses for damages because the incompetents failed to perform adequately. Clearly, if you allow incompetents and trial lowyers to define the rules of the game, your business will resemble fishing for trout in a leaching pond. On the other hand, *make* the rules of the game, then master the game itself, and your business will remind you of shooting fish in a barrel.

Bottom line: If you intend to outwit someone, you don't have to give fair warning. The courts understand that the principle of caveat emptor gives warning for you. Let the buyer beware, and let the shrewd prevail.

CAVIAR   I have no reason to be coy since the only people who will read this volume are self-selected young men and women destined to become members of The Club. So let's be honest about caviar. It is the most underwhelming creation on earth. It combines the texture of mucous with the odor of a fish market four miles downwind with the taste of lightly salted hog entrails. Gourmets refer to these traits as "the subtle nuances" to distinguish them, I suppose, from the uppercut you get when you take on a pickled herring. The implication is that lust for caviar separates sophisticates who appreciate subtlety from bumpkins who require the obvious. But it doesn't matter how you frame the issue. With caviar one expects fish and one gets funky Cream of Wheat.

Caviar is therefore "an acquired taste." Except for seagulls, no one with a full deck marvels over his first taste of caviar. We train ourselves to believe in it because it ranks first on the truly extensive and expensive list of things that have snob appeal. Like nothing else, it separates those who are worldly from those who are not. Eating caviar is a test, not unlike any initiation ritual, asking you to prove the depth of your commitment to your kind. Some of you will have been raised in an environment in which Beluga or even Sterlet caviar was consumed the way cheese crunchies are consumed in other households. For you all this is old hat. For those of you raised on cheese crunchies, it is essential that you lose your inhibitions and develop lust for caviar. Even more important, it is essential that you learn how to use caviar to test others. You can also buck up and be of good cheer because there is no test more challenging to your integrity, and once you pass this test, it's all downhill. Affect joy for the taste of caviar and you should be able to affect anything.

'CEPTING   An associate of mine who did his undergraduate work at Princeton is credited with giving a name to a common practice that I highly recommend: 'Cepting. According to my associate, 'cepting is the art of ferreting out the central idea, or concept, of an academic course, a particular lecture, an examination question, or an assigned paper. If you "cept-out" an exam, or get the "cept" of a lecture, you have succeeded in identifying the professor's central argument, which, of course, will help you regurgitate it successfully on an examination. The point of 'cepting is to please the professor (or should we say, "to grasp the course content") sufficiently to pass the course. As an intellectual exercise, 'cepting might be compared to speed-reading Cliff Notes. It allows an individual to grasp the point of something without having to read it or go through all the details, background, arguments, evidence, and other minutia most of us quickly forget anyway.

Consider this example. Beethoven's music, like Goethe's fiction, was part of the historical movement called "Romanticism," which validated individual experiences and emotional responses. Now there is a good 'cept to keep filed away. Some day, you will be napping at a concert. Your wife will wake you for the intermission and lead you into the foyer. Invariably, someone trying to be knowledgeable will throw out a comment about Beethoven's music, *strum und drang*, and suicides prompted by *The Sorrows of Young Werther*. To most people, none of this will make any sense whatsoever, thank God, but to you, armed with your 'cept, it will make perfect sense. You can reply comfortably, "Of course. The validation of private emotions among the German romantics was such a powerful motive that it almost had to be exaggerated at times, even to the point of self-destruction." Others around you will raise their eyebrows and drop their jaws momentarily as you shine in professorial splendor. "I never suspected that he had such depth," someone is bound to murmur. "He is much more complex than I thought." "Impressive grasp of history as well as Wall Street." "A veritable Renaissance man."

Of course I am being generous here. But the point should be well taken. 'Cept-out whatever you can. Store your 'cepts as in a card file. Each 'cept will provide a little frame of reference. You never know when good 'cepts might come in handy, plus they will help you to never seem surprised. They will give you an air of depth, sophistication, and worldliness that will serve you, particularly among the tea and charities set, as efficiently as the original Picasso hanging on the wall of your den.

CEREBRAL CORTEX   This part of the human brain, and in particular, the neo-cortex and the frontal lobes, is the latest part to evolve, the last to mature in individuals, and the one that differentiates humans from other primates and other vertebrates. It takes a leading part in all of the so-called "higher" brain functions, such as planning, language, ethics, aesthetics, morality, and abstract thought. No creature without a cerebral cortex could ever imagine a Utopia.

Its importance is also over-rated.

The motivation to compete, the impulse to greed, the imperative to dominate and control, in short, all the instincts we have that compel us to want to survive, whatever our circumstances, come from older, so-called "reptilian" parts of the brain. Without them, we would probably be content to sit in outdoor cafes writing poetry and discussing flower petals.

Use the cortex as a tool, not as a guide. It will give you an edge in business, particularly in your use of language, logic, and persuasiveness, and in your ability to plan. Otherwise, learn to listen to the deeper voices.

Perhaps this sounds harsh and uncivilized to you, particularly if you are waltzing through your sophomore Music Appreciation class, or you have just discovered Yoga and you now have a guru. I'm sorry, but we must be realistic about this thing. The world is a jungle and a battlefield upon which only the fit survive. Business is an adaptation to that real world, and it is no wonder that lawn sculptures of predators are popular among CEOs. Sharks, lions, wolves, hawks, and bears are survivors. Yes, humans can imagine a different world, a kinder, gentler, and more humane world, in which humane values replace the values of the jungle and the battlefield, and the *nocturne* replaces the anthem. But no one has yet figured out just how to make that world real and make it work. So until someone does, we must adapt to what is, not to what we might fancy. Ancient voices in your head will guide you. The newer voices are excellent tools and a pleasant respite while on holiday, but they can also lower your position on the food chain if you let them.

CHAIRMANSHIP   In the best of all possible worlds you will be CEO *and* Chairman of the Board of your company. Nothing provides singular, unified leadership like a single, unified leader. Nothing protects leadership like the leader himself. Nothing is more powerful than consolidated power.

To some, this will raise the issue of dissent. The political sector tolerates dissent and in a democracy, some dissent is probably advisable, though it is often annoying. Under unified leadership, a corporation can function, indeed should function, virtually without any meaningful dissent whatsoever, and the result of this spirit of unity should be peak performances for staff, greater efficiency for mid-level plodders, and for you, higher earnings, expanded perks, broader benefits, increased tenure, and a glowing reputation for autocratic ruthlessness.

The real trick is to stifle dissent while seeming to take it into account. How do you do this? Here is an example. Let's say that you want to mine gold on land bordering a wilderness area near headwaters of a blue ribbon trout stream. One of your team is an ardent catch-and-release trout fisherman with a strong background in conservation. He opposes the heap leach aspect of the project on grounds that damaging the wilderness or the fishery will cause high cleanup costs, trigger a backlash in public relations, and spoil his fishing. Otherwise, he has a history of being an effective and productive team player. How do you deal with him?

First keep in mind that dealing with him is the same thing as dealing with all like him; that is, the tree-hugging public. You can't simply remind him that no mining subsidiary worth its salt ever paid more than a token pittance in cleanup costs before declaring bankruptcy and turning the matter over to state and federal governments and their taxpayers. You shouldn't have to remind him that public relations and information control will gut any backlash. What you must do is take a green approach. Go duck hunting. Try not to shoot your host. Make sure your dues are paid to Trout Unlimited and that you have displayed in your office photos of your recent fly fishing vacation to New Zealand. Appoint a committee to evaluate the Environmental Impact Statement and address the concerns raised. Praise the individual who raised them. Meanwhile, work with your public relations people to develop exactly the right language to use when discussing the mine and the potential for catastrophic damage. Engage your science specialists to develop proofs that pollution *cannot occur* within the guidelines of your business plan. Aim for concepts like "cutting edge technology," "learning from past mistakes," "responsible corporate citizen," and "enriching the local community." Appear to be more concerned with wilderness and watershed than the malcontent himself. Launch an advertising campaign featuring butterflies and fawns and lots of happy trout – plus the benefits of secure employment in a region that desperately needs it. The situation will resolve itself.

After you have won the battle, share the joy and promote the malcontent to run your new field office in Ulan Batur, where he can spend the rest of his career evaluating high desert ore deposits and learning Mongolian. Effective and productive team players are a dime a dozen.

In the contemporary world, people are put off by displays of unbridled power, so learn to use yours with this kind of subtlety and you will keep it intact. In the long run, however, stockholders, employees, and other board members will remember that you were right, that you were bright, that your mine added significantly to the company's bottom line, *and,* most importantly, that opposing you is a form of self-immolation.

If you run into opposition from someone who serves on the Board of Directors, use the same basic strategy and apply lots of energy to bonding with agreeable members. Enough games of golf can solve just about any problem. In the worst case scenario, when a board member becomes intractable and favors his position more than his membership in The Club, find a good reason for your stockholders to distrust or despise him and see that he gets voted off the board in favor of a hand-picked newcomer whom everyone loves and respects, such as a retired Chairman of the Joint Chiefs of Staff or a Nobel laureate.

Always shoot for Chairman *and* CEO, which, of course, makes you the chief overseer of yourself. The more you consolidate power, the more you can wield it; and the more power you can wield, the more you will have to consolidate.

CHALLENGE

Think of life as a series of mountain peaks. All of them need to be conquered, and someone needs to take credit for climbing them. When climbing, do yourself a favor. Never pause. Wear waffle-stompers so that when others stop to rest, to pamper, to congratulate themselves, or to smell the flowers, you can stomp on their backs for leverage and leave a lasting impression. This will remind them and you of what it takes to reach the peak, and of who will always get there first. Challenge is challenging only if you hesitate.

CHAMBERS OF COMMERCE

The national Chamber of Commerce can always be counted on to speak our language, whether through lobbyists or its public policy statements. But don't overlook local Chambers of Commerce. Even though they are grassroots organizations supporting small businesses, they are always looking up to the next level. That is to say, in general, that they get most of their ideas from us. Think of each chapter as a little lap dog eager to please and happy to be of service to the big dogs. They will automatically be loyal to your needs and if you call on them for support for any reason, be it a labor dispute, an environmental issue, taxes, or ideology, they will respond positively and be flattered that you asked. In return, you might have to speak at a Rotary luncheon or a Lions' picnic but don't worry because they will welcome you as the biggest news in town since that tornado that swept away the trailer park.

CHANGE

Everyone in any kind of business knows that complacency is death, and yet our natural desire for stability often makes us forget just how important it is to promote change. Change is the genie in the bottle of commerce. If it weren't for the latest style, the new and improved, and the amazing breakthrough technology, profits would stagnate and all growth would cease. The faster the pace of change, the greater your turnover; and the higher your rate of turnover the greater your return on invested capital. Every change is a rebirth. Put simply, the more things change, the faster things that remain the same disappear, and the faster things change the more opportunities you create to make money.

That said, I want you to ask yourself how often you apply this fundamental principle of change to areas outside of your immediate business dealings. Specifically, I want you to think about Old Glory.

We have seen many changes in our nation since 1776. We have also weathered many challenges. But the challenges we confront today are more important for our future survival and prosperity than any we have ever faced in the past. We face gargantuan competition from emerging economies only recently converted to our way of commerce in Russia, China, India, and dozens of smaller nations. We face threats of annihilation from tens of millions of people sympathetic with terrorists, particularly from militant Islamic sects, who want to destroy us before our way of life gains stronger footholds in their cultures. Additionally, the borders of our nation are besieged by millions of illegal immigrants who will do anything to nibble at our prosperity. How do we meet these challenges? I say we take hold of change to direct the course of history before history, like a hungry python, tries to swallow us. How do we do that?

We change Old Glory. Our flag is the symbol of our nation and our way of life, and a simple change in its design would do more to promote our future prosperity than all the rhetoric and all the policies and all the military strikes in history combined. Our flag is the most potent bit of information the world has ever known. Let us broadcast a new and vital message that will dig into the hearts and minds of people everywhere and convince them at a glance that we are here to stay, and that *we mean business.*

I propose a constitutional amendment to alter the design of our flag so it will reflect more accurately a contemporary view of The American Dream that will win friends, intimidate enemies, and influence people everywhere to admire, support, and emulate our way of life and to respect our leadership . Specifically, I propose that we remove the fifty stars from our flag and replace them with forty-nine gold dollar signs and a bald eagle.[10] The inviting blend of red, white, blue, and gold colors alone justifies this change. But the symbolism speaks even more aggressively.

Let us announce to the world, despite trade deficits, that we are prepared to let the euro, the yen, the yuan, the pound, the peso, the ruble, the rupee, and the rial fend for themselves if they can – or give in to the dollar. We trust the dollar. Let us stand up and shout proudly to all the world that greed is out of the closet and that greed is good and natural and the most powerful motivator known to man; that money is the salvation for people everywhere; that our way of life is superior; and that when it comes to management of assets and means to acquire more assets, we are the best and the brightest. Let us proclaim from above our highest rooftops that we are determined to maintain our role of world leadership and that we *will* dominate world markets.

And finally, let us address directly those waves of immigrants and would-be immigrants clamoring to reach our shores. Let the symbol of Old Glory inform them: Don't give me any more of your tired, poor, huddled masses yearning to breathe *free* so they can add to taxpayers' burdens by taking advantage of our *free* education, welfare subsidies, Medicaid, and social services. Give me only ambitious, healthy, industrious farm workers, convenience store clerks, dish washers, maids, meat cutters, and landscape attendants; give me software engineers, motel managers, and accountants who can contribute. Give me people who can do the work that needs to be done for modest wages, and who can pay their own way and put hard dollars back into our economy.

And please, don't send me any more wretched refuse from your teeming shores; any more homeless and tempest tossed. We have enough refuse and enough homeless and enough disturbed of our own. Send me news of hard dollars coming my way: Tax breaks and incentives so I can build a profitable plant on those teeming shores and then your homeless refuse can earn some capital on their own turf and learn to take care of themselves.

---

10 We could hold a national lottery to see which state gets to be the eagle. However, I suggest that we not include our newest state, Grace, since it is the only state that is entirely metaphysical. Grace does not presently have a star and won't need a symbol in the future. Grace speaks for itself.

Why did past waves of immigrants come to America in the first place? Why did Serbs, Finns, Italians, Croats, Welshmen, Irishmen, and Germans show up at Ellis Island wearing signs pinned to their coats that said simply, "Butte America?" It wasn't because they were on a quest to get in touch with their true feelings, to freely express their beliefs, or to discover the meaning of life in the wilderness. It was because their relatives told them about jobs in the copper mines that paid cold, hard cash. Surely it is time for those of us born in America to give our nation the same recognition that immigrants have always given her. Surely it is time to put dollar signs on the flag and in our hearts.

It is no longer enough to hitch your wagons to stars. If you want to gain a fighting edge today you need to hitch your wagon to capital and then fight like hell to maximize your returns. Do that much. Take away the stars and add the dollar signs and one truly fierce-looking eagle to our flag and let the symbolism speak for itself. Do that much and the next time you stand to pledge your allegiance to our United States you will feel like you have good reason to lift your lamp beside this golden door – because that door will be 24 karat. Do that much and in time you will see gross domestic products you never imagined possible.

The greatest instrument of change is change itself. It is like a dose of fresh water from a fountain of youth. It revitalizes us because it forces us to pause, reflect for thirty seconds, then adapt. Change is good for corporations and good for America. And while it might be frightening to some people to reorganize a tradition to suit current trends, it can allow us to boldly assert our response to threats the world imposes. Dollars are our ace in the hole, and they will win you more happiness than a honeymoon. Certainly more happiness than a field of stars that only stand for dreams.

I offer one more suggestion for the future. Our coin and currency displays our national motto, "In God We Trust." That is true. We do. We are a deeply religious nation and I would never change that phrase. However, we are also a nation of atheists, secularists, humanists, agnostics, animists, and faithful believers belonging to every religion, denomination, and sect known to man. Consequently, among our religious majority, we find dozens of differing definitions of God. What in our culture besides this diverse religiosity is our most common denominator? I'll tell you what. It is greed.

Commerce. Capital. Making money. Greed is the one universal value that binds us *all* together. If three-quarters of our people look to God the Heavenly Father, nine out of ten also look to god the CEO, god the corporation, god the workplace, and god the market, and ninety-nine percent look to god the dollar. Even atheists appreciate sound earnings. Therefore, I propose at some appropriate time in the future that we ask Congress to authorize a second motto so we can print on new currency, particularly on larger denominations, the more militant phrase, "In Greed We Trust." Congress should have no problem endorsing greed as a motto, and the motto should please nearly every market sector in America. It will also challenge the rest of the world to live up to our motto or lose.

Dollar signs on Old Glory. "In Greed We Trust" on our money. If you are going to stand at all, you need to stand tall.

CHARISMA   Charisma is the lifeblood of leadership. It should be one of the three primary attributes of your character, along with greed and arrogance. A brief glimpse at history will demonstrate to you that even a moron blessed with an abundance of charisma can lead churches, armies, and whole nations to achieve their goals or to jump over a cliff on command. Imagine what you, the best and the brightest, can do when you harness and direct your charisma.

If for some reason you have little or no charisma, then you need to take up another profession, like dentistry, because you will never inspire anyone except the accounting department, and inspired accountants don't count.

If your level of charisma scores somewhere between the norm and the void, then do what you can to polish your skills. Most people with little charisma can bluff having more. It's like getting colored contact lenses to change or enhance the color of your eyes. I recommend that you watch the actor, George C. Scott in the film, *Patton,* or Burt Lancaster in *Elmer Gantry.* If that doesn't help, then take a clandestine vacation to Southern California and hire a plastic surgeon and an acting coach. After you recuperate and are ready, practice on your family. Pretend to throw a tirade or give an inspiring speech at dinner and watch your family members' reactions to see how well you performed. Like the actor, Roy Scheider, in the film *All That Jazz*, wake up every morning, look at yourself in the mirror, remind yourself that, "It's Showtime!" and at the very least, you'll get a running start.

On the other hand, if you were born with good charisma, don't take it for granted. Turn it loose and let it manage every aspect of your public personality. A charismatic leader can get by with amazing gaffs and be instantly forgiven simply because, at a gut level, people like, admire, feel submissive toward, and want to please, follow, and forgive him. The admiration people have for charismatic leaders is completely irrational but absolute. Look at Charles Manson, Adolph Hitler, and James Jones, for example. All three were impractical, unproductive, evil, and sometimes incredibly stupid men but all three were charismatic leaders and others wanted to follow them regardless of where they led. The best example, and one that you should follow, is former President Ronald Reagan, our finest President and savior of our economy. As a spokesman for General Electric and later for The United States, he demonstrated a quiet kind of charisma that was irresistible to ordinary people. Probably a few million other citizens in America were more qualified on other grounds to be President, but no one who ever held the office could work an audience of ordinary people like Mr. Reagan. As a result, this inspired and soft spoken actor from Tinsel Town developed such a large and powerful following that he single-handedly whipped Communism, buried the New Deal, defeated negative thinking, crippled labor unions, took graduation out of the graduated income tax, put God back into government, and obliterated drug use forever, saving millions of alter boys and pom-pom girls from lives of gang violence and prostitution. On top of all that, he saved Savings and Loans from themselves for the special, cut rate, one time price of only one thousand dollars per American taxpayer, spurred on by several million old timers and supporters thrilled to lose their life savings in S&Ls for a chance to help the Gipper win one and rescue an industry that had fallen on hard times.

That was one shining moment.[11]

The bottom line for leadership is to cultivate an image that inspires irrational admiration. Lock in loyalty and anything you want follows. Charisma is the key. Charisma shapes image and image is the magic wand of success.

CHICANERY   Shrewdness applied by someone else is chicanery. When you apply shrewdness, it is strategy, and when you are shrewder than your enemies, it is successful strategy. As a CEO, you are the "I" at the center of the storm, and you have the power to set value and to dictate what is right. Clearly, strategy is morally superior to chicanery: What you do in your own best interest stands head and shoulders above what your enemies do to unravel you. Thus, you can work your whole career without ever having to practice chicanery and no one can ever accuse you of being deceptive and underhanded. Always choose to do right.

---

11 President Reagan's bailout of Savings and Loans adds additional luster to his legacy. We all know that "consistency is the hobgoblin of small minds," and that President Reagan believed that government was not the solution, but the problem. In the case of the bailout, the Resolution Trust Corporation, the government bureaucracy created to oversee collapsed S&Ls, turned out not to be the problem, but the solution. This, like the President's deficit spending, demonstrates the width of the Reagan mind, which was never troubled by hobgoblins.

CHIEF   By definition, a CEO is a chief. But being chief takes some adjustment. For your entire career, from the first moment you go to work for a corporation until the moment you retire as Chairman of the Board and Chief Executive Officer, you will leave democracy behind and live in a world where wealth makes power and power shapes influence. Unlike our democracy, in which each person, regardless of means, is allowed one vote, in a corporation, each share of common stock is worth one vote, and so those with the most invested, the most to lose and the most to gain, have the greatest number of votes and thus the greatest influence. That is as it should be. Risk and reward are divided and shared equitably.

The structure of a corporation also reflects the fact that people are by nature tribal. It is a hierarchy strictly ordered into chains of command leading directly to the chief to facilitate efficient decision-making. Decision by committee, by contrast, is comically inefficient. That is one of the reasons why even democracies elect an executive to lead them. Congress can't. Congress can influence, but it can't lead. It has too many heads. Not just democracies, but all societies and all organizations need and look to leaders, autocrats, and chiefs, who can make tough decisions on the spot, as decisions are required, and not spend endless hours in debate, as Congress or a council of elders might. For the purposes of your career, emulate Julius Caesar, Napoleon, and Louis XIV. You need to lead, not contemplate.

Whenever you take the chief out of a chief executive officer then you are left with the shell of a man, a kind of business bureaucrat destined to mutter and muddle. The position of chief empowers you, as it should, since you have the most to lose and the most to gain. So take the power and wear it comfortably as a mantle. And always remember: Until they pull you down, the chief rules. If some of the field hands on your plantation don't like that fact, then sell them down the river and find people who do.

CHILD LABOR   Imagine that you are in a foreign city in one of those developing countries. On one street corner, a slick boy of twelve or fifteen stands by a curb selling drugs to those in the know who pull up as if to a drive-in window. There he is all day, selling crack and meth, listening to his iPod and talking on his cell phone, spitting on cars he doesn't like. Across the street another boy about the same age but a little scruffy, walks into a building, climbs the stairs, and enters a small clothing factory. He stays there all day too because he has a job, and when he leaves, fourteen hours later, he has a crisp new American ten dollar bill in his pocket. Which kid do you think will live to see his twentieth birthday? Which kid will make the better husband, father, and productive citizen? Which kid would you let your kid play with?

When children choose to work in order to better themselves, what kind of service is a community performing when it comes along and tells the child that no, he can't work and better himself? What, he should go spit on cars and sell drugs, and probably get shot or carved up for his efforts?

No one condones the exploitation of children, but providing a job for a child who wants one is not exploitation. It is development. It is community service, particularly if the child earns more money than he has ever seen before. He is also learning responsibility, punctuality, productivity, economy, discipline, obedience to authority, good citizenship, and a lot more. I am amused by children and I like to do everything I can for them, including giving them jobs so they can eat well, have a nice warm coat to wear, start a savings account, get a credit card, and buy some CDs, hip sneakers, and a pair of designer jeans. Hiring third world children is particularly good business. Not only do they spend, once they have money to spend, but we can produce the shirts they make for one-fourth the domestic cost and sell them for half the customary price, which increases our market share, doubles our return on invested capital, *and* helps the American consumer stretch her dollar. Everybody wins.

So what is the complaint about "child labor?" I don't get it so I decided to ask five of my acquaintances if they worked when they were kids. To a man, they all said yes. One fellow set up a card table just outside a train station during rush hours in Connecticut and sold bottled French spring water for three dollars a bottle and gourmet truffles two for five dollars. He got his inventory from his mother's pantry, so his cost of goods sold was zero. Talk about margins! Another fellow from Burlingame, California contracted to mow people's lawns. He had a crew of Mexicans who took care of the grass and he took a fifty per-cent commission for setting up the deals plus a twenty per-cent leaseback from the workers against their wages for tools he provided. Then, for a third of her action, he licensed the daughter of his parents' cook to sell them tacos and lemonade for lunch. Everybody was happy and he made a killing. Another fellow in Cupertino collected stray cats from his neighborhood and sold them to a research laboratory for four dollars each. He not only made money, he cleaned up his neighborhood and advanced the cause of science. Another fellow, as an ambitious young man, took a subway down to West 42nd Street and sold his sister's discarded underwear to perverts and got up to ten dollars per item. Talk about profitable recycling! One day, after deducting train fare, two hotdogs, and a Perrier, he netted one hundred and sixteen dollars. The last fellow I asked made out the best of all. He learned how to make baseball tickets using his home computer, and he tells me with a chuckle that they looked just like the real McCoy. He hung out near Yankee Stadium and scalped them to tourists. They were well enough designed that one in ten of his clients was able to use them to get through the turnstiles. He kicked butt, and with practically no overhead. In fact, he did so well in three years of work, that after he had saved a substantial sum, he proposed to his father that if he could save X amount of dollars, would good old dad match his savings five to one so he could buy a car? Any car? Daddy didn't think he had a worry, so he agreed without a second thought and to his surprise, the next day, he was obligated to outfit his son with the lad's first Jaguar.

Boys will be boys, you say, but just look at how hard these kids worked and no one complained about their child labor. Let the bleeding hearts take a vacation. Kids like to work and it's good for them. Each one of these fellows went on to become the Chief Executive Officer of an American corporation. When it comes to child labor, the proof is in the pudding.

Who's to say that a scruffy little Nicaraguan boy, or for that matter a shy little Malaysian girl, won't follow the same path?

CHILDREN If you choose to have children, provide well for them. Make sure they attend the finest nursery schools, kindergartens, prep schools, colleges, and graduate schools that your network or a substantial donation can buy. Teach them well. The worst thing a child can do is embarrass his parents. If you educate your children about the realities of life and teach them good manners they will make you proud.

Your children, as well as your wife, will certainly have sufficient motivation to behave as you want them to. Circumstances are instructive, and the most efficient educator in the world is the circumstance of "the will." Your last will and testament. Be sure to direct your family's thoughts to it often, and remind them periodically that it is never final until the eleventh hour. A family bound by mutual loyalty is a blessing.

CLASS In America, we avoid discussions of class distinction because they contradict the naïve definition of democracy so dear to us all. We discuss only lower middle, middle, and upper middle classes because those distinctions underscore the hope of upward mobility, and thus of the American Dream, even though the distinctions are meaningless. Our three classes are really only one class, the eighty percent of the population more or less evenly distributed not too far to the left and right of the median on a bell-shaped curve. The spread in annual income, for example, between the left end of the lower middle to the right end of the upper middle, or between, say, fifteen thousand and two hundred and twenty-five thousand, represents a factor of only fifteen. That isn't much compared to the spread between the mean and the ninety-ninth plus percentile; let's say between about fifty thousand and fifteen million, which represents a factor of three hundred. The latter *factor* is twenty times greater than the former factor. That suggests strongly that there exists somewhere on the curve an upper class and a corresponding lower class. One owns three-quarters of the nation's wealth; the other owns nothing. However, they are both sleeping dogs, and it is best not to disturb them lest the barking from the left side of the curve disturbs he serenity of the right. Membership in your class is one of the few things you'll ever encounter that is not enhanced by advertising.

CLONING　For those who can afford it, I predict that cloning of human beings will become a real possibility in the near future. Since your consciousness would not be transferred, but merely replicated, given present expectations, cloning will not meet the hope for immortality. However, it will meet the standard for passing on to another generation all that you are aside from your developed mind, and that is no small trick. Discounting the occasional third ear or the odd growth that looks like a mangled foot growing out of a collar bone, imagine the market for cloned celebrities, not to mention their pets.

The high price of cloning could act as a filter allowing clones of only the most successful and glamorous people to pass into the future. Of course there is some risk that scientists, engineers, theologians, anthropologists, artists, artisans, poets, policemen, dancers, miners, loggers, philosophers, scholars, teachers, nurses, naturalists, wildlife biologists, rehabilitators, carpenters, farmers, ranchers, mothers, chess masters, farm workers, plumbers, line workers, laborers, and lap dancers would be filtered out since most of these people seldom accumulate enough capital to be considered truly successful and they would not be able to afford cloning. Nevertheless, in time, to the extent that genetics governs an individual's future, cloning could create a whole new race of extremely productive, efficient, attractive, and career-oriented people potentially skilled at capital management, basketball, entertainment, and the distribution of controlled substances. These are professions requiring skills that could easily be redirected to those professions not cloned in order to meet demand for careers there if demand should surge. For example, who is to say that, given means, motivation, and opportunity, second editions of billionaire junk dealer Maury Milkem could not become an Einstein, a Grant Wood, a George Washington Carver, or a male Florence Nightingale?

If successful, this selecting of human genes could act in the same way as the selective breeding of domestic animals and racehorses. The proprietary clones could be sold in a free market for astronomical sums. Human inventory management could be a viable future career and even an industry. If the majority of clones were produced by top nations like the U.S., as is likely, and lesser nations produced workers by ordinary breeding methods, then we Americans would be looking at a very bright future indeed. If you think Model T Fords got people's attention, wait until you see a hundred Dick Cheneys roll off the line, each one equipped by genetic potential to deliver enlightened leadership and good cheer to millions of ordinary people. The thought brings tears to my eyes.

CLOSERS   I include two types of people under the heading of closers: High-energy arm-twisters who can close deals, and high-powered arm-twisters who can put an end to problems. You'll need both.

The first kind of closer must be extremely intelligent, have wit and humor, be absolutely fearless and self-confident, be more competitive than Tiger Woods, and he must have genius level skill as a negotiator. When you find a good one, pay him whatever you must and feed his ego. If he happens to be a she, give her a title and some underlings.

The second kind of closer one normally does not discuss, and you will need him at least as much for your overseas operations as for domestic. Ideally, he or she should blend the best attributes of a high-level spy and a soldier of fortune. Pick this closer from the cast of a James Bond movie or from the security staff of a U.S. embassy abroad. If you have to ask what this closer's duties are, then you might want to consider a different career, something like the priesthood or driving a turnip truck.

THE CLUB   This is the term I use, informally of course, to describe a sense of belonging that we CEOs share with others of our ilk. There is nothing organized, sinister, or conspiratorial about it. It is just a reminder that as CEO of a large or multinational corporation, or simply as a person of wealth, you too can always find warmth and friendship wherever you are, the same way ordinary people find it at rummage sales, their local church, YMCA, Kiwanis Club, or benevolent fraternity. To the extent that friends tend to be like-minded, share the same vision, and work for the same goals, it is good to socialize now and then, and, after a rousing chukka of polo or an eloquent toast at dinner on the eve of the Monaco Grand Prix, compare thoughts, share experiences, and chat pleasantly about how to shape the world and guide the lives of its billions of guileless inhabitants.

To be accepted into The Club means that others have recognized, in your life-long commitment to yourself, your career, and the welfare of the world's economy, a spark of genius that would bring pride and comfort to all the generations of members past, present, and future. Together, we make a family, a family of leaders. Together, we may face the always uncertain future with confidence knowing that, if need should dictate, we may draw strength, knowledge, power, and hard capital for a reasonable return from each other. As one collective voice we may hope to speak with a certain wisdom, purified by tradition and hardened by experience, a voice that will bring security, form, and exceptional profit to those shapeless tomorrows that await us.

There can be no greater success than the recognition, by you and by those who preceded you, that you belong to The Club, while so many others do not.

CODDLING   Help people who are willing to help themselves or who will pay a reasonable price in equity, favors, or gifts for your expertise. But never coddle. People who won't walk over ground glass to get what they want, or won't pay someone else a premium to do it for them, are not strong enough to keep what they want once they get it. Don't waste your time on them.

COLLATERAL DAMAGE   If you look at life realistically, you will realize that some people are just plain unlucky because they are in the wrong place at the wrong time. No one planned it that way. No one conspired to harm them. We would all be happier if no one got hurt. But the truth is that in any human endeavor a few people do get hurt. Military warriors call this phenomenon, "collateral damage," and by that they mean non-combatants who are inadvertently killed, wounded, or displaced because they were in the line of combat.

In the business world, corporate warriors encounter the same phenomenon. Build a chemical plant that employs thousands and makes millions of lives more efficient, more productive, and more comfortable, and almost without doubt, an occasional person is going to get sick or give birth to a freak. Collateral damage.

What can be done about it? The most effective means I know to combat the effects of collateral damage is to retain the best staff of company lowyers that money can buy. No one sues an army that fired a stray missile into a school for the deaf, but everyone wants to sue a corporation that inadvertently released a few toxins that wind blew into a schoolyard. An information campaign can go a long way to defusing public opinion. Threats of closing a plant can accomplish the same thing. Still, there is always a radical element that wants to sue the deepest pockets around. So be prepared to show them just how deep those pockets are. You can fight litigation for decades. Generally speaking, by the time your attorneys are finished with the opposition, they will be a generation older; they will be broke or dead; they will be embarrassed and discredited if your staff is first rate; and they will be glad to settle for a pittance. By that time, of course, you will be in the driver's seat and you can choose whether to settle or to bury them. When it comes to collateral damage, you can't have too many lowyers.

COMMUNICATIONS   We old timers will forever think the words, "public relations." However, a former associate of mine, a young man in the business, who went on to found his own PR firm, start his own lobbying group, and serve as a speech writer for one of our Presidents, one day enlightened me on the ninth tee at Pebble Beach. He informed me that the term "public relations" was no longer acceptable. "It sounds too much like a form of subtle mass rape," he said. "I can prove to you that that's what some people think when they hear the phrase in focus groups. It's all unconscious, but frightfully accurate!" I had never thought of it quite that way, but he is probably right. "Communications," he said, "reminds one of tea and cookies and warm, collegial conversation." Clearly, the communications image is preferred.

When it comes to communications, you can't overestimate the importance of words.

COMPENSATION   Look at it this way: On one side is you; on the other side is the rest of the world, including all of your stockholders and employees. One side is going to secure guarantees to walk away with the goods. Who would you rather that be?

Structure your compensation package to make it as large as you can get by with. At the same time, keep costs and employee compensation as small as possible. This will help you achieve your aim of shifting wealth in your direction. Start out right and keep on track because it is as difficult to cut an employee's salary as it is to add to yours once both are established. Don't be afraid to be creative.

Burnham Frever was a tower of finance and originality and you can learn from his example. The former CEO of WorldDom reported forty million dollars compensation for the last two years of his tenure. As the company skidded toward a bankruptcy encompassing more than one hundred billion dollars in assets, and Burnham was escorted out the door, he was granted a paltry million and a half per year as a pension. How can any CEO with an established life style based on twenty million a year live on that? It was shocking. These figures would have been a life-threatening embarrassment for Burnham if it weren't for the four hundred million dollars in off-the-books loans that the company had provided for him to cover his margin calls in a falling market. You can't be too creative when it comes to squirreling away a nest egg for a rainy day.

Here is a rule I lived by when I was CEO. Be as creative as you must to stash as much as you can and eventually, the day will come when the issue of your compensation ceases to be an issue. The wealthier you become the more respect you will gain, and people will stop second-guessing what you do. In fact, since personal worth is measured in dollars, others begin to doubt their own worth in direct proportion to the increasing disparity between their compensation and yours. In other words, the more you have the simpler it will be to diminish other people's income and expectations while increasing your own. This is a specific instance of a general principle that underscores the importance of compensation: The wealthier you become the more deferential and agreeable others become.

Now look at employee compensation. Pretend, for one wildly absurd moment, that you are a private in the army. A staff sergeant tells you that you shouldn't expect anything more than you have. The two of you are near enough to the same level that you are liable either to disregard the sergeant's opinion or to think that he is a moron. Now the Commander in Chief walks in and tells you the same thing. What will you think? You will be so thrilled and flattered that the President of the United States chose you to talk to that you won't think anything but you will be grateful for whatever you, a mere private, have. If you are a truly submissive type, like a puppy wetting the carpet when its master comes home, you might even be inclined, albeit briefly, to give back part of your private's earnings because you are so motivated to do your duty and so humbled by the President's attentions. At least for that afternoon, you are prepared to give new meaning to the term, "all-volunteer army."

You have the same power over your employees. Employees always grouse about how little they are paid. Not one ever believes that he is being paid what he is truly worth. Don't take them seriously. Amaze them now and then with personal handshakes and smiles. Give them service pins for longevity. Surprise them with vases of rosebuds for creativity, or post their photographs over flattering captions on department bulletin boards dedicated to excellence. When push comes to shove, despite all the grousing about money, employees are much more concerned about pleasing you -- and about losing their jobs and benefits -- than they are about their earnings. After all, if they were that concerned about money, and if they were truly worth what they think, then they would be CEOs, not grunts, wouldn't they? Compensate your employees with all the fear and flattery their egos can handle, but keep control of the capital.

Whatever the circumstances behind it, wealth creates images of greatness in the minds of those who don't have it. Use that process to advantage and certainly don't ever argue with it. Boost your compensation and tightly manage that of others so that you may boost your own again. The longer you persist and the wealthier you become, the easier that process will be.

COMPETITION   Along with greed, competition is the most powerful instinct driving all human endeavors. It is a law of nature that people compete. If that law had not governed people they would not have survived onslaughts from other animal species and foreign humans. Competition *is* human nature and all business is predicated on competition. All attempts to build business on the antithesis of competition have failed precisely because they violate human nature. Witness the cooperative ventures in the old Soviet Union, laughable failures all of them. We Americans like competition. We welcome competition. We are good at competition, and I encourage you to practice competition in everything you do until you are able to get the better of everyone with whom you compete, which is everyone with whom you come into contact. Competition is both the means and the end. We compete to live, and we live to compete.

However, it seems to me that in recent years a slow growing, subversive movement has surfaced, apparently an outgrowth of radical feminism, most obvious in large urban areas and small college towns. It teaches that competition is a male sin and that female cooperation, communication, and so called "nurturing" should take its place. Invariably, this movement is led by plain women with hairy legs who wear second hand clothing and weird hats knitted by Peruvian peasants. They promote world peace, public breast-feeding, healing, and mutual respect as the answer to all questions. They advocate taking toy AK-47s away from little boys, whom they want to turn into little eunuchs who play with dolls. They make decisions by group consensus, and they shun all sports except boring ones like hackeysack that supposedly teach cooperation. I would like to take these women and make them mothers and give each of their sons the ball on the Southern Cal 8 in a tied game with ten seconds remaining and make them watch him juke and jog ninety-two yards in front of national television for the winning touchdown against an undefeated and number one ranked Notre Dame. Then ask them if they would have been happier if their son had offered Notre Dame the football in a gesture of cooperation so the Fighting Irish could kick a field goal.

Come on, ladies, let's be realistic about this thing. Maybe you can't compete, but cheerleaders who can are getting the job done, and so are their teams. Get with the program. Buy some CoverGirl. Introduce yourselves to Mary Kay. Get rid of the gerbils in your armpits and get your hair styled. Then smile when your kid gives someone else's kid a bloody nose. Let his dad take him to the gym. Raise a winner, not a wimp. Creatures that don't compete become extinct. Roses go to the finest, not the frumpiest; and mountaintops are waiting for the fittest, not the Fauntleroys.

COMPUTERS   Are you getting the most you can from personal profile data sources? Are you losing business to more innovative competitors? Is your marketing department doing all it can for you, or has someone dropped the ball?

In tandem with other tools of information technology, particularly television, computers allow you to collect, store, organize, retrieve, and utilize enough data to manage consumers, to control their options and direct their choices, to shape their present world and their future, and to create in that future the perfect marketplace for multinational corporations. Give your unguarded loyalty to the machine. The Garden of Eden it replaced will never be missed by targeted consumers faced with marketing imperatives.

Consider, for example, three broad target groups. First, working poor who redeem coupons, join "bonus points" clubs even to get points they'll never use, visit Fantasy vacation sites on the Internet, and habitually buy impulsively to get deals. Second, small, insecure men who troll Internet sites featuring sexually dominant women; who order penis enlargement pills; and who also surf sports car, SUV, and NASCAR racing sites. And third, forty-something narcissistic, overweight, insecure, divorced, empty nest women. What are these groups up against? "From now until May 13, earn five hundred free bonus air miles with every purchase. But wait! Order right now and we'll throw in the carrying case free. That's a two hundred dollar value for only $29.95. Call in the next fifteen minutes and save an additional 30% -- *plus rebate!*" And: "Off road, the Turbo 590 gives you more than power. Feel the lift beneath your legs. Feel the thrust. It will take you places no man has gone before." And finally: "Isn't it time for you? Give yourself that soft, sensual luxury every goddess deserves. Shouldn't you do it now ... while you still can?"

Computers elevate marketing efficiency exponentially. With consumer personal profiles harvested from Internet and television use and correlated into data sets, your product clusters become magnets, not targets. Computers let you become that knowledgeable good neighbor, councilor, and vendor every consumer deserves.

Is your bottom line all it could be? Isn't it time you lit a fire under *your* marketing department?

CONDUCT   Every group of men and women needs a code of conduct to live by. I hope that this book will become yours and will help guide you throughout your career. I can summarize my best advice in one sentence, however, in case you won't finish reading this volume: Absorb Adam Smith; study Machiavelli; emulate our Founding Fathers, including Armour, Astor, Carnegie, Clark, Daly, Du Pont, Fisk, Ford, Frick, Gould, Guggenheim, Harriman, Hearst, Heinze, Hill, Huntington, Insull, McDuck, Mellon, Morgan, Rockefeller, Rogers, Schwab, Stanford, and Vanderbilt; and always conduct yourself in a manner that you think would make Ronald Reagan proud. If you do that much, you will make yourself and members of The Club proud too.

CONGRESSIONAL INVESTIGATIONS   Every now and then in the normal course of business, particularly during an election year, Congress decides to snoop. Avoid congressional hearings as often as you can, but if you should find yourself in the position of having been subpoenaed and you have no alternative except to testify or lose face, then testify. You can always take the fifth on the advice of your lowyer.

If you choose to speak, however, keep this thought in mind. Even for the best and the brightest, there are times when the world seems to conspire unjustly. When your forehead begins to sweat as much as the palms of your hands; when your lowyer seems at a loss for speech; and when you feel your courage slipping away, remember these words of wisdom found in an old aphorism. Yes, it's a cliché, and you have doubtless heard it a thousand times, but it will buck you up like nothing else and it will raise your courage and give you strength to stay the course. Always remember: When the going gets tough, blame your accountant.

CONSPICUOUS CONSUMPTION   What good is consumption if no one notices?

Let's say that you are out with some fellows shooting sandhill cranes on the prairies of Alberta and it's time for lunch. Which would be more fun -- and which would make a better story after the hunt -- eating a can of Vienna sausages, pork and beans, and a pickle, or eating a three-pound lobster with a bottle of Bernkasteler Doktor Auslese? Next time you drive from Saint Tropez to San Remo, would you rather take the coastal curves and villages in a Dodge Ram or a red Maserati? Set standards of consumption that ordinary people will envy. Otherwise, they will become too content to be any good at their job.

CONSTRUCTIVE FUTILITY   Once I visited a fading aunt in a nursing home. As I was trying to leave, a senile old man cornered me and told me his philosophy of life. He called it, "constructive futility."

He explained it this way. When you understand that an asteroid can smash into the earth, the Yellowstone super volcano will again erupt, or a nearby star will some day explode into a supernova vaporizing our entire solar system, you might be tempted to view human effort as an exercise in futility. However, since our eighty year span of life is, for all we know, the only chance at futility we have, you might also be moved to live "as if." As if things mattered. As if human effort counted for something. As if all our hopes and dreams were important despite their pending obliteration.

Armed with this view, according to the old man, people can subscribe to truth and recognize that, in the grand scheme of things, all we do is futile. But people can also choose to impose human value and personal meaning onto that futility during their lifetimes by living constructively, instead of cynically or destructively. Hence "constructive futility."

This fellow organized his thoughts quite logically. He avoided all flights into faith and ideology, and he refused to allow our future demise to serve as an excuse for inactivity or atrocious activity. No crusades or jihads; no Stalinist purges; no Hitler, Pol Pot, Idi Amin, or James Jones; no raptures; no delusions; no excuses. People have one responsibility, he told me, and that is to just live as if life matters, even though it doesn't, because if you can ask if it matters then it matters, at least to you while you are able to ask.

"So make it matter," he said, "to you and to all those around you. That is our human gift. We have the power to know truth and still choose the best illusion."

While I was digesting his advice, he turned abruptly to walk away. Then just as abruptly, he faced me again, smiled, and nodded to the empty lounge just past our hallway.

"If you don't believe me," he said, "ask that chicken."

CONSUMERS   If you think that corporations do not value human beings think again. As consumers, people are the most valuable and renewable natural resource we have. In many respects they remind me of gold. They are exploitable. Nature provides them for anyone who wants to use them. They are elemental. They are what they are and, aside from those who should be committed to asylums, you don't have to worry about them breaking down into something else. They are extractive. You can easily separate them from their host and refine them into a mass. They are malleable. Once refined, you can mold or beat them into any shape you like. And they are value-added. After you have shaped them, drawing out their instinctive desire to follow and their reflex to spend, they become more valuable than they were before. In the end, every consumer is like a gold ring ready for market. Some are ten karat, some fourteen, some eighteen, and some twenty-two or even twenty-four karat. Some are large and some are small. But every one is worth a certain amount of capital, and your job is to translate that capital into profit.

There is no reason to get emotionally or intellectually involved with consumers. Like your favorite pinky ring that holds your favorite pink diamond, you might grow fond of a particular investor because he delivers over and over again what he is supposed to deliver. That doesn't mean that you will have to listen to his ramblings or attend his son's Bris. Your job will be less confusing if you don't fall into the trap of anthropomorphizing consumers or of personalizing your relations with them. Think of them as extremely valuable statistics. Other than the occasional public relations contact, keep them at arm's length. Do not identify with them. Do not pity them. Do not lose all sense of proportion and believe that you are one of them. Just view them for the valuable commodity they are and of course appreciate them for what they deliver. Your treatment of consumers should be all about respect.

CONTRACTS   There are two kinds of contracts, yours and theirs.

Your contracts are binding agreements requiring other parties to adhere strictly to the terms therein. If they violate the terms of their contract, force them into compliance. Try to have them arrested. Sue them mercilessly. Charge them all penalties possible plus attorney's fees. Do everything in your power to make their lives miserable.

Their contracts, on the other hand, are tentative explorations of possible future agreements based on limited information available at a specific time and place. You may abrogate them any time at your discretion.

This might suggest to you that self-interest always supercedes abstract principle. If so, you are correct. It does. Furthermore, your self-interest supercedes all other self-interests. That is why there are lowyers. All cases of contract law pit one self-interest against another, and resolution is determined by which side has the better lowyers. The only principle in contracts is: Hire and keep the best lowyers money can buy

CONTROL   The idea of control is the central concept of civilization. I think that it arose slowly a few thousand years ago as a result of what historians call, "the agricultural revolution." The successful growing of foodstuffs and the domestication and husbandry of animals, for the first time in history, gave humankind the notion that people could control things – nature, the future, and their own fate. Prior to that time, the only hope to control fate was the use of magic and that was not successful.

As civilization advanced, so did the idea of control. Where once tribesmen wandered about governed by nothing more than their own whims, gathering a pear here and trapping a rabbit there, society learned to regulate its members and to require their adherence to a central plan. Magic evolved into religions, and religions became institutions. The idea of property ownership flourished and with it came the imperative to *defend* property against others and to *acquire* property up for grabs or claimed by someone else. Armies arose. Planners and strategists replaced soothsayers. Property ownership was directly tied to the notion that one could control the future. Carefully cultivated crops provided hedges against the next drought or flood. In addition, farmers became specialized. Some raised cattle and some grew grain. More specialized work took shape. Some workers butchered cattle and some ground grain into flour; some sold beef in markets and some baked bread in shops. As forms of labor defined themselves, the idea of occupations grew into the idea of careers. Tribes evolved into city-states and city-states into nations. We invented time and the clock. By the advent of the Industrial Revolution, humankind was so habituated to control that labor, the selling of one's time and skill, seemed almost natural. The rise of political factions and the loyalties they require accelerated the idea of control, as did the invention of banks and, in time, credit for the masses. Historically speaking, in no time at all, the idea of control transformed a happy-go-lucky wandering race of ne'er-do-wells into a disciplined, productive, responsible, loyal class of workers-consumers who owe their livelihoods to their employers and their assets to their lenders, and the idea of citizenship surpassed the primitive habit of personal anarchy. Today, the Babel of tribes and nations that once made up our planet is giving ground to the idea of one single borderless world, and the tradition of differing cultures is slowly being transformed into a new idea, a single, unified world bound together by free-market trade. Increasingly, humans are divided into economic rather than religious, cultural, social, linguistic, or political classes. And all this has been brought about by humans seizing control of their fate.

Look at the obvious. Without control, there would be no affordable, mass produced products made from natural resources because there would be no sense of ownership of nature to inspire their exploitation. Without control there would be no efficient production through cheap labor; there would be only packs of nomadic individuals who forage and hunt. Without control there would be no marketing, but only primitive and haphazard barter. Now ask the question, what best consolidates this control?

Humankind retains its herd and tribal instincts, and all human groups, from neighborhood watch to nations, control their members the old fashioned way, through tribal-like societies. Scouting groups, athletic teams, sororities, professional associations, unions, service clubs, church groups, political parties, you name it. They all have one aim in common: Take extreme edges off individuality and force conformity. In other words, control. Group consensus is more formidable than any lone wolf howling. But inefficiency arises with so many groups because the specific means to control vary and compete in direct proportion to the stated aims of each group. Is the Masonic Order closer to The Truth than Key Club? Is The Koran superior to Scientology? What group is best equipped to achieve the aim of total societal control?

You could ask: Where do corporations fit into this scheme of things? The corporate structure ensures internal control, and corporations have the wherewithal to chart societal control that benefits all participants. Furthermore, corporations are not ideological. They are pragmatic, and they focus on control itself rather than on some ideological lure to control. Read the *Talmud* or The *Times*, it doesn't matter, so long as you work, shop, and seek credit. Only corporations have broad enough reach and appeal to unify the Babel of human tribes, and people instinctively understand that.

Look at the whole of civilization. Without corporate autonomy, that is to say, corporate control, there would be only government control and no government will ever act strictly in the best interests of business or of consumers. Thus, increasingly, civilization entrusts corporate leaders with the power to control every aspect of nature and human life, and individual citizens worldwide vote on the results of corporate decision-making with their spending. What are the results of this trust? Corporations and their leaders have replaced royalty, aristocracy, the landed gentry, and even the world-conquering armies of the past. Where kings, queens, dukes and barons once ruled, today Exxtort-Mogul, Tarhill, Microfang, Fortressbanks, and W*ALLMINE! rule. Where Thomas Jefferson and men like him once managed their plantations, today thousands of regional and local corporations rule. Where once Cossacks conquered lands and sacked villages, today, the so-called Russian Oligarchs rule. Wherever you look you see corporations rising and consolidating control over every patch of land and every human group. The only thing standing between corporations and absolute control of this planet is established governments, and deregulation has begun the process of dismantling the relevance of those institutions.

Corporations rule. Think about it. We now control the assets of the world. People-as-consumers vote on our decisions with their spending to keep us in line and make us democratic. We in turn control most of the means and the methods used to shape public opinion. So we can *determine*, to a large extent, how people will vote with their spending. Meanwhile, corporate lobbyists already control a majority of government processes, and deregulation has become almost a religion. *We are a centimeter away from absolute and total control of this planet in its entirety.* In the very near future, we corporations will rule *all*. You must be ready to exercise this grave and historic responsibility.

From day one on, go into training. Train yourself to exercise control over every aspect of your life. Control your wife, your children, your dog, your reputation, your friends, your co-workers, your peers, your subordinates and, while climbing the competitive ladder, as much as possible, control your superiors. Let control of others be the guiding light of your life. It is, as you have seen, the light that led our ancestors out of chaos and into civilization. Under your direction, let it now lead civilization into an age of commerce powered by The Grand Economy.

COOPERATION   Studies conducted at the Carlson School of Management at the University of Minnesota demonstrate that when money is on people's minds, they behave more selfishly and cooperate with others less. Researchers concluded that even the thought of money makes people feel self-sufficient and independent.

I think this research backs an additional conclusion. People inclined to cooperate with others do so because they lack confidence in their own independence and because they think they can gain an edge by working with others. A weak warehouseman who needs to lift a heavy box enlists the cooperation of stronger men. That way, he gets his job done and looks better to his supervisor. In other words, cooperation is a function of personal need and self-interest, more than of altruism. Throw money into the equation, and the cooperative spirit morphs quickly into personal greed. This reinforces my lifelong belief that "the spirit of cooperation," so touted by its advocates as a cure for human nastiness, is in most cases the mentality of losers.

Cooperation is two things. At its best, it is leverage gained by convincing people to pool their resources. For example, if you assign a team to come up with a solution to a difficult technical problem, chances are they will reach their goal quicker working well together. In this case, keep money off the table and keep them focused on the praise they will get if they succeed. But cooperation is also the refuge of last resort for losers who cannot keep up. It is the modus operandi that drives panhandlers. Furthermore, people who preach ideological cooperation, as in socialism or communalism, are playing a game of diminishing returns. To the extent that they succeed, and distribute wealth broadly, the recipients of that wealth increasingly will be motivated to cooperate less and go it alone to gain more wealth.[12] In time, the only people left to cooperate would be those who cannot compete at all: Losers and people maladapted for survival because they suffer from low intelligence, disabilities, or too much empathy. To the extent that cooperation is a temporary tool used for specific ends, or is a springboard to self-sufficiency, it is a good thing, but as an end in itself, it is a losing proposition.

This might not have been true for primitive peoples, however, and here the anthropologists who tout cooperation are probably correct. Cooperation benefited primitive peoples and helped them to survive, and the reason is simple. They did not have money to chase. They chased buffalo and picked bananas and they did both better as teams. Only after the idea of capital came about did personal, self-directed motivation take over in the form of greed. Only then did rugged individuals follow their will and create new ways to do things, such as *herding* buffalo and *growing* bananas. We call the results of that takeover, "civilization." It is based on fierce com-

---

12 This underscores the great flaw in Marx's thought. The spirit of revolution cannot be sustained in the proletarian class because the more that workers succeed the less inclined they are to revolt and the more inclined they are to abandon their comrades, open their own businesses, and invest for their own benefit.

petition between men and it leads to more buffalo and more bananas for everyone, plus a Lamborghini for the guy in the big hut who came up with better ideas and made them work.

Bottom line? Inadequate people demand cooperation; winners expect competition.

CORPORATE CHARTER Typically, corporations are registered, chartered, or otherwise authorized to do business by the Secretaries of State of each state. Recently, socialist radicals have again suggested that corporate charters should be given out for twenty years only, and that to renew its charter and keep doing business, every corporation must pass a so-called "good citizen" litmus test. If the corporation fails the test then its charter is revoked and it goes out of business. This test includes references to treatment of workers, social responsibilities, and the environment.

Well, if corporations are, legally speaking, individuals, then shouldn't individual citizens also be required to pass this "good citizen" test to continue doing their business or to vote? Anything less would be discrimination. Yet these tests themselves would resemble the kind used in the Old South when literacy tests were required of prospective voters in order to disenfranchise African Americans who were not allowed access to schools. Bottom line? This is a ludicrous idea suggested by people who hate free enterprise as an excuse to promote socialism.

A charter is to a corporation as a birth certificate is to a person, and as long as any corporation chooses to survive and is able to survive, then it has an inalienable right to survive, just as citizens do. Would you risk having your birth certificate invalidated by taking a test of your "good citizenship?" And who, please tell me, is going to presume to define good citizenship anyway? Who will administer these tests? And what about stock markets and investors? Are we going to let money managers, widows, and orphans invest in companies that might be disenfranchised at any time? If you ever run across one of these radicals, I suggest you ask them how many jobs they provide for their community, and how much they pay in taxes.

When a new mom sends birth announcements to her relatives and friends, she expects the good news to be greeted with happiness, blessings, and the expectation of longevity. A spanking new corporation deserves no less.

CORPORATE WELFARE Whoever coined this term should be forced to get a job. There is no such thing as corporate welfare. There are government incentives aimed at helping corporations deal with difficult situations, but this is not welfare. It is investment. My favorite bureaucracy is called the Overseas Private Investment Corporation, not the Overseas Private Welfare Corporation. We're talking about investment. Rational investment. Investments in progress, in development, in new jobs, in profits that lead to expansion, job-creation, and more tax revenues; in all the factors that are helping to build the new, worldwide free market system, The Grand Economy. What entity is more deserving of public investment than a public corporation? Who provides? Who forms the backbone of every community? Who installs a Henry Moore or a Brootus Kingkitsch in their entryway for the whole world to enjoy? I'll guarantee it's not some unemployed trailer park slattern with six kids, five ex-husbands, and four bounced checks in the mail, or some thirty year old ne'er-do-well "Veteran" standing on the roadside with a cardboard sign advertising, "Sometimes People Need Help." Recipients of welfare are not required to earn their stipends. Recipients of investment capital, on the other hand, must be able to work hard, work smart, and demonstrate a reasonable return on that capital. Behind all the personal, institutional, or government investments in corporations there is one rule of thumb that applies, and it is a good one to remember in your private life: Keep capital to make a modest return; invest it to make a good return; give it away and get no return. Even government is not stupid enough to give it away. Even government expects to earn a good return, and while they might not always get it because investment involves risk, at least they expect it.

CORPORATION   A corporation is a body authorized by law to act as an individual in business. It has all the same rights and privileges guaranteed by the Constitution that individual human citizens have, such as the right to free speech. When it does things right, its officers are rewarded for having steered it well. When it does something wrong, it is liable and may be punished for its wrong-doing. Similarly, when it performs badly and loses money, it suffers public scorn. In such cases, however, boards of directors try to preserve the integrity of the company and keep it from falling into incompetent hands. Typically they provide handsome bonuses for the existing, experienced officers in order to keep the management team together to prevent the company from sliding any farther than it already has.

The popular perception that corporate personhood allows us to influence people and governments more than any ordinary citizen because we have more money and can afford more donations and commercials, is folly based on public ignorance. Income or net worth has never been a test of the rights of citizens to be heard, at least not in our modern times, and I don't think the public would care to have their rights judged according to their relative degree of wealth or poverty. It is not a question of whether a poor man should be allowed to speak out only five minutes while a rich man can speak for twenty. The point is that both should be allowed to speak. Obviously, if a rich man can stretch his advertising budget a little farther than a poor man, then he can hold the microphone a little longer, but that has nothing to do with rights and everything to do with abilities. The same is true of corporations. A corporation that funds a lobby group or a political advertising campaign has no more rights than a homeless bum. It just has the ability to exercise those rights more robustly. Some individuals might possess more resources than other individuals, but resources are not addressed in our constitution and are not an issue. No one is getting screwed just because a corporation decides to be a good citizen and speak out. Don't parents, Boy Scout leaders, teachers, coaches, and religious leaders speak out? I prefer to think that corporations are accepting a role of citizen responsibility in offering the public guidance, advice, and consul, not unlike the way, with such unbridled enthusiasm, some dedicated Catholic priests set aside their private ecclesiastical duties in order to minister to the children in their care.

COST-BENEFIT ANALYSIS The only rational way to live is to apply quantitative cost-benefit analysis to every endeavor in your life, whether personal or professional. You have all read plenty of case studies featuring cost-benefit analysis in various business situations. But have you thought of ways you can use the same analyses in your personal life? Business is not just business. It is life. It is a way of life – the best way of life -- and you should strive to live by the established principles that make corporations what they are. Can you imagine your life, if you became a CEO, so integrated and so whole that your personal life and your professional life became indistinguishable? That is, after all, the ultimate goal of a CEO's code of conduct.

Let's take a simple example. Let's say it's your birthday and your wife has invited you to your favorite five star restaurant for dinner. Just the two of you. You are listening to the menu. You have a passion for food. But your memory flashes images of other CEOs you know who also have a passion for food, some of them human cream puffs, grotesquely obese and sluggish, not only at the table but also on the links and in the boardroom. They sweat like laborers. They reek of secret self-indulgence. They have lost their competitive edge to their girth, and they do not look like warriors. They look like creatures from a zoo. You vow never to resemble them. You are determined that right now, even on this special occasion, you will exercise perfectly rational cost-benefit analysis and thereby demonstrate your superiority.

Suddenly, the waiter recommends the exceedingly tender filet mignon with portabella mushroom and port wine sauce. You can almost taste it and your salivary glands go wild. But wait. You have some idea of the benefits, lots of protein, iron, and vitamins plus a high, high degree of pleasure. But what are the costs? Even though your doctor gives you a clean bill of health, you are forty-eight years old, male, balding, and statistically at risk for kidney stones, gall bladder disease, obesity and late-onset diabetes, colon cancer, high cholesterol, and heart disease. Red meat is very risky. There is no windfall profit to be made from its added risk. You are just on the threshold of your peak years and you cannot afford a health setback. Clearly, the risk of eating the exceedingly tender filet mignon with portabella mushroom and port wine sauce trumps the nutritional reward, which you could get by other means, and also trumps the reward of a high, high degree of pleasure, for pleasure, after all, can and should be governed by discipline, and is of no real consequence.

Foods such as the exceedingly tender filet mignon with portabella mushroom and port wine sauce will be just as available to you in retirement as they are now. Just as available when dining with meat-eating friends, and not your wife. Available to you, in fact, any time you want. Any time.

Fine. You order the braised halibut with no sauce. Throw in a fresh lemon. Add the iceberg salad with no dressing. There. Brilliant. You have effectively eliminated risk from your meal and gained the nutritional reward. Actually, you have added to the nutritional reward by incorporating omega-3 fatty acids from the fish oil. Your cardiologist will be thrilled. But your pleasure centers are still crying out, so you turn to the anti-oxidants and tannins and other beneficial compounds that keep the French and Italians healthy, and you contemplate your favorite red wine, even though it is not a good match for the fish: The '75 Chateau Figeac. It is still on the restaurant's wine list. Your palate yearns to swirl the bold and astringent '75 Chateau Figeac, here priced at $3,900.00 for the bottle. Might not the pleasure in drinking the wine, its well-documented health benefits, plus the prestige in ordering it and having it served in a public restaurant, far outweigh the slight added risk of the price? Alas, you know that the fish and the '75 Chateau Figeac would ruin each other, and so you settle on a current vintage Chablis Grand Cru, the Vaudesir of course, and your sommelier's face brightens. You proceed, confident in the knowledge that your quantitative analysis has been flawless and that you have done the rational thing. Furthermore, since your wife did not forgo dessert, the incredible *pain de genes au chocolat* that melts as it touches your tongue and then wants to cascade down your throat more lightly than music; since she did not forgo this dessert as you did, this meal will give you plenty of ammunition for future discussions with her about weight, fitness, and good health.

And the fish, judged by its astounding aroma, is fresh. Obviously fresh. So fresh that everyone in the room can detect and attest to its freshness. Meanwhile, on your Limoges china plate, Brussels sprouts in shades of green and bile contrast sharply with roach-colored wild rice and little steamed carrots the color of raw snapper. Yes, presentation is thoroughly professional. And, of course, the wine is classic, mildly acidic, lean and ascetic; dry as sand from the Sahara Desert. All in all, the meal is a well-executed, professional, risk-free achievement. The chef can be proud. The waiter can be proud. The Maitre d' can be proud. Onlookers, your wife, and your doctors can swell with pride. Your sommelier can burst with admiration. There is simply no substitute for cold, hard, rational, quantitative judgment.

So you repeat to yourself, "happy birthday, Bucky," and "Here! Here!" for a job well done; then turn your attention to the aromatic fish.

CREATIVE DESTRUCTION

When wolves were re-introduced to Yellowstone National Park a few years ago, some of us who own homes near Jackson Hole, Wyoming got worried. We thought the wolves would wander south and destroy our elk herds. We were wrong. Today the elk herds are bigger than ever. The real losers were the Yellowstone area coyotes. The wolves took out a lot of inferior competition. Since 1942, Economists have called that process, when it is triggered by innovation, "creative destruction," which is just another way of saying, "survival of the fittest."

That's what happens to local mom and pop stores when a company like W*ALLMINE! moves in. W*ALLMINE!'s innovations in inventory management, supply chain, labor costs, and marketing are so effective that they sink more complacent competitors, who were content to get by doing things the old fashioned way. When your innovations wreak havoc in existing markets and you witness the wholesale slaughter of your competition, remember that your creativity has reached the second and third most important goals of your career. You have stimulated corporate success. And you have created a more efficient worldwide economic machine.

When your personal tribute for being so creative equals your achievements in the destruction of others, then you will have fulfilled your primary goal. You will become the alpha dog in your neighborhood. The only step left is to widen the reach of your corporation until, like W*ALLMINE!, it dominates every neighborhood in your sector in every corner of the developed world.

CREDIT   Always work with friendly bankers. While I preferred not to work with bankers at all, I always did and I was nearly always happy afterward, because when you already hold the chips, you can easily cut a sweet deal to hold a few more on credit. But this goes without saying. Let's talk consumer credit.

Whoever invented the idea of consumer credit was one of the great geniuses of history. Today, without tight usury restrictions, credit sales offer some of the highest profit margins in business. It's not just the interest. When you add on processing delays that increase your float time, service fees, origination fees, participation fees, annual membership fees, late fees, service contract fees, ATM fees, transaction fees, user fees, then throw in a couple of fees for your secretary's hooters, you have a real winner. Credit is a win-win-win-win proposition. The consumer gets that big screen TV he always wanted, and you get the interest, the float, and the fees. If he defaults, repossess his purchase, resell it, and you'll end up collecting one and a half times for it. You can't lose. What hurts is consumer bankruptcy, but we're working on that.

The greatest innovation since the invention of consumer credit is the extension of credit to children. Most sixteen year olds work. They deserve credit. Send them a credit card or open an account for them and you will start them down a consumer path they will never leave. Get to them when they are young and you will teach them all about the world of consumer goods and services. You will point them in the general direction of fiscal responsibility. You will offer them the opportunity to share in the good life. You will gain their faith and loyalty, and you will show them what a better life is all about. When you think about it, kiddy credit does for young people today what scouting and Sunday school used to do, plus it gives you the chance to make a few extra bucks along the way.

Children deserve our undivided attention. After all, tomorrow's riches, a brand new climate, ten billion people, Islamic democracies, and our gross domestic debt will be all theirs.

CREMATION   Metaphorically, cremation is the total annihilation of a competitor. Used in its traditional sense, cremation of dead bodies today is a beacon of opportunity burning on the horizon of the future. Someone needs to capitalize

Think of human death as a manufacturing process. As populations increase, deaths increase, so you have a classic growth market in funerals. You have an almost infinite supply of natural resources in human bodies, and your cost for these raw materials is zero. You have accelerating demand, as population grows and families have to deal with more corpses; high inventory turnover, since one body can produce only one product; and low advertising costs since you don't have to promote the concept of death. In addition, as available land becomes increasingly scarce and existing land values rise, driving the cost of cemetery space to unreasonable heights, your competition is already on the run. Finally, cremation, the manufacturing process, by which you add capital value to the basic commodity, is cheap and uncomplicated with core technology already in place. You burn bodies, cull out precious metals, package remains in urns, and then sell the product back to a captive market for a profit. Best of all, you don't have to worry about warranties and returns. These factors reduce your risk to near zero. Talk about opportunity in a growth industry!

To thoroughly exploit this opportunity, you need to apply some imagination to the existing market structure and update marketing procedures. Take scattering as only one example. It is estimated that more than fifty percent of all cremation consumers scatter the product rather than set it on a mantle or a table. In times past, families used to gather for a scattering, often traveling hundreds of miles to a preferred location. Who has time for that any more?

I have given this considerable thought, and, with my wife's help and inspiration, this is what I came up with. Take four acres of bare land, much less than conventional cemeteries would need. Divide it into Serenity Segments, such as Rocky Mountain Wildflower, Appalachian Autumn, Timeless Sea Breeze, and Great Plains Horizon. You get the idea. Landscape accordingly. Provide a cobbled, winding Serenity Lane under shade trees with piped-in breeze and birdsongs.

In addition, build an exclusive Elysian Fields of Finance segment for those bereaved who can afford the best. There you can let your Serenity Lane turn into little models of Church and Wall Streets. Build a nice fountain to receive the loved ones and surround it with miniatures of reinforced steel and concrete.

Consumers can take a slow Final Drive along the lane to the setting they have paid for, roll down their windows, scatter the ashes, and still keep that lunch date or important business appointment. For background, religious folk could choose from various add-on options, such as prerecorded prayers, or music featuring the Vienna Boys Choir, Black Gospel, New Orleans funereal jazz, a chorus of Tibetan nuns, or an Ave Maria solo sung by a leading hot diva of the moment. Imagine sending a loved one to heaven on the wings of a beautiful voice like Streisand or Madonna? Throw in a few add-ons up front, like a full-scale pickup window espresso bar featuring home ground beans and exclusive house blends, and a drive-through New York style deli for those on their lunch hours. Consumers would never once have to leave the comfort of their own automobiles.

Give your service a snappy name so consumers will understand that this is one place they won't have to get bogged down and jammed up. For example, who wouldn't be proud to give their loved one a practical yet sensitive send-off using, "Toss-n-Go?"

Americans' hearts and wallets are big enough to support three or four Toss-n-Goes in every designated marketing area coast to coast. If the pilot works, franchise. You could make a killing.

CRIMINAL   A criminal is someone who can't afford a good lawyer. Never find yourself in such a position. When the sharks start circling, call in all your markers, hire the best lawyers you can, and climb back onto the yacht. You will recognize many of the fins of those who want to take a bite out of you, but don't take it personally. You might feel the same if they were on trial. They are part of the feeding frenzy that always follows after an enemy, a loved one, a dear friend, neighbor, associate, or other miscellaneous acquaintance shows vulnerability, and they will feel better once they have tasted blood. It doesn't matter whose. Just make sure it isn't yours.

In most circumstances, lawyers are vile, but in this circumstance, they are wonderful because they are your only friends and their loyalty is absolute. They sell it by the hour. Just be sure you can pay your bills -- and keep your friendships – until the charges are dismissed or you cut a sweet deal.

CULTURE   Before the beginnings of industrialization, when the seeds of The Grand Economy were sown, the world's populations were divided into cultures based on each small group's special heritage. Each culture had its own unique language, religion, art, methods of commerce, social structure, taboos, value system, military traditions, and sexual rites. In other words, the world was in a state of absolute chaos. Can you imagine trying to sell riding lawn mowers and Barbie Dolls to a thousand completely different cultures?

Today, homogenization is replacing diversity, and the American model of enterprise has overtaken parochial traditions. This breaking down of differences between peoples is the only thing that allows multinational corporations to function with any degree of efficiency. Marketing principles here will work just as well there. Wages here, adjusted for cost of living needs, are relatively the same as wages there. Cultures belong in museums. Today, like machines with exact, interchangeable parts operating all over the world and connected to a single source of energy, units of The Grand Economy will not tolerate inefficiencies caused by differences.

The other use of the term "culture," as in High Culture, refers to the degree of cultivation or sophistication to which one has risen. It matters only to members of university faculties, who perceive themselves as the caretakers of deep thought and true civilization, and the very rich, who have time on our hands and money in our pockets to play with paintings, symphonies, and fox hunts instead of romance novels, backyard grills, and *People* magazine. The more wealth you acquire the more Culture you will have, which you can demonstrate to others when you want them to accept or admire you. If you had a privileged upbringing, all of that will be second nature. If not, it is as easy to acquire as a Bentley. Just follow one rule of thumb: Whenever in doubt, that is, whenever you think that you are in over your head, act incredulous, as if others were dwelling on the obvious. For example, let's say that at a cocktail party someone takes aim at you with a comment like this: "Everything depends on style. Look at the differences between Roth and Bellow, for instance. Each wrote the same novel a dozen times but Bellow's style elevates his work to the strata of originality. Don't you agree?" To this you might reply: "Style, James? Really? That's an astute perception." You then look at the other people listening, smile wryly, and continue: "We would never have imagined that style would play such an important role for the Nobel Committee, let alone for the rest of us, would we?"

Cultured people would rather be tortured to death than be obvious, so they will never really challenge you or push the matter beyond what they fear is your knowledge, because if they did so, they would risk starting a discussion that could prove that you know more than they do. Obviously, that could put them at a mortal and humiliating disadvantage, and even make them look stupid. They won't take that chance. More likely, if you parry them correctly, they too will smile wryly, nod, and chuckle, as if still in possession of secret knowledge superior to yours, then slink off to whither away in misery and search for acceptance in another part of the room.

Checkmate when you can and when you can't, choose poise. Like a stalemate in chess, the element of uncertainty in conversation guarantees you advantage at least equal to that possessed by your opponent, and if you refuse to self-destruct, then the worst that can happen is that your queen will lose her edge but keep her throne.

CUSTOMER SERVICE   Your customer service departments will require special training and supervision. Your view of customer service needs to be tough minded and realistic, while your service representatives' view must be warm, fuzzy, and unrealistic. Most customer service contacts will be complaints, and in most complaint situations, the customer will attempt to screw the company with lies, hostility, and inflated expectations. Your goal is to keep customers from screwing the company. The service representative's goal, therefore, is to listen and do nothing, but encourage a majority of customers to feel like they have succeeded in screwing the company. If you reach your goal, then you should be able to add a net one-quarter to one-half percent to your bottom line. In no other area of business can you realize a higher return with so little time and energy invested. So how do you set up a first rate customer service department?

First, put the right person in charge. Look for someone whose personality combines equal parts of Mr. Rogers and Nurse Ratched. This special person must want to welcome customers with love, gentle kindness, and understanding, which will enhance the corporate image and disarm the complaining customer. Even more, she must yearn to give customers what she believes they most need and, if the truth were known, deeply desire: An enema. She also needs to be a good trainer, and to possess charismatic leadership skills to keep her staff properly motivated, because this staff will have the highest turnover rate of any department in your company. A good customer service representative will last only about six months and that will be about two months longer than you want him or her to stay. A good CS department head, on the other hand, will rule her domain until she dies.

Second, set up a first line of defense which customers must penetrate before they can speak to a service rep. Get an automated telephone answering system that requires the caller to choose from a confusing array of options and to remain on hold for at least seven minutes before speaking to a human being. When your staff is busy playing video games or eating pizza and hosting a baby shower and can't take calls, the automated system will refer the caller to an automated voice mail box if the caller knows the name or extension number of the representative they wish to speak to. If they don't know the name or extension they are trying to reach, then they will have to return to the main menu. And, of course, they can't know the name or extension number they are trying to reach unless they guess right because names and extension numbers are not listed anywhere and because all reps will use different names and different extensions every day. If anyone makes it through to the actual voice mailbox and leaves a message, it will not really be recorded so no one will ever have to waste time and return the call.

In other words, the system is set up to encourage most callers to give up and go away. Since every call is a claim, and therefore an attack against your bottom line, the more callers you can discourage the better. Only the persistent few should ever actually get to speak to a service rep.

Third, hire and train the right service representatives. The ideal candidate for service representative is a naïve, articulate, upper-middle class floater with no ambition or business skills, age twenty-two to twenty-eight, someone who was raised to communicate, avoid confrontation, listen to others, always be polite to everyone, and empathize with underdogs, like dolphins, Bambi, and angry customers.

Newly hired service reps need to undergo rigorous training, which should take about twenty minutes. Teach them always to be sympathetic to every customer and to do everything in their power to satisfy every caller. As service reps, of course, they have no power. They must also understand that their primary objective is to listen and be supportive, so train them never to argue with a customer. The customer is always right. Properly conveyed, that attitude will make more than half the callers go away, feeling like they have won.

Once they are trained, seat your new reps in close proximity in an open room, no cubicles, so no one can speak to a customer without being monitored by peers and supervisors.

When actually speaking to a customer, the service representative's first response is to tell persistent people what they want to hear to appease them, then pass the buck and shuffle them through five or six layers of appeal until they would rather gouge out their eyes than call again. Each layer should weed out about one third of those callers remaining. Their next job is to support the claims of the remaining callers. However, before any claim can actually be approved for settlement, the caller must take the positive recommendation of the helpful service rep up to a Supervising Customer Service Representative, who is presently out of the office and who, in turn, must send the caller to the Senior Vice President in Charge of Customer Service Claims and Settlements. It is a good idea for morale to change daily who gets to be the Vice President and to include newly trained reps so they don't feel left out.

For those rare individuals who stick with it and reach the final layer of appeal after five or six weeks of runaround, your department should arbitrarily deny claims for half of them, and for the rest it should give them about half of whatever it was they wanted. Flip a coin. It doesn't matter who gets what and who doesn't. Studies show that those who stick with the process that long will not give it up as long as they have a chance, so it is cheaper at this point to deny half of them outright and buy off the rest than to spend any more time on them. Remember: You just want to make them go away.

This is why jobs in the CSD run through a revolving door, because after about three months, the reps get frustrated since company policies, to which they must rigidly adhere, will never allow them to satisfy any customer in the way they are taught they must.

The people you deny you will lose as customers. Good riddance; they are malcontents and losers. The people you buy off, in contrast, you will need. They will think they are winners. Trot them out in your annual statement and your training manual to show just how special customers are to your company, and use them to demonstrate to shareholders how well you take care of the public.

Ideally, customer service departments should be located away from the company's main campus or administrative offices. The spirit under which CSDs operate is different from the corporate mainstream; plus you won't want the nice guy service reps mingling with aggressive young executives and ambitious wannabees, who never leave their table hungry. It's hard enough to find good help without internal casualties.

If you find that your CSD is granting too many claims, you might want to try a different strategy. One excellent solution, growing in popularity, is to outsource your CSD to Third World or Emerging countries, where wages are much lower, service reps speak English as a foreign language, and customers are forced to communicate like tourists whose rented taxi broke down in an isolated village in rural New Guinea.

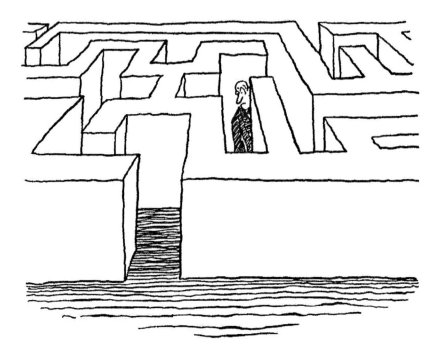

"When actually speaking to a customer, the service representative's first response is to tell persistent people what they want to hear to appease them, then pass the buck and shuffle them through five or six layers of appeal until they would rather gouge out their eyes than call again." p. 106

DEATH   Try not to think about it unless someone comes up with a cure. If that happens, invest.

DEBT   Owners of capital and ordinary people both subsist on debt. The difference is that we owners of capital are the creditors and interest we collect adds to our wealth, while ordinary people are the debtors and interest they pay reduces their wealth, which stimulates them to take on more debt. Clearly this is an elegant system of give and take.

To sustain this system you must do three things. First, you must stimulate ordinary people to want more than they can afford. Second, you must keep their earnings at a reasonable level so they cannot afford to pay cash for all that they choose to purchase. And third, you must make credit available to them so they can borrow more money to buy what they want but cannot afford. Following these three steps will allow you to stimulate additional sales, and therefore profits. In addition, ordinary people will pay you a reward for following these three steps in the form of interest and various service charges that stimulate even more profits. That's what I call a win-win situation.

Consumer debt is a giant blood bank always open when you need a quick transfusion to quench your thirst.

People of means, of course, do not carry debt. We might briefly incur a debt of convenience, but otherwise why pay someone else a few points to do what you don't need them to do?

Corporations, on the other hand, use debt like any other tool. Sometimes the added leverage of debt leads to returns much greater than the cost of money. In cases like these, when your liquid assets are tied up elsewhere, debt is imperative. Never argue with numbers that crunch. I also believe that you can have fun with debt.

How is that, you ask? Each of us is born with creative instincts that might have been channeled into art, music, theater, or invention. Truly, business does not offer many opportunities, outside of advertising, to play with those creative instincts. However, debt is one of those opportunities. What is debt? Think about it. Is it simply an amount owed to someone else? Can't debt be made up to look like a different character, such as an asset or an expense? Perhaps even income? Remember that enough unexpected income can turn a quarterly statement into a greeting card.

Don't be afraid to play creatively with debt. You have to be a little careful how it shows up on your balance sheet, but with the right accounting trails you can place debt just about anywhere you like. Put it where it does the most good. Think of yourself as a film director whose task is to transform the Wicked Witch of the West into a Little Flower Girl.

To be a fully rounded person you need to express your creative side. What better way to do it than to enhance your financial image in the process?

DECISION MAKING   When faced with important, complicated, and stressful choices, some people contemplate while others make decisions. Whom would you rather follow?

Always show that you are confident, in charge, and decisive, even when you don't have a clue what you are doing or have just flipped a mental coin. The world loves clear, simple, black and white choices. Provide them, and people will follow you anywhere.

DELUSION   People create fantasies to feed their hopes and allay their fears. When they are hopeful enough or frightened enough, they start to believe their fantasies, and if they believe their fantasies long enough, their fantasies replace reality and they become true believers.[13] That is, they become delusional.

Politics, religion, and self-image are the three areas that most encourage delusion. I can't count the number of times religious zealots have sold all their worldly belongings and congregated on a sacred hill so they can be picked up and carried off to a better world, only to suffer disappointment. Political ideologues fall prey to almost the same scenario. They too congregate on The Hill to conjure Utopia, only they don't sell their worldly belongings. They sell influence so they can add to their worldly belongings. Disappointment follows after they are investigated and voted out of office. In one way or another, though generally on a smaller scale, all people follow a similar pattern, characterized by reach that exceeds grasp by a couple of light years. Beneath their veneer of dissatisfactions, plain people desperately want to believe that they are gods and goddesses; mediocre people that they are geniuses; and vulgar people that they are sophisticated.

Knowing this quirk of human nature, you should know how to exploit people's delusions for profit. Obviously this is not a difficult task, but one that requires subtlety. You always want to provide some kind of reinforcement for the delusion, but you never want to actually share it. The trick is to supply products and services that delusional people demand, and thereby become their resource; but never put your corporation into a corner by directly claiming that the delusion is reality. If you did that, then when the bubble bursts, you would lose future credibility. In other words, sell every goddess a potion that makes her skin glow; just don't try to measure that glow with a light meter.

---

13 The phrase *The True Believer* was coined for the title of his first book by Eric Hoffer, that remarkable laborer and longshoreman who read whole libraries, authored ten books, and won The Presidential Medal of Freedom.

DEMAND   In a free market economy the law of supply and demand is comparable to the law of gravity in physics: Every commodity, product, and service is governed by it and none escapes it. The shrewd CEO must abide by its dictates or trade in his Rolls for a bus ticket.

Everyone knows that marketing research is focused on understanding demand. If you don't know what consumers want, you can't very well provide it. Fewer people understand how efficiently advertising, used in conjunction with marketing research, creates demand. Today, in general, demand defines supply only because the supplier defines demand. Remember the Pet Rock? Before the blitz, no one ever went prospecting for a pet rhyolite to replace Fluffy the sheep dog. The majority of consumers don't know what they want until their acquisitive nature has been tickled by it.

Give people choices. Present those choices as imperatives, one after another in rapid sequence, and consumers will gobble them all up. It is possible to create demand in the marketplace for just about anything you can imagine, so the nature, the relevance, the usefulness, the quality, or the longevity of the product is irrelevant. What matters is the desire to have what others might have and the fear of being left behind.

Recognize consumers for what they are. Give them a clearly focused dose of demand so they will stampede to the marketplace, give up their fleece, and extend their credit to the limit. To maximize efficiency, keep them on the edge. Extend them more credit and increase interest rates as needed to cover additional risk. Offer them trivial rebates which sixty percent of them won't bother to collect, or double your prices then offer bargain two-for-one giveaways. You can also reduce prices from inflated margins and throw in a freebie trinket that looks and sounds valuable. Use all the tricks of the trade to convince them that they have nothing to lose by making their purchase and that they would be missing the boat if they didn't make it. Most demand is a corporate imperative interpreted by consumers as their own spontaneous desire. Don't argue with their interpretation. In a "consumer-driven" economy, consumers must always believe that they occupy the driver's seat.

DEMOCRACY   Strictly speaking, in a true democracy, every person gets one vote on every issue, and the majority rules. So far as I know, no nation has ever practiced true democracy. Athenians from the fifth century B.C. gave it a whirl, but they excluded human property such as women and slaves from voting, so honest historians count them as a near miss.

Most of us defer to the vague, popular definition of democracy as a set of principles in government ensuring rights and freedoms for citizens. I emphasize the term "citizens." Given terrorism and other chicanery in the world, I don't think the rights Americans enjoy should be extended to non-citizens on American soil. Most of these people aren't used to them anyway, and if they are serious about living in this country long term, they should earn their citizenship. Meanwhile, bring them in temporarily and let them work. It's a good way for them to learn what our democracy is all about, and, since they work for next to nothing, they dilute our domestic work force and keep it from demanding unrealistic wages and benefits. That is, they democratize our labor force.

I also emphasize the term "rights." In America, you have the right to do with your life whatever you choose; to make of yourself whatever you wish; and to satisfy every desire you have so long as your actions don't impede the other fellow's rights to do the same. Each of us gets the same chance to step up to the plate and swing. Each of us gets an equal chance to become a billionaire.

Finally, and most importantly, I emphasize the term "freedom." Presently we enjoy extensive freedom, but we could still do better. Think about some of the freedoms we have enjoyed in our past. How much better would our world be if we had no income taxes, for example? Or no inheritance taxes? No capital gains? No anti-trust legislation? No ceiling on interest rates? No nit-picking rules about working conditions? No limits on the age of employment? No suffocating environmental rules? No prohibitions against offshore setups, and no penalties once you are there? We must all understand that business will take care of business. In a world of absolute freedom, businesses compete and consumers vote with their dollars. If one plant is undesirable then consumers will buy from another and the laws of supply and demand and consumer choice will create *de facto* any regulation that might be needed.

Still, compared to the rest of the world, we are free as birds. So guard your freedoms well; always try to expand them; and never let them slide. Fight efforts to regulate and legislate and control. Our world may not be perfect, but without the freedoms we currently enjoy, it would be impossible to accumulate wealth to such a degree as we have. Therefore be ever vigilant. If we ever lost our liberties we would all be forced to live in fear and hopeless poverty like Cubans and North Koreans.

You don't even have to look that far down the scale to get an ulcer. Just for a moment, think about present day America. Think about the economy we now have and then add just a few socialistic regulations like those instituted following The Crash of 1929. Think about what you have or what is nearly within your grasp right now, and then take a cold, hard look at the alternatives in a world determined to redistribute income downward and regulate business to meet goals set by a socialist ideology. Go ahead, ask yourself: Do you really want to work for a hundred thousand a year as part of a stifled cadre of executives more intent on pleasing regulators than investors? Could you honestly live in a two thousand square foot standard issue pre-designed cul-de-sac hovel furnished from a display showroom? Do you want to drive a Subaru? Worry about how to pay for the slip? Wonder how to afford a few days' holiday on the Côte d'Azure? Give up that creaky old castle in Newport or skiing in Grenoble? Purchase a Monet *print*? Golf at a public course? Gamble at a public table? Eat steak at an Outback? If these questions don't shake you up, then consider this: What if you had to count on Social Security as a major part of your golden parachute?

Take away even our most obvious freedoms and life could become an unbearable nightmare composed of want and deprivation.

DEPRESSION   Economic depression is no longer possible. There are too many vested interests that would be hurt by it, and too many controls have been instituted since the 1930s to permit it. Nevertheless, many consumers and economists believe that depression is not only possible but also likely at some unspecified time in the future. If you view this attitude as a market demand, then you can profit by it. The sale of hard monies, like gold and gemstones, and of real estate and tools of survival such as guns, ammunition, storable foodstuffs, bottled water, generators, and a host of other useless paraphernalia, plus certain securities alleged to act as a hedge against hard times, can offset some of the decline in the purchase of normal products by this doomsday sector whenever it becomes militant. However, most consumers most of the time understand that even the phrase "financial depression" is an oxymoron.

Since financial depression is highly unlikely, there is no good reason to experience psychological depression. However, if for some reason you do feel depressed, I suggest that you experience The Authentic. Take one of those vacations that will guide you through places inhabited by "real" people: Indian reservations, inner cities, barrios, and peasant villages in Mexico, South Asia, or Africa; that sort of thing. Nothing will perk you up and make you appreciate your own life more than mingling with the masses, the poor, the diseased, and the desperate.

DEREGULATION   Deregulation did for CEOs and corporations what the Declaration of Independence did for the colonists. It gave us a nation and made us answerable only to ourselves.

DERIVATIVES   Derivatives offer sophisticated investors the chance to manage or exploit risk by betting on or against the future performance of anything, from common stocks and corn to a company's credit rating and your mother-in-law's weight. Derivatives also allow swapping. For example, if company A gets a two percent discount on Girl Scout Cookies, which company B wants but doesn't get, and Company B has a fixed rate loan at one point over the Federal Funds Rate, which Company A wants but can't get, then the two companies can work out a deal to swap: A pays B the two percent cookie discount while B pays A its loan rate so both companies can get what they really want, and if there is any change left on the table the principles work it out in green fees for Friday tee times.

The hedge game can also be played as an end in itself. Because they are risky, derivatives can lead to frightening losses but also to gigantic profits. During the last two decades, derivatives have grown so much in popularity that between over-the-counter markets, exchanges, and private handshakes at Buckaroo's Waterhole and Bull Riding Salon, the value of derivative contracts reaches into the hundreds of trillions of dollars in notional value, representing more capital value than all other markets for financial instruments. The best part is that most of these deals are unregulated. These markets have grown so large that shrewd players no longer measure derivatives' values in mere dollars. Instead, they created a new index, the ISDI, or Inferred Steroidal Dollars Index, which daily sets the ratio between dollars and millions. For example, an ISD index of 1.3 means that a contract worth twenty million dollars is really worth only 15.3846 steroidal dollars. As you can see, derivatives are part of the final frontier, where big dogs play big games by big rules or no rules. But this is not worrisome. While risky in principle, two reasons indicate that derivatives are safe for knowledgeable players. First, they must be safe because nearly every rock solid financial institution consumers know and trust is swimming in derivatives up to their armpits. And second, derivatives traders and the owners of capital behind them are among the smartest and most trustworthy people on earth, second only to televangelists.

Derivatives also demonstrate that business does not have to produce anything, sell anything, or manage anything beyond theoretical risk to justify its existence. It can simply gamble with numbers representing capital on any scale from small to epic. In other words, whether you are a bull, a bear, a wolf, a hedgehog, or a raving lunatic, you will find plenty of players and plenty of amusement in derivatives.

One of the pioneers who developed the modern markets for derivatives, and one of the main reasons for their current popularity, was Endrun Corporation. The world thought Endrun was an energy company. In fact, it was a derivatives trading firm specializing in energy related Inferred Steroidal Dollars. One entire floor of the Endrun world headquarters in Mega, Texas was a huge derivatives trading pit called, "The Coliseum." It was open to any trader certified by the Texas chapter of the Ringling Brothers Board of Derivatives Trading Certification and Clown College, which quickly qualified all qualified applicants except communists, child molesters, and Oklahoma University football boosters. Endrun also provided a core clientele, with more than three thousand off-the-books subsidiaries and partnerships, each doing battle like gladiators against the uncertain future and each other. They demonstrated just how profitable derivatives can be. However, as traders learned how to fool the company and the company learned how to fool itself, they also demonstrated that derivatives were key to one of the worst financial collapses in human history.

There are two lessons to be learned here. First, don't forget that old saying about never gambling with scared money. Play with derivatives all you like because you can make a lot of money, but play only with gambling money. Money you can afford to lose. Leave capital earmarked for investment, operations, and your personal comfort out of the game. And second, watch for irrational fools who play derivatives rationally. You should be able to pluck them at their own game.

DESIRE   People are notorious for letting their desires screw up their lives. Look at the French artist, Paul Gaugin. The man was a stockbroker, for God's sake, and with a top-drawer firm. He had a wife and children. He was an aggressive, outgoing young man with a good dose of the Right Stuff. But he gave in to his desires and ended up poor, miserable, and syphilitic in godforsaken reaches of the South Pacific. The man died alone in a grass hut!

You are blessed with greed, the unbridled lust for money. This is all the desire you need. It allows you to focus all your energy on your career. Do it. Use all the discipline you can muster if you need to, and never allow yourself to be sidetracked by more passionate desires. People who follow their bliss nearly always end up in a mess. Follow your career instead, and all the carefully wrought strategies that frame it, and chances are good that you will achieve success, wealth, power, and prestige.

Life is short. Don't waste yours by developing outside interests -- and chasing foolish desires that contribute nothing to your bottom line.

DEVELOPMENT   When Europeans colonized North America, it was a wilderness that offered hardship and poverty with plenty of potential. Today the United States is the most vibrant economy in the world's history and it offers everyone a chance for prosperity and relative ease. We call the difference, "development."

What used to be swampland is now a productive mall. What used to be deserts are now profitable orange groves and retirement communities that pay property taxes. What used to be a forest, inhospitable to all but a few birds and squirrels, is now a viable source for the export of saw logs that will lower our trade deficit, and of value-added palettes of dimension lumber that will keep employment high and provide shelter for families. Development does not come without some cost, of course, but what is the alternative? Which would you find it easier to live without, the First Care clinic in your mall, or a flock of ducks? Orange juice and municipal water, or scorpions and tarantulas? Your job or a few spotted owls? You have to make choices.

If you think there is a meaningful alternative to development, think again. What we human beings inherited in this planet and what people refer to as nature, is a collection of atomic and molecular building blocks that can be assembled and reassembled in just about any form we choose. What we inherited was merely the assemblage that resulted from four and a half billion years of chance interacting with the laws of physics and chemistry over time in a biological evolutionary stream. With genetic engineering we have the power to replace chance with human reason and make the evolutionary stream into a rational strategy designed for our good. We can remake forests, deserts, and swamps to benefit ourselves and future generations. We are learning how to remake plants, animals, and yes, even human beings, to suit our desires. It is happening right now, and it will continue to happen at an accelerating pace. The genie is out of the bottle. And the opportunities for growth and profit from genetic engineering are unparalleled. In time, nothing on this planet will resemble what we now know as nature except those few structures that we choose to keep unaltered, and everything else, every resource, will be reinvented and harnessed to the service of human beings. We can honestly say that a miraculous future awaits us, one that no one living today would recognize. For that we must thank the idea of development.

DISCLOSURE   Would you publish your Social Security number in the *Los Angeles Times*? No? Then why would you show anyone your actual personal earnings statement? Why would you give anyone unpublished information about your corporate earnings? Or corporate business in general?

Aside from quarterly and annual reports, which can display the production values you want to display, never voluntarily disclose anything to anyone. Your business is not the business of your wife, your family, your friends, your enemies, your associates, your employees, your stockholders, the press, the government, or God. You are answerable only to yourself. If other people express dissatisfaction or outrage because you refuse to reveal the inner workings of your financial existence, screw them.

However, if you are forced by massive public pressure to disclose, then turn the matter over to the spin-doctors in your public relations department. If you are forced by law, then let your lowyers speak. Never believe for one moment that you, by yourself, can disclose as well as spin doctors or lowyers. That would be arrogant.

DISCONTENT   The world is filled with people who do not have the wherewithal to harness life for their own benefit. Many of them become malcontents, losers, complainers, and whiners, and they are all filled with discontent. These are people who want a free ride. Life is too tough for them. They complain about others, "the system", "the establishment," and people who are successful. In truth, they are complaining about their own inadequacies and failures.

Guard against discontent. It can spread through a corporation like a wild fire. Get rid of the discontented and have a no-tolerance policy toward negativism of any kind. Make sure your human resources people document everything. Most people who are discontent have low self-esteem caused by inadequacies they have been unable to cure. Some are addicts. Some are fat. Some are old. Some are stupid. Some are ugly. Some are impotent, frigid, neurotic, or otherwise inadequate. Some have mental or physical defects, or believe that they have been victimized by others in ways that damaged them. Some are just lazy and don't want to compete. There are many reasons for low self-esteem. However, none of these inadequacies is a viable excuse. Nearly all of them can be fixed – diet, counseling, plastic surgery, dozens of fixes come to mind – if the person has sufficient will.

Purging the ranks is never easy. Low self-esteem is not sufficient grounds for dismissal. But poor job performance and violation of company policies are sufficient grounds as long as you document infractions, keep all relevant performance reviews, and go about the firing in the right way. For example, getting rid of a three hundred pound malcontent will be more difficult than getting rid of a one hundred and fifty pound malcontent. Charges of discrimination, wrongful discharge suits, and violation of personal rights are always risks. So keep the three hundred pounds – or any other source of low self-esteem – off the table and the table will last longer. Make sure that every targeted employee has received below-average job evaluations for three consecutive quarters and that each one has clearly violated company policies. Make sure that you have signed, documented warnings in each target's personnel file. And be certain that each target has been offered counseling. Follow the book and you can purge your ranks without a wrinkle. Just do what you must to cover your tracks and get rid of them.

Remember this: If your cup is not half full, it's because you don't know how to empty the bad half.

THE DISEASE SCENARIO   Pharmaceuticals wrote the book on how to create demand for a product. Once their industry was deregulated and they were allowed to advertise directly to the public, they quickly learned how to create a disease to match a pill, terrify consumers, provide free samples to the medical community, and then induce the individual consumer to demand the pill from his or her doctor. Demand has increased so much that manufacturers can raise their prices and charge enough for their products to make record profits and still pay astronomical advertising and marketing costs. Good consumers foot the bill to finance the forces that make them good consumers. It's like asking a company to pay for its own hostile takeover. This brilliant strategy has made the drug companies billions, and other industries need to adapt it more aggressively to their own needs.

Let's look at two examples. Just about every child suffers, now and then, from hyper-activity and clipped attention. It's an annoying condition that we used to call, "childhood." Perhaps five percent or fewer children suffer it continuously as a result of actual pathology. However, when someone comes along and defines it as a disease then provides a pill that fixes the disease, nearly every frustrated parent in America sees the disease in his or her children. Since good parents want what's best for their children, and good pediatricians and counselors never want to be outside the avant-garde loop, everyone jumps on the bandwagon. For an added bonus, before you know it, adults are spotting the same disease in themselves and sales that exploded can now blow the roof off. The best part is that everyone benefits. Drug companies get fat and family members that used to hate each other now get along like zombies at a voodoo picnic.

Then there is acid reflux, an annoyance that people suffer after they eat too much. We used to call it "indigestion," and "heartburn." Since nearly everyone in America eats too much, what was once a minor annoyance, fixed with some calcium carbonate, is now a dangerous epidemic. Fortunately, the disease can be fixed by taking an expensive pill. Best of all, both conditions, short attention span and heartburn, when viewed as Attention Deficit Disorder and Acid Reflux Disease, require a *lifetime* of prescriptions for sufferers who want to be on the safe side.

Some people question the tobacco folks for creating life-long demand for a product that is addictive. No one can fault pharmaceuticals on these grounds. All they have done is present options so consumers can make rational choices. That's what the marketplace is all about. The fact of the matter is that the disease scenario is the best marketing scheme ever invented. It is better even than addiction because it doesn't risk massive lawsuits and public relations suicide. It is a template that you should apply to every marketing strategy you can whenever you can. Is your car engine noisy? Have you seen a termite lately? Does your lawn have crabgrass? Is your portfolio overloaded with cash instruments? Does your belly bulge? Is your dog bi-polar? Do you have a gray hair? Do you sag? Do others get the best of you? Is the circular saw you presently own dangerous? Are you socially awkward? Does your hair frizz? Do you suffer from chronic insomnia? How long a list do you want? Life can be a series of dreadful threats, each waiting for a magic fix. Define the threat and provide the fix and you will cure for your lifetime whatever financial ills you have.

DISSATISFACTION   Back in the naïve old days, merchants lived by the rule that they should always satisfy their customers. Fortunately, thought on that subject has changed and become subtler. My basic rule of thumb is, *never satisfy your customers*. A satisfied customer either leaves the marketplace or becomes complacent. Why drive customers away with satisfaction?

Gratify the customer's immediate desire, yes. But then be certain that within hours, if not at the point of sale, the customer experiences new dissatisfactions that he or she must resolve with new purchases.

Dissatisfaction is the key to good marketing. Is this person too fat? Does that person have too many wrinkles? Wouldn't this person like to drive a car almost like the car his favorite rock star drives? When was the last time you ate a *real* steak? Look, this lawn mower does much more than my lawn mower! Hey, this dog food has new and improved flavor! Create dissatisfaction at every turn and consumers will rush to your business to bid on satisfactions. Then give them more dissatisfaction. Our economy is built on yearnings for more and for better, and those yearnings are made possible only by dissatisfaction with one's status quo, whatever that might be. In a perfect marketplace, we would offer consumers a hierarchy of products, each one a little more satisfying than the one beneath it, and the top product far beyond the financial reach of any but the most privileged. Try to keep consumers climbing a product ladder, forever dissatisfied because something better always exists just out of their reach; forever acquiring to resolve that dissatisfaction. Forever unable to reach final bliss, but always able to reach.

DIVERSIFICATION   Don't keep all your eggs in one basket. Get several baskets and then buy the chickens that lay the eggs. That's diversification.

DOGS Pick your family dog as carefully as you picked your wife, your son's nanny, and your daughter's boyfriend. Then have him trained with the same care. The dog will reflect on you just as powerfully as any of your other possessions, including your homes, your cars, your Italian shoes, and your custom designed jewelry. If you own a stupid dog that befriends everyone, people will tend to think of you as an oaf and a fool. If you own a dog that looks and acts like The Terminator, people will think by association that you are vicious. If you own a simpering, Barney Fife dog that mutters when it means to bark, people will be inclined to view you as weak-willed, uncertain, and submissive. *Never* get stuck with a dog that reminds people of Barney Fife. Pick a dog that makes a positive, aggressive statement.

Ideally, and particularly if you don't intend to kick the beast for effect, find a dog that is larger than average, powerful enough to tear the throat out of a rhinoceros, well-mannered as a British duke, bold yet cautious, clever, astute, exciting, charismatic, impeccably groomed, and handsome as a Westminster grand champion. And give the dog an appropriate name, not a pedestrian name like "Bowser," or a specifically human name like "Frank." An associate of mine gave his dog the excellent name, "Bones," because the dog by breed appeared mildly portly, like its owner, and because the name invoked memory of his hallowed society, something other members, but not every person within earshot, would recognize.

If you pick him astutely, train him rigorously, and name him cleverly, your dog can be your best flattery as well as your best friend.

THE DOLLAR There ought to be a monument located on The Mall somewhere between the Washington Monument and the Lincoln Memorial to commemorate what made our country great.

DOOMSAYERS There is a word you are liable to run across, as I did, in the *Reader's Digest* vocabulary quiz. The word is "fey." It means a foreboding of calamity or death. Literary people often use this word to describe each other's bad attitudes. I don't think there is room for this word in the boardroom.

There are two attitudes in this world. One looks up and says, "Can do!" Like the people who cracked the human genome. The other looks down and says, "It can't be done," like skeptics who claim that you can't design perfect human beings who will live a thousand years and even if you could you wouldn't want to because in a thousand years humanity might be extinct or living in caves under an ice cap. You know the kind. Pessimists. Doomsayers. Fey people.

Weed doomsayers out of your organization. They are much too fey.

DREAMS   The world could be divided right down the middle between dreamers and doers. Some people are happy to let ghosts of imagination perform what real people might achieve: Dreamers. Others will not rest until they have built what they want: Doers. I don't have much use for dreamers.

You want to dream? Fine, dream on. Dream the impossible dream. But let that dream be a seed of action, not a pacifier. A dream without a plan to develop it is like a building without tenants. It gives no return, no income, no investment profile, no activity, no growth, no increases in rent, no security, no power, no prestige, and no write-offs to reduce taxable revenues to an acceptable net. It is merely a shell and an excuse for inactivity. Dreaming is for poets, painters, idealists, and other malcontents who haven't got the drive to build what they really want, so they talk about it or show it and wait for someone else to come along and fix what's wrong or build what's right. It will never happen for these people. The only dreams that come true are those that start in the wallet, advance to the drawing board, and finish as final entries on a balance sheet. The only exception to this rule is the occasional lottery winner who bought a chance at his dream and got lucky. At something more than one hundred million to one odds.

One dream that can come true is the American Dream. It is poorly named, and that fact might explain why so many people fail to achieve it. It is a strategy, not a dream. Invest a hundred dollars in your strategy. Make three hundred. Extrapolate. Research. Come up with a solid business plan. Turn your three hundred into a thousand, your thousand into ten thousand, and your ten thousand into half a million. Before you know it you are on The Big Board and when you walk into a room, you can almost hear the hair on the back of people's necks rise. That's when you remember what it was like. How ordinary people budget for fuel bills, eat out only four times a week, spend holidays at a public zoo, borrow money to send their kid to a mediocre state college, and walk through banks feeling no more important than a cockroach. Call it a dream if you wish, because the alternative to achieving the American Dream is a nightmare. You must understand that every dream realized is the end result of a practical plan shrewdly executed, and its success is measured by its bottom line.

DRESS   We have all heard those tired clichés about first impressions and clothes making the man. For all practical purposes, they are true. You will never take your place among the nation's business leaders unless you *look* like a nation's business leader. Most of you will have learned how to dress at home or at school. If your home life deprived you of that education or if you did not attend prep school, then I suggest that you start with the basics: A subscription to *GQ*. If you don't know that *GQ* stands for *Gentleman's Quarterly*, then I suggest that you assemble a starter kit and order catalogues from Brooks Brothers, L.L. Bean, and Abercrombie and Fitch.

The well-dressed CEO must follow only one simple rule: For every occasion there is an accepted proper dress code. Learn it and follow it. Whether you are opening gifts with the wife and kiddies on Christmas morning, attending a soiree hosted by the ambassador of Brazil, or participating in the execution of one of your colleagues at a board meeting, there is one way to dress for each occasion. When you can write the manual on how to dress for every occasion, then you may take the term "dress" off your daily agenda and concentrate on the more subtle art of how to outdress others.

Is it possible to be more correct that correct? Is it possible to be brighter than bright and better than good? As a member of the club "Best and Brightest," you will learn how to draw positive attention to yourself in a crowd of men all dressed seemingly alike, for example, in black ties, tails, and patent leather pumps. No one said it would be easy, but something as simple as the hand-engraved insignia on your pinkie ring can make all the difference between fitting into the crowd and assuming your rightful place in its hierarchy.

Here are a few basics for beginners. Know the psychological values attached to cuts, colors, and patterns. Let's say that you are meeting over lunch with the CEO of a weaker company, a quarter of whose stock you have just acquired in a hostile move. Would you choose tasseled loafers, tan trousers, a single-breasted tweed sport coat with a green wool tie over a buff-yellow soft collar button down oxford cloth shirt? Or might you choose a double-breasted, broad chalk stripe navy suit, inch and a half wide braces, starched white shirt with stiff cuffs and collar, carat diamond cufflinks, and a silk silver and crimson rep tie that could bring to mind a bloodstained broadsword? It isn't rocket science.

Long before you can afford to do so, stop buying off the rack, if that's where you buy, and find a good tailor. Hong Kong and Singapore are good places to start. Tailors there will be less costly but will require more guidance. Once you step up to New York's finest, or to a good outfit in Rome or Paris, you can pretty much turn them loose. The ultimate, of course, is a bespoke tailor from an old firm of several generations located on or near London's Savile Row. Plan on flying to London twice yearly for fittings. Once you have a truly intimidating tailor, learn to take off your coat in appropriate places and leave it draped over a chair or hanging on a coat rack while you leave the room. Now and then when conditions are right, others will reconnoiter your coat and even feel the material. The effect on them will be well worth the effort.

Whenever you encounter others less well dressed than you, less appropriately dressed, or whose taste is incorrect in any small detail, crush them immediately with a look of disdain that would wither a marble statue. Learn to make subtle but biting comments that won't brand you as a snob but will leave your victims bleeding and terminally uncertain while their friends will struggle to suppress a sneering chuckle. In this way, as in other ways, use style to inspire admiration and to instill fear in others.

What about changing standards? Increasingly, casual (some would say downright vulgar) dress is becoming the norm in America. A few years ago, jeans were appropriate attire for the boy in the mailroom. Today, some young and even mid-rank executives, male and female, find them appropriate for Friday's business, and some young women assume that Casual Fridays are a license to dress like lap dancers. Rather than despair, I suggest that you take advantage of this trend. Call an unplanned staff meeting on a Friday afternoon, and watch the skin on your employees' cheeks turn grayish-green when you walk into the room, the last to arrive. No one ever visited a royal chamber and had to ask, "Which one is the king?" The relative splendor of your appearance compared to their own shabby and tasteless togs will remind everyone in the room of which individual sits atop this food chain. Furthermore, their regret will be good for at least two weeks' worth of high quality sucking-up.

One final word. Don't wear short pants. Not unless you are dressing for court sports or boating. Short pants are for short people: Children. Seersucker trousers or linen casuals will do nicely for you in warm weather. The difficulty is simple: Short pants reveal. Do you want others to think that you are vain or off your guard? Do you want to invite their ridicule? Remember the cardinal rule of rulers: *Never reveal yourself.* Think of your wardrobe as a kind of impenetrable armor afforded by few, emulated by many, and admired by all.

Does clothing make the man? That is entirely up to you.

THE DUPONT CHART   Almost no one knows or cares today what a DuPont Chart really is or what it measures, why it is necessary, or how it works. However, it is absolutely essential to have one, and to make sure that it is working correctly. It must measure what it measures with absolute perfection, and it must be prominently displayed. Don't let it slide. Assign it to your CFO and hold him personally responsible for its accuracy.

Why? Because when old school investors happen by, they will need to see the chart to know that all is well. In the mean time, lock your young Turks in their play room and let them ratchet up their software with all the bells and whistles that factor into the financial mix variables like current stock value, projected growth rate, virtual profits from hedge strategies, and the effect of the South American popcorn crop on Indonesian oil production. This will tell you much more than stogy old generalities such as return on assets, return on equity, turnover, and leverage. After all, a corporate culture must be grounded solidly on whatever is fashionable.

It should also respect traditions that work. What better tradition than brackets on your wall displaying fundamentals that only a graying CFO could love?

"Almost no one knows or cares today what a DuPont Chart really is or what it measures, why it is necessary, or how it works. However, it is absolutely essential to have one, and to make sure that it is working correctly." p. 127

EARNINGS   When the Chicago Bears play the Green Bay Packers, is the outcome determined by which team had more fun? When Al Gore and George Bush contended for the presidency, was the outcome determined by which gentleman acted more gentlemanly? Life gets down to basics. People keep score and in sports and politics winners score more when they hit harder, run faster, and talk the talk louder. Business is simpler. Our scorecard records only one item: Earnings.

As to personal earnings shoot for the moon and disguise as much as you can to avoid criticism. I hope that you are aware of the gains we have made in the past thirty years and how much you stand to benefit from them. Back in the bad old days, a third of a century ago, the best CEOs made only a pittance, some thirty times as much as the average worker. By 1993 that multiplier had risen to one hundred and thirty. Today, in these better times, the figure is around four hundred. And that is just the norm. The American turkey has been carved. Now with full plates we are equipped to maximize profits to gain *real* wealth. For example, play the game right and pump enough oil, like retired CEO of Exxtort Mogul, Lou de Rappest, and you can bump that CEO-to-worker ratio to a thousand or more. At twenty thousand dollars per hour, you can afford to worry less about Social Security going belly up. These are good times. Treat them well.

As to corporate earnings, if you don't have them, you can't show them, right? Wrong. You can always show earnings if you just redefine a few entries. Move a few debts to assets or some loans to future sales reported in the present, that sort of thing. You can also boost earnings, if you are in the right industry, by puting pressure on your wholesalers to buy, whether they need to buy or not. According to our best information, All-ford "The Twister" Doonit, CEO of Brasen-Meizer Squeaz, developed such a devastating chokehold on his customers that he was offered a job with the Worldwide Wrestling Federation soon after he got fired from the drug business. Of course some sectors don't need to boost earnings. Oil companies have learned to merge and cooperate like moms planning a PTO picnic. Worldwide, the oil pipeline, like the world's diamond pipeline, can change diameter daily to meet projected earnings. But in good times like these, when Exxtort Mogul alone pulls in one hundred million dollars daily in profits, that's a good indication that reducing diameter to boost earnings even more might be redundant. In times like these your real challenge is to hide earnings not flaunt them. At least look like you are putting all of that windfall to good use, such as reinvesting it in vital new somethings that will save America and comfort the poor.

Bottom line? Don't sweat annoying details that stand between you and your earnings goals. Pursue your goals relentlessly, and plan for a retirement that will put you in a Winners' Hall of Fame. Along the way, whenever you show an earnings report, display your company's earnings and the many good uses to which you put them, the same way a decorator displays Norman Rockwell prints in a dental office. Frame them subtly so they almost blend into the wallpaper. That way they won't clash with anything, but will provide a happy distraction from a process that might otherwise cause the clientele to scream.

ECOLOGY   Ecology is the study of the interrelationships between living organisms and their environments. As it is practiced, ecology is based on the false premise that those *present* relationships always have positive value and should therefore be preserved. Imagine what our world would look like if humans had been around and ecologists had been in control during the age of dinosaurs. Instead of millions of acres for grizzly bears, alligators, snow leopards, and rhinoceroses, we would be setting aside millions of acres for tyrannosaurus rex. Welcome to Jurassic Park.

Things change. Species disappear. New ones emerge. The Laws of Survival dictate that species adapt to change or perish, and since nearly all ecosystems in the future will be human ecosystems, humans will decide what will be allowed to adapt and what not. In other words, not only the animals listed above, but all wild creatures will become extinct in the relatively near future except cockroaches and those creatures that can demonstrate some important use to human beings. Like anything else, wild species, both vegetative and animal, are subject to the hard scrutiny of cost-benefit analysis, and if we cannot justify the cost of artificially maintaining them because we recognize a benefit that is worth more than that cost, then those species will be allowed or encouraged to become extinct. As a matter of fact, if you yourself don't adapt to these changes, you too might disappear.

I suggest that ecologists learn to adapt while they still can. Of course they won't, and then we will have to decide how long to mourn before we replace them with genetic engineers.

THE ECONOMY   We no longer have complete cultures or societies and in time nations will become obsolete. Today, in the infancy of the Age of Commerce, we have economies merging slowly into The Grand Economy, one worldwide system of free market commerce whose universal language is capital. That revolution has already begun to take place and there is no going back and no wish to go back. Even reporters now discuss "the economy" instead of "the nation" or "our society." Gross National Products have become Gross Domestic Products. Christmas is no longer measured in quaint terms of Santa's elves, religious mystery, human sentimentality, and good cheer. It is measured in terms of retail sales, hard dollars exchanging hands and spreading prosperity. When a catastrophe strikes, like a hurricane or a flood, we instinctively measure its ferocity, and our loss, in terms of dollars, not vague sentiments or changed lifestyles. "The hurricane did three hundred million dollars worth of damage." That is a statement that strikes home. It is one that we understand and can relate to. Capital measures our worth in every way imaginable. When was the last time you heard a reviewer praise a movie because it analyzed cultural traits or attempted to present a thought? Reviewers report that the leading film grossed eighty million dollars in its first week. In a review I remember for a film about the history of skate boarding, the reviewer did not characterize the sport in vague and subjective terms like "healthy," "obnoxious," "entertaining," or "self-expressive." He said, "It's a productive outlet for youth." Productive. The same is true when we discuss emerging nations. We do not hope that they become humane, enlightened, happy places to live, any more than we pretend that Dorothy and Toto never left Kansas. Instead, we hope that they take their place among efficient and competitive nations. As surely as Neanderthal man belonged to a clan, birds belong to a flock, and fish belong to a school, we now belong to an economy. To The Grand Economy.

As a CEO, you should take pride in the efforts of all those who came before you to help transform *homo sapiens* from an itinerant, short-lived, provincial, unattractive, unwashed, inefficient, superstitious, and impoverished lot into a stable, trained, civilized, productive, realistic race of workers/consumers who plan to meet old age with a high standard of living. Instead of dying miserably from a simple bacterial infection at age thirty-nine, most ordinary people now fantasize about playing bridge and eating cheese while resting poolside at their club at the age of eighty-five in their sunny, gated, retirement communities. We defy the destructive forces of nature, and we do so because we belong to The Grand Economy. After all, it is the economy that generates wealth, and from wealth all things flow.

EDUCATION   The most important mission of any free market democracy is to educate its citizens. All of them. That is why I recommend vehemently that you acquire and use to your specific advantage mass communications facilities of all kinds. Only if you own broadcast media, or you exert sufficient influence through spending on advertising, can you then design media content to meet your needs. Call it curriculum development. Target adults too, of course, and do it relentlessly, but focus on children as your main targets. Their little minds are less cluttered and easier to fill. Remember: Children spend more time watching television and movies, listening to music, and playing computer video games than they spend in school and their minds are more accessible at home. Most of them sleep through school anyway. It is essential, therefore, to control entertainment production through sponsorship, research and development, funding grants, advertising, and ownership of production facilities.

Most importantly, gear the cognitive level of content to age nine through fourteen, just as Hollywood does. You'll be able to reach ninety-nine and a half percent of the population. People in the targeted mental age group will believe that the world was designed specifically for them. Younger children will think that the level you portray is a goal to reach, and older children and adults, since they have all been through it and are and comfortable with it, will accept puberty as our culture's developmental norm. This is why we call our world a "popular culture," and not an "unpopular culture," or a "mature culture." In addition, make selective donations to schools, donations that will enlighten students about their place in the economy and the kind of work you will expect them to do; your commitment to their needs; and your product lines.

Children are present and future consumers and potential employees, and a majority of them control or deeply influence their parents' spending habits. And of course a large number of their parents and other chronological adults are fun loving folks who will continue to enjoy their own adolescence through their golden years. Nurture them all with care. Education is the key to tomorrow's bottom lines.

EFFICIENCY Just as a perfect machine cannot allow imperfect parts, a world calibrated to efficiency will not tolerate slackers. Let those in backward countries idle away their time in cafes and theaters and town squares while our new world takes shape and its work begs to be done. Let others chatter like jays while we hone our skills and build our markets and reap our profits. The final stage in our evolution is the one in which mankind seizes control of the process of evolution and redirects it toward predicted ends. Only those who understand efficiency will understand how and why to redirect that process. Only those who have become the future will know how to build it. Do not be left behind because you cling to old and quaint habits. And never waste your time on unproductive pursuits that lead nowhere.

For example, let's say that you love to travel. Understand that there is no room left in the real world for happy wanderers who idle off to exotic lands merely to see, hear, smell, touch, absorb, and learn. Whatever your destination -- the Andes, the Himalayas, the Amazon, the Sahara -- go into training. Set goals. Devise a marketing plan. Take your extreme bicycle, skis, snowboard, climbing gear, or whatever turns your crank, along with a video crew, and *capitalize!* Use your time efficiently. Conquer something. Prove your worth. Set some kind of weird record that will give you fifteen minutes of celebrity and a couple of gigs on talk shows. Then watch the doors open. In other words, learn to direct all your thoughts and all your activities toward your bottom line. Otherwise you are wasting your time while others get ahead.

Get into the habit of pushing yourself in everything you do. At the end of each day, look back on the past twenty-four hours and evaluate your performance. Be critical. Devise ways to increase your efficiency. In a competitive world, every minute of your life is a judgment.

EMPATHY   Fortunately, this is one of the most rare and least developed of all human abilities, and I mention it here in the same spirit as one would mention poison ivy in a hiking manual. Empathy is the inability to recognize self-interest as the primary human survival skill. If you find traces of it in your character, eradicate them at once if you want to develop The Right Stuff.

EMPLOYEES   Imagine a band of sheep grazing on a mountainside in Nevada. Your job, as the sheepherder, is to round them up into a single, cohesive unit and, keeping them together, herd them over the mountaintop, down a slope, across a highway, through a stream and up again onto a new pasture where their job will be to graze until all the grass is gone, at which point you will then have to herd them on to the next pasture. You have to keep the sheep from panicking, from wandering, from slipping entirely away where they could fall prey to the wolves, bears, mountain lions, and coyotes that wait nearby. You have to keep them from being run down by cars, from drowning themselves, and from getting lost and discouraged.

And you must keep them healthy despite intolerable weather, disease, their incessantly poor judgment, and infestations of insects. The only help you have is from a couple of well-trained sheep dogs. Along the way, you must keep an accurate accounting of all the sheep and their condition, and at the end of the season, you must turn in a fine harvest of wool and mutton and turn a profit. Do you think you could pull this off?

Now multiply your band of sheep by several hundred. Turn them into human beings with human complexities, including neuroses, discontent, and hostility. Throw in a Saul Alinsky or a Mary Harris Jones and a few dozen rabble-rousing rank and file union sympathizers, several hundred malcontents, a handful of industrial spies, a few violent felons, a few thousand recreational drug users, drunks, and ne'er-do-wells, plus a mountain of government regulations and a spate of nosey, do-good reporters out to bury you, and you will have some idea of the task you will face as a CEO.

Workers are the natural enemy of management. They require constant supervision and monitoring. Fortunately, they are disposable and can be easily replaced; though replacing one always involves inefficiency since a new one must be trained to fill a vacant spot. They will lie, cheat, and steal from you. They will waste hours every week talking on their cell phones, text-messaging, listening to their iPods, and chatting around the water cooler. They will have the same aunt die a dozen times, always on the third of July or the Tuesday following Labor Day. They will slack, nap, sneak off to sleep, undermine, sabotage, and slink away in the middle of a shift to have sex under a stairwell. They will use the toilet a dozen times a day, always on company time. They will idle away hours on IM, on games, in chat rooms, and on eBay and other websites, ready to restore a work window the moment a supervisor passes by. They will pad their hours and shorten their workdays, and if they had the opportunity and thought they could get by with it, they would beat you senseless for pleasure, steal all your money, sell your daughter to a slave trader, and bend your golf clubs over your Lamborghini. Never trust an employee; never turn your back on one; and never allow sentiment for one to impair your judgment.

To keep employees in check and, in a few cases, to stimulate productivity, install a program of incentives and rewards, such as a five year pin, a nylon bowling jacket after ten years, small bonuses at Christmas and, for meeting projections, an employee of the month photo in the company newsletter. Sponsor their softball teams with the corporate name and logo embroidered on their tee shirts. At the same time, establish systems of control. Monitor their computer use. Time their visits to bathrooms. Install "security" video cameras to remind them that you are always watching them. Work with a few trustworthy individuals to act as snitches, and pay them for good information. Just remember that your task is approximately the same as that of the sheepherder, only you do have one great advantage. You won't have to personally bite off the testicles any of your employees to ensure their docility and to keep them from running amok. Designed correctly, your company's policies, in the hands of the right supervisors, will accomplish that for you.

There are no mysteries in the study of human relations when it is applied to employees. If I may mix my metaphors, you are the engineer and they are the engine. Without the engineer, the engine is a useless conglomeration of parts. Every day is a race, and the race will separate winners from losers. You know what *your* talents are. When you unleash your brilliant and flawless strategy and apply your talents aggressively to extract everything you can out of your engine, then you should take the checkered flag and win the trophy, and your competitors should be left with a nasty pile of envy. Give yourself a pat on the back for a job well done and get ready for the next race.

Unfortunately, things don't always work out as they are supposed to. Sometimes you can apply a perfect strategy. You know it is perfect because you developed it yourself without one single bit of stupid, misguided input from any other human being. You apply your strategy and you stoke your engine with enough energy to rocket to the moon and back, and *still* the thing breaks down and you lose. During dark moments like that, remember that despite your talents, you are only one man, and you can't do everything yourself. Also remember that you counted on people who let you down.

It is always a good idea, after your engine fails you, to assemble your losers in one big room. Silently, make eye contact with each person. When they begin to look at their shoes and squirm, express five seconds of consolation and then go berserk. Humiliate them. Ream them. Demote them.

Vivisect them. Fire them. Throw the entire mess on the scrap heap and tomorrow start building a new engine; a better one; one that will answer the call.

Never let employee incompetence drag you down.

EMPLOYMENT   As the members of each generation mature, they fulfill the destiny set for them in The Grand Economy: They divide into employers and employees. They separate into the owners of capital and the owners of trinkets. They become providers or they become consumers.

You must think of this big picture when you consider the issue of employment. It is important to provide employment not only to provide productivity, but also, as Henry Ford discovered, because employment gives people enough money to become consumers. Give them too much money, however, and they will become complacent spenders saving for an early retirement. Give them too little and they will become ineffective spenders. Pay them just right, and they will stay harnessed to the workplace and live a full life span as robust consumers chasing dreams they can always see but can never quite grasp.

It is important to note here that the ideal of retirement has become an anachronism. As a CEO, you must develop an enlightened attitude toward older workers. Why relinquish spending consumers just because they happen to be of a certain age? Why encourage them to leave the vitality of the marketplace? Keep them employed until they die. More to the point keep them in need of employment and encourage them to work until death, pain, or disability stops them.

Apply simple mathematics. The longer a consumer is employed, the more income he or she has to spend. The more a consumer has to spend, the more he or she will spend. Besides, most ordinary people, who spend all their time working, never develop any meaningful interests. For them, retirement would be boring and unhealthy. People do better when they are challenged. So challenge them. Pitch in and make the idea of retirement for workers a bad and unfashionable, if not impossible, idea until it becomes a relic of the past. Keep them productive and keep them spending, and that means *keep them working.*

"Without cheap, abundant energy, all would be lost and we would have to live like savages. It follows, therefore, that we must exploit, utilize, and defend the cheapest and most accessible forms of energy at our disposal."

ENERGY Energy is the lifeblood of commerce and the inspiration for convenience. It powers steel mills, runs trucks, lights neon signs, heats toasters, empowers television sets, paves the information highway, keeps the hot tub at a steady 102°, and warms the Jacuzzi, the sauna, the lap pool in the basement, and the Olympic-sized pool adjoining the veranda. Without cheap, abundant energy, all would be lost and we would have to live like savages. It follows, therefore, that we must exploit, utilize, and defend the cheapest and most accessible forms of energy at our disposal. If that means lopping off a few mountaintops in West Virginia, pumping oil out of an Alaskan wildlife refuge, or fighting a war here and there, then so be it. If spokesmen for a few caribou, some liberal descendants of third generation coal miners, and a handful of peaceniks want to complain and be taken seriously, fine. Let them participate in the American system of government. Let them hire lobbyists.

The new millennium brought America its first MBA President, and, adding in the Vice President, its first team of oilmen in the White House. Their election demonstrated not only that voters, polling place officials, and the Supreme Court of the United States can be educated, but also that the public understands the importance of reliable sources of energy. Despite its unpopularity, historians will remember the war in Iraq as a turning point in free market history. It demonstrated to OPEC and to new mass consumers of energy, such as India and China, our resolve to maintain dominion over the world's oil supply. Even more, the war itself and the parallel increases in fuel prices in America, opened consumers' eyes to the reality of the future: The need for new exploration, for profitable forms of alternative energy, and most of all, for a revitalized nuclear industry. Like a strong Texas gusher, nothing but good can flow from the legacy of this administration. The public is now aware of the reality that our demand for energy is so insatiable that the rest of the world will not be able to supply our future needs adequately. As a CEO, you must support a realistic energy policy and if you have any sense at all, you will get in on the rush while there is still cheap commodity to be extracted; you will invest in research and development for new sources of energy; and you will find ways to profit from a very large boom inevitable in tomorrow's nuclear sector.

As for the conservation of energy, it is good sense and makes for good public relations to turn off a few lights during the heat of summer and lower the temperature on your thermostats a couple of degrees during the coldest nights of winter. I recommend doing both with enthusiasm.

ENVIRONMENT   There are two kinds of environments, the one nature provides, which is a random circumstance into which you were thrown without choice, and the one you build because you like it. Never second-guess your own will. It is the attribute that differentiates you from lesser animals, who have no will, and from lesser men, who don't use what little will they have. Build your world the way God built the world of Genesis and you can't lose: With confidence, command, and uncompromised self-interest. In other words, build it in your own image. Then you will have an environment worth defending.

ENVIRONMENTALISTS   Loosely speaking, there are three categories of people in the world: Those who choose to do the world's work,
like you and me; those who sell their labor, eat, sleep, drink, breed, and
watch television; and those who will attempt to stop you from doing the
world's work. Included in the last group are environmentalists, people who
give their loyalty to the chaos that is nature rather than to the carefully con-
structed world of human invention. They believe that a rare frog is more
important than the livestock and crops that feed hungry people. They believe that chance, which directs nature, is a better guide than planning and
development, which utilize nature to satisfy consumer demand. Environmentalists are obstructionists and like any other obstacle to progress they
can be ignored, when not directly in the way, or removed, when blocking
the immediate flow of commerce.

What do most Americans think about environmentalism? Clearly
they don't understand all the subtleties of the issues. And while they are
certainly not activists, a substantial majority of Americans nevertheless
consider themselves to be environmentalists, so don't dismiss environmentalism out of hand, and don't take it for granted. Show respect for these
people's sentiments while working to enlighten them. A tear in your eye
when you talk about Bambi will put a dollar in your pocket when you
build a strip mall. Plus these people will love their mall and they won't
remember for a minute the noisy, dirty, disease ridden waterfowl that used
to dominate the stinky marsh that is now covered by a parking lot, a Cin-
eplex, and a pizza place to die for.

In short, be tough, be tactful, and be one hundred per-cent uncompromising. To grant activist environmentalists one small point is to validate their entire agenda. Just be quick to show the non-activist public how
much more commerce can offer them than chaos. In time, you will prevail.
As technologies advance to abate the few environmental problems trace-
able directly to industry, environmentalists will become the road kill of The
Grand Economy.

ENVY   Wherever you go, others will envy you. Be glad. Their envy is your reward for jobs well done, and their envy forces them to look up to you. Accept their judgment. For your part, you will know that you have reached your goals when there is no one left for you to envy.

EQUITY   An associate of mine from Silicon Valley once described his Karma as "my slice of the great big cosmic apple pie." I like to think of equity in the same light.

Equity gives substance and value to properties that would otherwise, say, in the hands of a deeply leveraged person, be merely assets. Equity is a man's connection to the universe and a reflection of how cleverly and ruthlessly he has worked during his career. It is both his reward, for he will enjoy his equity, and his punishment, for he must yet manage it. Equity gives meaning to a man's life. It interprets his life and his work. It frames him around points of reference unique to his personality. And it will follow him out of this life, leaving his stamp on his trusts and foundations, and on his wife and children, as they vie for a slice of inheritance.

Each time your net worth doubles, take a few moments of quiet time just for you. Think of the place you are carving for yourself in that vast, uncharted region where only the editors of *Forbes* and *Fortune* dare to tread when they select their honor rolls. If your equity is great, they might elect to list you. If it is truly cosmic, they might put your portrait on a cover.

If you care for it with all your heart and soul, your equity could become your bridge to immortality.

ETHICS   The term "business ethics" is an oxymoron, not because we business people are immoral, but because we are amoral. Corporations are amoral. No great CEO ever pushed a moral agenda. Business people are like all other people: Some are more ethical than others and some are less; some are saints and some are devils. The fact remains that we are in the business of business, not morality, so if you are required to take a course for your MBA called "Business Ethics," smile, 'cept it out, and move on to the real stuff.

Later, at the peak of your career, if you are called to testify before a Senate subcommittee and live television, recall some of those 'cepts and you might be able to present yourself as one of the saints.

EVOLUTION Two centuries ago, all people either walked or were moved by horses. Many of them got ambushed. Burdened by time and risk, imaginative people began to come up with better ideas. The result? Today, people can sit in hot tubs on jet aircraft flying from New York to Tokyo at five hundred miles per hour, close a two billion dollar deal over sushi on the Ginza, and return home the next day in time for dinner at Ruby Foo's and a show. Those who change to meet challenges and solve problems survive and prosper. Those who don't perish. It's called evolution and it's the way things work. Followers of Darwin called that process, "survival of the fittest." We call that process, "survival of the fittest." Evolution is the key to progress, and it demonstrates clearly that the more things change, and the more efficiently you adapt to change, the more change you will have in your pocket.

EXCELLENCE CEOs reward lower executives, managers, and middle managers with terms like "excellence," which mean whatever you want them to mean. So when staff employees do what you want them to do, call their performance "excellent." It's one of those warm, catchall, feel-good terms that will stimulate an employee's loyalty and subservience. Apply it to individuals sparingly so it keeps its force. But use the term generically wherever you can, particularly in emails, newsletters, and posters, to create an atmosphere in which people feel like their work is meaningful and important and their talents are recognized. You can never have too much excellence.

EXECUTIVE   An executive is one who executes: Plans, strategies, policies, rules, leadership, and unwanted employees. Executives dictate; others obey. Executives plan; others daydream. Executives define norms; others fit in. Executives advise presidents; others vote. Executives weed out losers and replace them with winners; others blend in. Executives provide the brainpower and backbone to make things happen; others put in time and a little effort. Executives provide the world's work; others feed their families by working. Who should be extremely well compensated for what they do?

EXTRAORDINARY RENDITION   I include this term because it is picturesque and because it underscores an important lesson in communications.

At first glance, "extraordinary rendition" sounds like a category for a Grammy Award. Without reading *The Wall Street Journal*, who would guess that it means the U.S. government sending a person to a foreign prison, where he can be electrocuted, castrated, roasted, and eviscerated, without violating the law or incurring blame to the U.S.?

The term itself has a delightful lilt to it, and it demonstrates the important strategy of befuddlement. Whenever you need to befuddle investors or the public, particularly after they have learned something about your company that they didn't like, trot out your wordsmiths. If they are any good, they will be able to fog the brightest day or brighten the darkest night with a couple of well chosen words, like "extraordinary rendition." As long as the words sound picturesque and delightful, and they thereby create an extraordinary rendition of something you'd rather not render to the public, you will accomplish befuddlement and keep the villagers content.

FACE MAN   You all know the face man, sometimes called a "front man". He's the handsome guy in your fraternity who spearheaded your annual rush, the first hand to greet all those prospective pledges. He's still working his magic in your corporation whenever you have clients, potential customers, or investors you want to impress. A good face man is worth his weight in, well, silver. Look for memorable cheekbones, flawless hair, straight white teeth, fresh breath, a big genuine smile, a firm and robust handshake, an aura of charisma, and the ideal jaw.

When you find all that in one human being, chances are better than even that your face man will need a second, someone to stand by him whenever he is in public and to refocus his attention on his job when he attempts an opinion of his own or blurts one out unexpectedly.

Follow two rules: 1. Always use a face man on your home turf, when you want to make a good first impression on people who are sources of capital, and on neutral ground, when the event has no immediate relevance to your business beyond good will, events such as a beauty pageant, an athletic contest, an awards ceremony, or a prayer breakfast. 2. Never use a face man in public on someone else's turf when business is at stake or reporters might ask probing questions.

The face man's job is to rein in impressionable people who have something you want, usually money, so that closers can then go to work on them. Send him to a fashionable gym daily, and, if he is light Caucasian, to Hawaii every now and then to work on his tan, and he'll serve you well until he starts to look old and you have to replace him. I recommend taller than six feet but not towering, average build with well defined physique, smooth voice, and perfect hair. Don't forget the jaw. The jaw is a face man's most important feature. It must be broad, straight, sculpted as a rock and show a slight cleft in the chin. Nothing turns women and other men off more than a wimpy, weasely jaw, or a soft and sloping jaw that disappears into a double chin. Don't settle for a mediocre jaw. The face man stands for your corporation. He must be the real thing.

FARMING   A hot new word of advice to young executives might surprise you. It is farming or, more correctly, agribusiness.

The First Agricultural Revolution gave us farming and freed our species from having to hunt and gather for a living. It showed us how to make nature more productive and more predictable. The green revolution, which included widespread use of fertilizers, herbicides and pesticides, growth hormones and antibiotics, and carefully selected hybrids, particularly in developing countries, was our Second Agricultural Revolution. Right now, we are in the first stages of the Third Agricultural Revolution, utilizing genetic modification, which will free our species from dependence on nature for the design, quality, and quantity of our crops and livestock. It will also free us from inefficiencies inherent in small-scale production.

Within half a century, family farms and ranches will have all but disappeared as corporations buy up their land and consolidate it into holdings that offer agriculture the same efficiencies of scale and the same productivity that the assembly line offered industrial manufacturing.[14] This, combined with crops and livestock genetically altered to better suit growing conditions and the marketplace, will maintain the cost of food as more mouths bid on it; will make produce appear fresher and less damaged when shipped hundreds or thousands of miles; will make all foodstuffs more abundant and available to more people; and will dramatically increase profitability in the sector.

---

14 The growing movement to buy locally grown and organic foods will offer some resistance to the Third Agricultural Revolution. However, producers in this movement will fall prey to creative destruction as multinational producers innovate. Supply chain efficiencies, product standardization and reliability, advantageous pricing, reduction of international trade barriers, and introduction of plantation organics will swiftly outpace local producers' ability to compete. The W*ALLMINE! model will prevail.

We all know what the world needs: A steer with the body mass of a hippopotamus and a bright red spotless spherical tomato that can stand up to the Jaws of Life while being trucked from Mexico to Maine. I am here to tell you they are on the way. The fact that new, genetically altered or engineered species of plant and animal life can be protected by patent, just as new drugs are, has stimulated a rush of research and development. Results are already widespread in the marketplace but they represent only the tip of a massive iceberg. Half a century from now, when irrational critics, like those in the European Union, have been silenced, virtually all growing will be licensed. Crops will be resistant to hazards such as bad weather, drought, frost, disease, predation, and shipping damage. Livestock units will be similarly protected and designed to maximize bulk and nutritional output while minimizing traditional waste in skeletal structure, mobility design, and non-edible parts. The biochemist, the genetic engineer, the agricultural engineer, and the research veterinarian will play pivotal roles in production, replacing quaint cowboys, country animal doctors, feed salesmen, and crop dusters. As the scale of production accelerates and holdings are consolidated, control over the nation's land base will revert to publicly owned corporations and many presently unproductive reserves will be put into production. Waste will be reduced to a minimum as surplus wetlands, untended forests, and unirrigated prairies are turned into food plantations. Adequate facilities for recreationists will be set aside and developed to accommodate boaters, skiers, golfers, gamblers, theme park enthusiasts, and nature lovers, and these too will offer new frontiers for profitability.

What is the future of farming? Pay no attention to the whiners still scratching dirt on land their great-great grandparents homesteaded. Ignore the fear mongers who see Frankenstein's monsters jumping out of engineered spare ribs. It's time for change. All farming needs today is a little capital, a little practical vision, a hi-tech laboratory, and the will to compete in world markets. Those who cannot adapt will move off the land or go back to reading Mary Shelley. Those who adapt and innovate will make themselves, their stockholders, and their investment bankers proud. And they will bring to our nation's rural communities a new style of professionalism unlike anything those communities have ever witnessed.

FEAR   Nothing motivates a crowd in a theater more than the word, "FIRE!" When you need to steer, induce fear. The mob will take over and trample its way to any destination you desire.

FEEDBACK   You have all heard the phrase, "out of the loop." That's one place you never want to go. Every successful information system provides a feedback loop. Be sure to keep yours intact. A top CEO not only has eyes on his fiercest competitors, his enemies, his friends, and his closest allies. He has ears near the SEC, The Fed, key congressional committees, and the Attorney General's office, to name just a few. Old school ties can never be cinched too tightly.

FEUDALISM   Feudalism wasn't such a bad way to organize societies and economies. It just needs a little fine-tuning and modernization. If we could develop the same orderly working relationships between management and labor that the Middle Ages had between Lords and vassals, we could upgrade the entire system to everyone's benefit. Take the thirteenth century, for example. Try to imagine it on steroids. Keep the absence of national governments – which means no interference from government do-gooders -- and the decentralization of operations around regional hubs. Throw in modern technology. Provide mass communications that terminate in cottages and cell phones for serfs. Add our understanding of capital markets and the dynamics of supply and demand. Institute wages but keep them standard and meager. Break down boundaries between fiefdoms. Nix witch hunts, but keep stories about plagues, trolls, and Mongol hordes. They will give the masses something to fear and hate other than you, and will give you good reason to protect and control the masses for their own good. Build product networks and supply chains. Advertise and market. Provide hospitals for lords and drugs for peasants, boar burgers and mead for everyone, and lots of credit cards. Throw in W*ALLMINEs! and Fortressbanks in place of village cathedrals. Bingo. What have you got? The Grand Economy at its most robust.

It's something to think about.

FINANCE   Who is the most important person in your life? Your parents? Your wife? Your mentor? No. The most important person in your life as a CEO is your CFO, your Chief Financial Officer. He will make all things possible. Choose him, therefore, wisely because you will need him and because he will also be in a position to become your Brutus. In the best of all possible worlds, you will have the goods on him, and if you don't, then find them. However you do it doesn't matter. The point is that you must have his absolute loyalty.

Once you have your man, keep him. So long as he performs, take him with you as a permanent part of your team wherever you go. Encourage his creativity and help him understand that he is not bound by any laws, any standards, or any precedents whatsoever. He is answerable only to you. Let him do his job with as much originality as possible, and let your lowyers and ad men worry about the details. A good finance man is worth a million times his weight in gold and as a rule he will require no more that his weight in gold. He's a bean counter, and a lot of bean counters are in it for the challenge. If so, he will measure his success by your wealth more than by his own. He is also the only person to whom you should say, "You're the man." As a bean counter, he is not accustomed to flattery, particularly with a macho overtone, and one or two enthusiastic "You're the man!" compliments thrown his way should buy his dedication for another year.

One word of warning. Some CFOs aren't just bean counters. Some are potential CEOs and act like it before their time. Reilly Fasthand, for example, of the Endrun debacle, cared about his own earnings more than he cared about his stockholders, his employees, his reputation, the law, and his wife. No one can fault him there. In fact, I know that it was a particularly difficult sacrifice for him to serve his wife to the law on a platinum platter, but Reilly was a tough guy and he could handle it. Reilly's problem was that he forgot his place. In his pursuit of personal earnings as a CFO, he left his mentor, confidant, and leader in a vulnerable position, and that was unforgivable. True, Bucky Leize was at fault for exercising too much faith and too little control. But even a great CEO and a great Chairman can't do everything himself. Just make sure that your CFO is smart enough and loyal enough to cover everyone's tracks. Run him through your ringer periodically just to make sure.

Now one word about finance per se. The only way to finance anything is to use other people's money (OPM). We all know that. The conclusion follows that you should never finance anything through a commercial bank unless you absolutely have to or you own the bank. The bank is already using OPM and they have already padded their margins and fattened their fees – and they get to use the float. Rather than use a bank, stack your own deck and deal an initial public offering. Pad your own margins. Fatten your own fees. And float the money yourself until it's waterlogged. That is, go directly to the source of capital, the great American public, and use that one infallible method of separating people from their money: Gambling. Forget about a stogy secondary market offering. Save that for nickel and dime needs. Stir up some real excitement. Create an entity. Float your IPO and pump it up until it looks like a free ride to the summit of Mount Everest. Nothing exhilarates speculators more than risk, and each one expects to return from his adventure alive and bathed in glory. You put up the ten percent hype and, with a little nudging from your underwriters, gamblers will put up the ninety percent hope – and pay for the privilege. Short of an assault on Fort Knox, this is the surest way to gain a fast infusion of capital. I call this GRF, or Grass Roots Financing, because it takes about as much effort as mowing your lawn and the piles of clippings you harvest are all green.

FINANCIAL STATEMENT   The financial statement is a statement describing your company's financial situation. Since your company's financial situation is no one's business but your own, you will do well to think of your financial statements as: A. Public relations gestures. B. Marketing aids. C. Good advertising. Once you have that package firmly in mind, you can fill in the blanks A-B-C and move on to the next quarter.

THE FLAT WORLD   One effect of The Grand Economy is to create a flat world. That is, a level playing field upon which every player has the same opportunity as every other player to compete and to score. In real terms that means, for example, that the cost of labor in Brazil, Bangladesh, and Ohio should eventually be the same, and that trade barriers and inequities between governments should all disappear. On such a playing field, the only rules of the game are the mechanism of supply and demand and the mandate to compete. Like natural selection, the end result of life on a flat world will be the most well-adapted and efficient economic machine possible, and whatever results from its operations can only be judged as right, particularly for multinational corporations. Whoever would have thought that Utopia would materialize on a flat world?

The metaphor of a flat world, replacing the old fashioned idea of a spherical world, shows real progress in the way some economists think. With a little more effort, they should be able to come up with an even newer and more progressive theory that places our flat earth where it belongs, at the center of the universe.

FLEECING   The art of fleecing, in the agricultural industry, is the art of taking off the coat of a sheep, despite its protests, in order to make a profit for the sheep's owner. The art of fleecing in business is the same thing, except that the businessman doesn't actually own the flock. He merely provides a voluntary system of controls and incentives designed to help the flock guide itself to the fleecing. He advises them where to graze, keeps them tightly unified, protects them from alien predators, neutralizes the naysayers in their midst, offers them coupons and discounts, and opens the shed door so they can jump in, have fun, and leave behind the burden of their available capital.

Now, among some people, the term "fleecing" carries a negative connotation, particularly among fleecees who sometimes claim that fleecors are disreputable. This is an assertion to which I can only reply, "Baaaaaaaa, humbug!" After all, most fleecees if left on their own would follow a nickel over a cliff to find a dime. At least after they are fleeced they get to walk away under their own power and charge a new coat to their MasterCard.

What's good for the shepherd is good for the sheep.

FOOD   Look at the top tobacco companies. They should all be belly up by now, but they are profitable as ever. One reason is their diversification into food. Talk about a ready-made market! Look at the fundamentals: People eat. They always will. Then they have babies and the babies eat. People have new appetites every day. I am bullish on food, despite the complexities of the sector.

And I am bullish for a second reason, beyond fundamentals. Something like a third of the world's population is underfed, malnourished, or starving. How many mouths will that represent when the world's population increases to ten or twenty or more billion? Food is an aggressive growth sector. But there is much more to it than that. After water, food will be the most powerful weapon of the future. Those who control food will go a long way toward controlling The Grand Economy and all its members, little and large.

FOOLS   Treat every person as a fool. Odds are that you are right. If you are right, you won't have wasted your time suffering fools. If you happen to be wrong, then the target of your scorn will exercise sufficient initiative to prove his worth and you will see what else he is made of. You can't lose when you treat people equally.

FREE MARKET   The free enterprise system, more commonly known today as the free market, and soon to be known as The Grand Economy, will be, within a few decades, the only economic system operating on earth. To find its fast track, remember three points.

First of all, forget about small business. It will putter along in local villages as it always has and little business owners will continue to work themselves to death to make enough money to go fishing three Saturdays a year without feeling guilty.

Second, to get in on the real action of the future you need to think big and think international. The door is wide open. We have already beaten the last great challenge to our system, and today the Russians are regular capitalist pirates. Even the Chinese are making Adam Smith proud. Now is the time to jump in and teach them what competition is all about.

Finally, keep the free in free enterprise. That is, keep governments out of business and free markets everywhere will flourish. However, you never want to quibble over small points. If a government offers you an incentive to expand overseas, such as reduced regulations, favorable legislation, a subsidy, a tax credit, or a tax reduction, without any objectionable strings attached, take it and run. Isn't the whole point of government giveaways to keep the free market free from destructive influences, such as government meddling?

Life's a paradox.

FREEDOM   We all tend to think of freedom as unscheduled time coupled with the means to use it however we wish. Ordinary people struggle their whole lives through an endless battle between time and money. Those who spend time have no money since they have no careers, and because they have no money, their freedom is constricted and illusory. Where can they go? What can they do? What happens if they get sick? On the other hand, those who have stockpiled money have no time because they work twelve hours a day at two jobs to save money, and their freedom is also constricted and illusory. In truth, it is the illusion of freedom and the hope of future freedom, that keeps both groups on track and pacified. So long as they have that illusion or that hope, they pose no political threat.

Real freedom is possible only to people of real means. We can take all the time we want whenever we want. And we have more money than God would ever want. Our lives should serve as examples to ordinary people, giving them hope.

I must add that most people's idea of freedom, meaning lack of structure and responsibility, would create an unhealthy state of mind for the economy and for individual citizens. Actual freedom is best left to those few of us who have a good idea of what to do with it: Golf. Finance takeovers. Buy Impressionist paintings. Sail the Aegean. That sort of thing. Don't believe that you would be doing workers any favors by increasing their pay while cutting back their required workweek, like France has done, only to watch a decline in worker's gross productivity and motivation. We all depend on self-esteem and it is always higher when workers produce more. Keep workers productive. They will be happier producing more and hoping for a lucky lottery ticket than they would be with a raise and a few hours of additional freedom, but lower productivity. Furthermore, even a miniscule taste of the good life, such as five hours a week free time, will only whet their appetites for more and fill their hearts with discontent. Why sow discord? For most ordinary people, isn't true freedom really found in the structure that someone else provides for them?

Give plenty of structure to your workers. Demanding structure. At the same time, give them a hint of hope. Strive for that magical balance between rigid control with enhanced productivity and a ray of hope peeking through the transom that says, "Some day...some day...." Some day your illusion of freedom will be granted. Give them all that and you will give them more real freedom -- from despair, from low self-esteem, from mental poverty -- than even they can ever waste.

FRIENDSHIP   It's a simple enough rule to live by: Reward your friends and destroy your enemies. The destruction of your enemies does not have to be limited to acts of good taste. Use any means at your disposal, so long as you don't harm yourself.

The rewarding of your friends is a more complicated matter. In its pure, or naïve, form, simple friendship exists among simple folk of modest means with little to gain or lose. You know the scenario. Three or four buddies get together to go fishing and cook hotdogs. They drink too much beer and let their guards down. They laugh, argue, and tease each other and drag themselves home exhausted. By Monday, they are rested, and all is forgotten and forgiven.

For people in high-stakes careers, with plenty to gain and lose, friendship is obviously a much more risky and more complicated proposition. Nevertheless, a *kind* of friendship can be available to you and I recommend it heartily. To wit, those who help you and support you, at some risk to themselves, I would consider friends. However, keep in mind that envy is a part of every friendship, and if you are unguarded toward your friend his envy might take over and surprise you. There is no fiercer enemy than a friend who is twisted with envy. To guard against this kind of betrayal, I recommend that you use a quantitative, measurable standard to judge whether or not your relationship with someone might be considered a friendship. In general terms, I suggest a gratuitous giving ratio of three to one. For every act of friendship you proffer to an individual, that person should proffer at least three of equal or greater value to you in order to earn and maintain your friendship. The one-sided nature of this imbalanced relationship should test your friend's resolve and make his or her friendship more believable. In addition, I suggest that you view every friendship with only one eye, reserving the other eye always to watch your back. Once you have established friendships, maintain them so long as they are useful, and use them whenever you stand to benefit.

So how do you reward your friends? You allow their friendship. After all, friendship is its own reward.

FUTURE   Remember that line from the film, *Gone with the Wind*, "Tomorrow is another day?" Remember that nearly every major religion asserts the existence of a life after death in which good is rewarded and bad is punished? The reality of ordinary people's lives never quite matches their hopes, so they invent better futures. Therefore, if you want your business to succeed, appeal to people's fantasies more than to the humdrum realities of their daily lives. Feed their dreams. Promise a better tomorrow. Expand hope. Give shape and form to fantasy. Isn't the future a place where robots do all the work and where people live two hundred years in perfect health; where beautiful people surround you and you have more wealth, influence, and prestige than you ever imagined possible? Isn't the future the Big Rock Candy Mountains come true? Tell consumers what they want to hear about the future. Give them products and services that seem to foreshadow that future. Do only that and you and your corporation will lead them over and over again directly to your bottom line.

"Isn't the future the Big Rock Candy Mountains come true?" p. 155

THE G WHIZ GAMBIT   For decades, Downhome Power Company was a trusted darling of widows and orphans, a solid, dependable utility with consistent earnings and a robust dividend, trading on the New York Stock Exchange at around sixty-five dollars per share. Stockholders put their life savings into the company. Employees planned their retirements around it. Downhome and the Rock of Gibraltar had more in common than apple pie and ice cream.

All this proved to be pretty boring stuff for CEO G. Lewis Cannon, known to his friends as "G Whiz," because he was such a sharp guy. The company offered little opportunity for growth or adventure. Earnings, regulated by a state agency, were always sound but never exciting, and the company seemed to run itself. To be perfectly honest, I think G Whiz was underpaid, under appreciated, filled with energy, and, because he was a really sharp guy, bored out of his mind. In such a position, what's a CEO to do?

G Whiz needed a challenge. He needed to have some fun. He needed to climb a mountain to see what was on the other side. And the strategy he devised proved to be so successful, as a monumental failure, that I have dubbed it with the name, "The G Whiz Gambit." How did it work?

Before making a move, G Whiz sought advice from the big dogs at Goldin Baggs, the investment bankers. For a small cut of the action (about twenty million dollars in fees after the dust settled), the big dogs helped G Whiz devise and execute a plan. First, Downhome Power set loose its spin-doctors and its lobbyists to convince the state's Republican legislature and governor to deregulate the energy business. That set the stage.

Next, in a surprise move, including a brilliant end run around its stockholders, the corporation sold its power generating facilities and its transmission lines. Net result: 2.7 billion dollars. State citizens groused but dutifully began the process of adapting to substantial and accelerating increases in the cost of energy and to new power companies. No real problem there.

Finally, Downhome Power announced that it intended to abandon the only business it ever knew to become a major player in the currently fashionable but highly competitive communications hardware and infrastructure sectors. Downhome Power put itself into dry dock, and then launched its fledgling little subsidiary dinghy, "Tune In America, You Bet!" with all the fanfare of the Titanic. Tune In acquired contracts and major facilities from QuickieComm, which had its own problems, and set about trenching and hanging fiber optic cable all over the region. The gamble began to fail almost immediately, of course. While the company strove to become the alpha dog of land lines, investors everywhere must have discussed its retrograde progress on their new *wireless* cell phones and on email via new high speed *wireless* Internet. The corporation's stock plummeted to thirty cents per share and the humiliation of an NYSE delisting. However, Tune In America, You Bet!'s top management team had an amazing adventure, more exciting than anything they had ever done, and they rewarded themselves by taking all that was left in the 2.7 billion dollar kitty, 5.2 million dollars, in bonuses. G Whiz took about 2.7 million. In the scheme of things, of course, this is pretty humble peanuts, but it allowed G Whiz to build his new three million dollar home near a handful of Hollywood stars, retired dentists, and New York mobsters on picturesque Fatkat Lake in the heart of the Sugar Rock Mountains, and to forever rub the noses of his critics in his personal well being. Good job, G Whiz! This kind of gambit demonstrates that however bad circumstances can get, there is always a way for a clever, gutsy CEO to have some fun and emerge with a profit. Keep this lesson in mind. And if the villagers start to look like a lynch mob, gate your property and keep that Lear jet fueled and ready. Take a few vacations and before you know it, the lynch mob will fall back into its familiar pattern of quiet desperation.

One caveat. While this gambit demonstrates a viable strategy, its execution clearly was less than efficient. Measured as a return on invested capital, 5.2 million on 2.7 billion comes in at a shade under two-tenths of one percent. At the time, one could have done ten times better from a passbook savings account in a Nigerian bank. As a case study, perhaps the G Whiz Gambit is better remembered as a lesson to investment bankers everywhere. You earn your fees for advice dispensed regardless of outcomes. Clearly, *you* are in the right business.

GENOCIDE   Every group of people is always superior to every other group of people. When competition heats up between two groups, even though they might have been close neighbors for years or centuries, the group with greater power wishes to exterminate the group with less power and sometimes it makes its wish come true. After all the other nations of the world have taken several years to analyze, debate, and comment gravely upon the slaughter, they announce that a genocide has taken place. By then, of course, the weaker group has been annihilated and the genocide has stopped so, following the announcement, everyone returns to business as usual except a handful of leaders from the stronger group who might or might not be charged with crimes against humanity, a process that requires another several years.

Business offers a better idea. It allows corporations to exterminate other corporations without spilling blood. In this way corporate warfare satisfies basic human instincts. Junior League moms and church choir dads employed by a corporation get to despise other people and subject them to rape, hideous tortures, sadism, and death by vivisection, all symbolically, while the rest of the world observes but does not feel obliged to pass judgment except to subpoena an executive or two for crimes against securities. In time, displaced workers and angry stockholders move on, indicted executives unfurl their golden parachutes, and everybody wins.

As a model for society, corporate tribalism offers a more civilized approach than political tribalism, and it is just as satisfying to the baser urges within us. It can also generate profit, something no genocide has ever done.

THE GENOME   Whatever it took nature a billion or two years of trial and error to produce, we will be able to improve during the next half century and beyond. Understanding the human genome and the genetic structure of all other species will enable us to recreate reality according to our own needs and desires. I can't even imagine the market potential it is so vast. What used to be considered big profits will soon be thought of as pocket change. Think about a child with Henry Kissinger's voice and Britney Spears's brain all in one package. What about a Chihuahua the size of a Clydesdale? I am only partly kidding. The near future will see the demise of natural processes and the emergence of human imagination as the prime mover and designer of the world. Some of those computer video games you played as a kid and now play as an adult while you are supposed to be finishing that sales report might well become reality.

Remember that line from the film *The Graduate*, when a well-meaning neighbor told Benjamin what he should do with his future? "Plastics," the man said, and, ironically enough, he was right. Today, I am taking each of you aside and I am whispering into your ear a single word: "Genetics." This will be the greatest business opportunity in history, a gold rush like none ever experienced. If you want to be a hundred times wealthier than the wealthiest CEOs are today, then start planning now. Of those who get there first, a small handful of tough, clever survivors will get the most.

But you had better hurry. Not long after you get there, you could be up against a new breed of Chiefs armed with the predatory instincts of a gray wolf and the adaptability of a cockroach.

GIFTS   If you are inclined to express sentiment send cards. Count on your secretary to pick out the least subtle and most expressive. Just remember than any bum on the street can – and surely will – express sentiment. It is the wholesale marketplace of the human heart.

If you want to influence people, on the other hand, and do some groundwork for future business, give gifts. The giving of gifts can be a rare and powerful motivator, highly regarded by the recipient. Who doesn't like to boast that the CEO of a Fortune 500 company personally gave him this rare manuscript or that Monet? Gifts should be part of a broader strategy, so give with feeling and with a deep commitment to the ultimate goal toward which the gift is aimed. As a rule, give generously but not so generously that you risk looking like you are ingratiating yourself. Consider the recipient and what buttons he likes to have pushed. For example, if the recipient is sentimental about his family and he has a young daughter, give the kid a brace of swans for Christmas so they can glide around for years in full view on the family pond. Or if you want to impress a potential ally who once invited you to join him at the Kentucky Derby, an emerging racehorse might portray the depth of your feelings better than, say, a bottle of rare claret. It might also inspire greater returns. The point is to use your wit to select exactly the right gift. Unconsciously, if not consciously, a recipient who accepts such a gift will consider it an obligation, which is another way of saying that you have found a way to slip your foot into the doorway of his heart. Remember: 'The gift without the giver is bare.' I take that to mean that you are part of the gift. In other words, your gift gives you license to exert influence over the happy recipient.

The great philosophers and religious leaders were absolutely right: When done in the right spirit, giving will always return more to you than you had to spend on the gift.

GLOBAL WARMING

When Florida becomes an island and coniferous forests spread to the North Pole, complacent CEOs will continue to argue and to believe that global warming is an unproven hypothesis. Their companies will decline accordingly and history will remember them as idiots. Forward-thinking CEOs, on the other hand, will accept the overwhelming evidence, and they will make the largest investments of their careers right now in research and development to position their companies for a future bonanza. History will praise them, and if they are truly clever, they will be able to cash in on the climate change personally while they are still alive.

R and D and strategic planning on global warming need to concentrate on several fronts at once. Here are six keys to help you profit from global warming, and one plan to make a killing.

First and foremost is the extraction of existing stores of fossil fuels, some of which will require new technologies, and, once the door to extraction has been re-opened, the exploitation of new non-energy mineral deposits should also boom in places like Antarctica, Greenland, the Arctic Circle, and our national parks and other preserves.

Second is the strategic understanding of world pricing structures for fossil fuels. How do those structures affect both consumer markets and efforts to maximize corporate revenues? In other words, how can we squeeze a few more cents of profit out of every dollar consumers spend on fuels? Couple with this a comprehensive plan on how best to use mass concern and occasional panic to motivate slacking consumers when markets temporarily stagnate.

Third is a clear understanding of precise climate changes predicted and their relation to geography, water, agriculture, population distribution, transportation and product distribution networks. Once you understand how these relationships work, you can develop short and long term strategies to adapt to climate changes with minimal disruption to productivity and profits.

Fourth are definitions of new fuels, how to use them, and how to get them to consumers. Before you develop new products you need to design new distribution networks.

Fifth is a consumer education strategy designed to establish and exploit the new markets that will emerge while transitioning out of old markets. Since change worries people at the same time it excites them, you will need to design communications models that portray consumer spending as the shortest path to security. Keep in mind that management of public attitudes is always challenging when nature destroys cities, kills and maims thousands, and threatens to exterminate species. However, an aggressive information strategy led by top-notch ad men should be up to the challenge. It all comes down to positive imagery.

Finally, you will need to instill in your people the desire and the ability to think outside the box, particularly since the box itself might be carried out to sea by a tidal surge, burned to a briquette by a firestorm, or turned into toothpicks by an F7 tornado.

Consider one example of thinking outside the box. As many as fifteen percent of the world's consumers live on coasts at sea level within spitting distance of an ocean. That includes the heavily populated East and West Coasts of the United States. In other words, nearly a billion consumers worldwide are going to have to move or develop gills as oceans rise and natural disasters like mega-hurricanes and tsunamis strike. Where will they move? Where will people in the U.S. move? People are still migrating to Texas and the desert Southwest, despite ever-higher temperatures and ever-lower water supplies, but a few extended heat waves coupled with drought will divert that migration north and to higher altitudes. People in general will want to move inland and upland. The problem is that Aspen is already full and lower altitude ski resorts are drying up. What's left? Where will they go?

Outside the box, I predict that, properly motivated, many will move to places heretofore considered backwaters, places like the mountainous half of Montana, where I happen to own a ranch. Research is not conclusive on local climate changes that will result from global warming, but at first glance, this state offers higher elevation skiing, moderating winters, reduced snowfall in urban centers, and increasing winter and spring rain in some semi-arid mountain and mountain valley areas. Although during winter, the northern reaches of this state are condemned to sixteen hours of darkness, summer brings sixteen hours of daylight. Land that twenty years ago sold for five hundred dollars an acre already sells for ten thousand dollars and more per acre and the sky is the limit in the future. Packaged with just the right imagery depicting a safe island of fun in a sea of impending disaster, real estate development designed to protect consumers from the worst effects of global warming while giving them an authentic, back-to-nature life style, could lead you to fast and enormous profits.

Take a close look at this area. The mountainous part of this state is free from the kinds of weather events that will plague other areas, such as hurricanes, tornadoes, tsunamis, and large-scale flooding. It is far enough north to resist many of the tropical diseases, such as malaria, that will spread to temperate zones. Drought, earthquake, extended heat waves, and massive forest fires, plus effects from the odd volcanic eruption in Washington, Oregon, Northern California, or the Yellowstone basin, are the only primary threats to habitat. The state's local population is tough, educated, and independent but largely naïve, and they have a strong work ethic. Wages are currently half that required in big cities, and the state offers amenities that consumers like, such as wildlife, hunting, fishing, kayaking, mountain climbing, bicycling, hiking, snowmobiling, breathtaking scenery, bird watching, lots of open space, a relaxed pace of life, sparse population, and a surprisingly rich cultural life. You can find high quality dance, theater, music, film, writing, cuisine, and sports easily, not to mention rodeo, square dance, logger days, barroom brawls, pow-wows, livestock auctions, and an annual maggot race held on a bar top during the depths of winter to ward off cabin fever. Currently, Montana averages only six or seven human inhabitants per square mile, about the same as Australia, yet already, housing developments and luxury condos are sprouting up all over near the larger towns that have views. Other parts of the state, particularly on the plains east of the continental divide, are quaint but terminal backwaters. Montana's chilling climate, traditionally viewed as somewhere between harsh and uninhabitable, could benefit from global warming if you discount dust, thirst, smoke, fire, and the effects of increased population. The bottom line is that Montana is a massive development waiting to happen. The population could triple or quadruple in no time at all, and those with enough foresight to capitalize on this potential will make a killing. There is still time.

One word of advice if you move to Montana. You can buy plenty of wool socks and respirators once you are there, but bring your own capital. After the state is as developed, paved, and populated as metro-Denver, an abundance of capital should be available locally. Until then, you need to think of Montana as an emerging third world economy.

Other western areas like northern and central Idaho, parts of inland Washington and Oregon, northern Utah and Nevada, and huge chunks of southern Alberta and British Columbia also have potential. If you discount minor discomforts from an emerging desert climate, all of these areas offer fun with apparent safety from the worst effects of global warming. They are all nature-lovers' Disneylands with relatively cheap admission and few policies to obstruct development.

The point is, when it comes to global warming, don't get bogged down in the blame game. Accept the realities and plan for future profits. Change is always a stimulus to huge profits if you view it as such and if you exercise your imagination correctly.

Now picture mom and dad sitting on their new redwood deck attached to their new log home overlooking a pristine stream with deer cavorting, birds singing, and not another human being in sight. Aside from smoke in the air, it is a perfect day in paradise. Dad checks his portfolio on his wireless Internet connection while mom gets ready to uncork her chardonnay and turn on the hot tub. Meanwhile, a tsunami wipes out Seattle. A hurricane devastates Charleston. Tornadoes rip through Kansas City, Des Moines, and Birmingham. Houston, Phoenix, and Las Vegas hit one hundred and twenty degrees with rolling blackouts, and the Ohio River Valley is flooding.

Do you think that you can't make a buck from even *the perceived threat* of global warming? Think again.

GOALS   Someone with ambition has to imagine the future before it can happen.

For every CEO, controlling the future is a prime management directive. The most powerful management tool you possess to shape the future is goal setting. Without rational goals, nothing is accomplished. Tied to and defined by goals, every human activity acquires purpose. In addition to strategic planning, set rational goals for attendance, tasking, efficiency, productivity, earnings, and every other aspect of your business. In your personal life, set goals for body weight, exercise, home projects, retirement, golf score, and every other aspect of your domestic scene. Set goals for your wife and children, who, by nature and by their circumstance will tend to slack, and you will see a marked improvement in their productivity. Goal setting is a lifelong habit that should direct every minute of your day and night. The more goals you set the more goals you can meet. The more goals you meet the more you can achieve. And the more you achieve the more goals you will need to set. Just make sure that your goals are rational.

If a life of achievement is the only life worth living, then a life without rational goals is a life wasted. Take Walt Whitman, for example. Remember the poet, Whitman? We all had to read from his *Leaves of Grass* at school. Here was a guy who had such good instincts for self-promotion that he could have built an advertising and marketing empire before the age of mass media. Why didn't he? Whitman lacked rational goals. All he wanted to do was sell his book of poetry which, at the time he published it, was considered by everyone except the French to be weird, vulgar, and unseemly. He pumped it, promoted it, wrote great fake reviews for it -- and sold six copies in his native land. If he had focused on selling chewing tobacco or a cure for warts or some other rational goal, Whitman would have found his way to Madison Avenue. Instead, he gave up marketing to write more poetry. What a pitiful waste of talent.

THE GOLDEN PARACHUTE   The defining feature of the modern CEO is his Golden Parachute. Just how good is the CEO? You need to ask, just how golden is his Golden Parachute?

As a CEO, it is only natural that you, a proven winner, consider yourself to be the most valuable person on the bridge of your ship. A good leader is the most valuable commodity on earth, and no one will be more protective of the good leader than the leader himself. Therefore, protecting yourself from financial disaster is not only natural; it is the most responsible thing you can do. An organization without a true leader is an organization in chaos and if you take the steps necessary to protect your status as a leader, you will do your part to suppress disorder.

Your first responsibility as a CEO, therefore, is to take care of yourself and build a golden parachute of savings gleaned from earnings, dividends, bonuses, incentives, low interest or interest free corporate loans, forgivable loans, 401 Ks, IRAs, trust funds, personal properties, securities and tax exempt securities, stock options, and whatever else you can get your hands on. Everything else will be included in your pre-written termination agreement, so have your lowyers weave a big basket. Throw in severance pay and your annual retirement benefits, exit bonuses, deferred compensation, health insurance, life insurance policies, gifted annuities, and a contribution for the non-profit charitable family trust you will head. Don't forget to add in buyout guidelines, club memberships, theater tickers, retention of corporate properties such as automobiles and vacation homes, your portfolio of news clippings, awards, and other documentation of your achievements, liability limits, and anything else you can design, including the language used to describe your future dismissal, whatever the circumstances behind it. Finally, line up an aggressive agent. Set fees for consulting, speaking, and ad hoc lobbying, and be ready to add your name to a top drawer speakers' bureau.

Once your golden parachute is locked in and your lowyers have made it impenetrable to attack, you can proceed to your other duties with remarkable self-confidence.

GOODHAND, HONORÉ   Even in death this woman refuses to go away. She remains a thorn in the side of American Industry.

In case you were raised in Andromeda and don't know the story, Honoré Goodhand was employed during the early 1970s by Malfi-Zentslicher, a chemical company founded in picturesque Bavaria in 1934. Born in 1947, Goodhand worked at a Texas Malfi-Zentslicher plant that manufactured Cyclone brand bee pesticide, Bunny Buster pest poison, and various radioactive isotopes for federal government research. She became a union activist and accused the company of unsafe working conditions. In 1975 she was severely contaminated. She created a stink, and on her way to meet an *Austin Un-American* reporter to cause trouble for her employer, in November, 1975, her car left the road and she died. Her death was ruled an accident and was not investigated further. Her family, blaming the company for her contamination, sued Malfi-Zentslicher on behalf of her toddlers, and the company eventually settled for a used Vanagon and no admission of guilt, plus incidental cash estimated at two hundred million dollars. That should have been the end of the story.

However, because of allegations made by her radical supporters that she was intentionally contaminated and forced off the road, the saga lives on. Both allegations seemed dicey at first because Goodhand breathed and ate polonium-200, to which she did not have authorized access. Furthermore, there was some evidence that her car had been forced off the road, and the notes that she was taking to the reporter were not found at the scene or anywhere else. In my opinion, Malfi-Zentslicher defense lowyers answered all these charges brilliantly. The fact that Honoré Goodhand was a socialist, trouble-making malcontent who used no conditioner whatsoever on her hair clearly explains why she would sneak around until she gained unauthorized access to highly radioactive polonium and then eat and breathe several grams of it to make herself mortally sick in order to annoy her employer. Russians do that sort of thing all the time. And just last week, I read about a drug addict in New York City who ate a quart of rat poison he found laying around just to embarrass his landlord who couldn't afford an exterminator. Likewise, the allegations that Goodhand was an irresponsible person, a bad mother, and a flake, just as clearly explain why she would take drugs and fall asleep at the wheel of her car. In addition, the deep impression of a pickup bumper creased into her trunk was easily dismissed as prior damage presumably resulting from Goodhand's bad driving when she attempted to parallel park. What about the missing documents? What documents? If they are missing then no one can substantiate their existence, so what's the controversy?

This case came down to "he said-she said," and she wasn't there to say anything. Besides, who are you going to believe, a fine, upstanding German corporation born in 1934 authorized by the Atomic Energy Commission of the United States Government to produce top secret products essential for securing our National Security, or a twenty-seven year old neurotic pot-smoking tattooed proto-feminist union radical closet lesbian? The allegation that Malfi-Zentslicher had someone murder Honoré Goodhand is just plain ludicrous. Corporations don't kill people. People kill people.

In 1976 Malfi-Zentslicher paid off the balance of its war reparations and closed its Texas chemical plant. In 1982 the company disappeared altogether in Argentina. In 1987 the AEC ceased to exist. The plant is gone. The AEC is gone. The company is gone. At the time the company disappeared, even Argentina was gone. Why isn't Honoré Goodhand gone?

I'll tell you why. People love underdogs and they love martyrs. There is a lesson here. At the first glimpse of a malcontent, fire the person before she has a chance to embarrass you in public and become a folk hero, and long before you have no choice left but to get caught up in another one of those final solutions that clearly resulted from a series of unfortunate coincidences caused by yellow journalism, public ignorance, prejudice against corporations, threats to national security, unnamed terrorists, weapons of mass destruction, and really bad weather in Saskatoon. Fast reaction up front will save everybody a lot of grief.

GOVERNMENT   A little government is not a bad thing so long as the right people have access to it. When it comes to directing the habits of citizen consumers, however, I think that corporations can do a much better job than governments. Here are some thoughts that you can address to consumers.

Is government representative? How many bureaucrats are there compared to elected representatives? Did you vote for or against any of them? How many times a year do you vote for your representatives? On the other hand, every time you spend one dime, you are voting to assert your choices. Do you want more cowboy movies? Do you want an SUV or a fuel efficient green machine? Do you want organic carrots? Do you prefer the fluoride toothpaste with whitener, or the apricot flavored gel that comes with a stripe of anti-bacterial mouthwash and a breath freshener? What about the exciting new transparent gel that comes with the anti-cavity super fluoride, the whitener, the mouthwash, the breath freshener, *and* a thirty year variable rate mortgage?

As you vote daily with your dollars, corporations all over the world register your exact preferences and react. Ask yourself, who is in a better position to assume a role of leadership in America and in the world, governments who push their own political agendas, or businesses that exist to serve your needs? Corporations know you. We know your habits better than the FBI, better than your minister, better than your closest friends, and better than your mother. When you log onto a website that provides you with that secret little pleasure you so enjoy, we know. They don't. When you buy stuff with your credit card, we know. I could go on and on. If it's privacy you're looking for, you were born into the wrong century. What you need to understand is that every corporation is vying for your dollars and so every corporation records and adjusts to your needs. We help you refine and clarify your needs through advertising. We make it easy for you to satisfy them through aggressive marketing, saturation distribution, and easy credit. We reward your decisions with rebates, sales, and coupons for more. Together, we form that perfect partnership of supply and demand, and you, the consumer, with your dollar vote, hold all the power. Who needs government when you have someone in your corner looking out strictly for *your* needs? Who wants governments when all they do is interfere with that supply and demand relationship with too many taxes, too much social engineering, and too much regulation? Like you, we stand for freedom, and let the chips fall wherever *you* decide to spend them.

THE GRAND ECONOMY   A worldwide system of unregulated free enterprise governed by immutable economic laws and managed by the best and the brightest for the benefit of all

Imagine a world in which market sectors replace borders, corporate logos replace national flags, and every consumer is wired directly to every market and every other consumer. All mysteries would disappear as communications specialists answer every consumer question. War, terrorism, and protest would become obsolete as markets provide mutual dependency between peoples and jobs for almost everyone. The battle against nature would shrink to insignificance as technologies provide comprehensive solutions. The chaos and confusion caused by different languages, currencies, customs, religions, ideologies, clothing styles, and social habits would vanish in time as homogeneity and standardization transform humanity into a melting pot of commercial partnerships. The ultimate life goal for which all peoples have searched in vain for thousands of years finally would become a universal reality: Economies of scale joined with high productivity and low labor costs yielding affordable prices with expanded margins.

Once set into motion throughout the world, The Grand Economy will operate like a gigantic frictionless machine generating enough surplus capital to overcome entropy and achieve a state of perfect, self-sustaining perpetual profit for its primary investors.

GREED   Greed is the misunderstood stepchild of the human heart. For centuries it was considered a cardinal and even a deadly sin. As recently as 1956 Thornton Wilder, when discussing "winning children" and how they get what they want, had this to say: "All children, emerging from the egocentric monsterhood of infancy – 'Gimme! Gimme!' cries the Nero in the bassinet – are out to win their way – from their parents, playmates, from 'life,' from all that is bewildering and inexplicable in themselves."[15] Wilder is pointing to greed. He still thinks of it as a form of egocentric monsterhood, but note his emphasis on winning.

Without knowing it, even Wilder was beginning to understand the true nature of greed. Look around you. Look at the subprime mortgage broker, the televangelist, the professional athlete, the actor, the rapper, the lobbyist, the corner W*ALLMINE! grocer, the dedicated politicians who lead our nation, and the guy in the Porsche who just flipped you off as he passed you on the freeway. Look at the great CEOs and other leaders I discuss in this book. All these people share one trait in common: The need to take; to win their way; to grab their entitlement and run, whether that is money, power, money, position, money, prestige, money, policy, or influence. Or money. That is, they are all driven by greed. Would anyone today in his right mind consider all these winners egocentric monsters? If so, then we are all becoming egocentric monsters.

The truth is that those of us blessed with an abundance of greed have broken our yoke of oppression. We have finally become liberated, just as homosexuals, people of color, and certain other downtrodden groups of men, women, and animals have become liberated, from the prejudice and misunderstanding of others. It is a new era. We are free! Free! Free at last to express ourselves with the liberty of a Martin Luther King, Jr., the creativity of a Michelangelo, and the joy and dignity of a free-range chicken.

I date the start of this great era to the 1970s and early 1980s. Two events in particular marked its true beginnings: The election of Ronald Reagan to the Presidency, and the publication of a particular syndicated newspaper column by Louis Rukeyser, for many years host of Public Broadcasting System's *Wall Street Week*, entitled, "What's Wrong with Greed?"

---

15 *Paris Review*, Winter, 1956. From an interview with Thornton Wilder on "The Art of Fiction" conducted by Richard H. Goldstone.

The Reagan Presidency speaks for itself. Mr. Rukeyser's column spoke for millions of Americans who, particularly since The Great Depression and the era of liberal moralism that it spawned, had suppressed their normal desires for wealth under a shadow of guilt, good taste, and embarrassment. His column marked that point in history when millions of Americans came out of the closet and announced to the world that yes, they were greedy, and no, there is not a damn thing wrong with that.

Let's take a closer look at greed.

Has there ever been an Olympic champion, man or woman, any race or nationality, who didn't say to himself, "I'm gonna win. Gimme that gold?" Has there ever been a CEO who didn't say the same thing? Even Wilder understood that winners are driven to take whatever they can.

Greed is the full expression of an individual's drive to survive. It is the need to win and to score more than others. In the context of the economy, greed is a way of describing the natural human instinct to improve one's lot in life and to accumulate enough wealth, power, and influence to be safe and self-sufficient. Isn't all this the American Dream? Is there any motive of which people should be more proud than the drive to win and to stand on their own two feet? If that suggests to some people a Nero in a bassinet crying, "Gimme! Gimme!" then I say, long live the emperor. If you stand tall and be proud of who and what you are, greed will serve you the way you serve your employees, your investors and your customers; the way God serves the faithful; and the way emperors serve their subjects. It can also make you very rich.

In addition, as a powerful motivating force, greed will sustain you during moments of self-doubt. Everyone, even the most seasoned CEO, has existential moments during which he questions himself: "Who am I?" and "Why am I doing this?" "Am I a good person?" and "What is the meaning of life?" At such moments, I recommend that you sit back, close your eyes, and allow your instinct of greed to take over. Count your assets. Calculate your latest net worth. Think about the thirty thousand square foot retirement home you will build some day on Jupiter Island. Think about clearing more than a billion dollars in a hostile takeover and the subsequent divestiture. Greed will quickly overpower every "how, who, what, where, and why?" you ask.

At the same time, while there is nothing wrong with greed per se, you should guard against appearing too greedy, or avaricious. It's fine to be gay, but would it be smart to go to your job in drag? Appearing avaricious is a mistake since it reveals an excess in your character and thus, a personal vulnerability. Hide avarice and learn to treat your wealth as if it were at most a footnote to your career. In other words, if you have an abundance of greed, and you can learn how to seem utterly indifferent to its rewards, then clearly you have a large dose of the right stuff.

Okay, let's say that you have the right stuff. You have earned your MBA and you are ready to jump into the world and make your mark. Exactly what miracles can greed perform for you? Let's take a look at one shining example: The man with the most; the highest paid CEO in America.

Raubert Freiherr Ubergeschaffen, like many men raised in California's Golden Triangle, gave himself a new name that sounded more democratic. You know him as Bobbyu, CEO of Just Bobbyu's Little Holding Company.

Bobbyu is the quintessential Nero hero in the bassinet. He wins everything. He is described by his trainees and by anyone who does business with him as, "that three thousand ton Godzilla on steroids." At last report his wage was $192,307.69 per hour, or $3,205.13 per minute, or $53.42 per second. In other words, every eleven minutes, Bobbyu takes home as much as the average American earns in one year. If you are the best, that is what greed can do for you.

Bobbyu is also careful never to appear avaricious. In public interviews he scorns mere money as a meaningless trifle. He reminds us that Attila the Hun and Genghis Kahn kept their scores with dead bodies. He keeps his with mere dollars. Money keeps score and rewards successful decisions, that's all. The money itself means nothing. Similarly, while acquiring several television networks, film studios, radio conglomerates, advertising companies, a large chunk of the Internet, and exclusive rights to the English Language, he has repeatedly warned against consolidation of power and ownership of the sources of public information. Who in this world could possibly make better decisions on what to feed Americans' minds than a knowledgeable media tycoon who scorns money and supports the democratization of information? His leadership is even more inspiring when you consider that he was never seduced by that stodgy, stifling, misguided anachronism we call "the school system" that attempts to impart antiquated concepts of community, right, wrong, perspective, wisdom, and responsibility. Instead, he does things his way.

Remember those stiff, puritanical teachers who looked like they were being slowly strangled by tight sphincters? Remember how they preached that with freedom comes "responsibility," that educationist's code word for ramming "values" down students' throats? These teachers were so uptight they actually believed that self and freedom should be restrained as well as set free; that minds should be expanded in addition to being narrowly focused; that children should be forced to attend school, where they can be cultivated, coached and mentored and work their way up, rather than set loose to express their inner selves with only their selves to guide them. Like a truly heroic leader, Bobbyu refused to let anyone stuff him into a box. He invented his own rules. He allowed his parents to parent him only when it pleased him; he attended high school only when he felt like it; he dropped out of college after two hours; he got his start from family connections; and he never looked back. He is the finest example in the known world of what it really means to cry, "Gimme! Gimme!" and mean it. And that is the secret to ultra-success. You really have to mean what you want.

So what is the bottom line on greed? As you plan your life, expect to live large and be selfish. After all, if you don't take good care of yourself, who is going to take care of you? The state? The Salvation Army? Your mother? Live large and be selfish. It is the most responsible thing to do. And no one is going to strike you dead with a bolt of lightning just because you have the ability to look out for number one, particularly if you act like it's not a big deal. If our present economy demonstrates anything, it demonstrates this: If you can't celebrate greed, you have nothing to celebrate; but when greed alone directs you, you could have more to celebrate in eleven minutes than ordinary people will have in a year. Above all other human traits, greed will help you win your way.

And by the way, in case you haven't heard, research shows that rich people live longer and have fewer illnesses than the other ninety-nine and a half percent. When the proof is in the soufflé, eat the soufflé, *and* be proud of it. Just keep your cool and call it gruel so the villagers won't get restive.

GREENS   In every economy there are small groups of people who genuinely do not care about prosperity or who have simply given up hope of any upward mobility for themselves. In their desperation they search for something to believe in that seems larger than themselves and more pristine and more promising than the world of work. These characters often become greens and they are big trouble. They can disrupt the flow of business and call into question the status quo that serves us all so well. Their numbers are liable to increase in the twenty-first century as weather patterns change, natural resources are depleted, oceans flood island nations and coastal cities, extinctions are publicized, human populations explode, new diseases spread, and revolutionary technologies emerge. Be prepared to deal with them.

The best way to neutralize these greens is to discredit them. Encourage comparisons that will stimulate the rest of the public to ridicule them as dangerous malcontents. Using the power of public relations, advertising, and imagery in the print, visual, and electronic media that you use or control, including the Internet, set standards for normal Americans, loyal Americans, productive Americans, patriotic Americans, and wholesome Americans. Let those standards contrast sharply with your projected images of the greens. How do they fix their hair? What kind of clothing do they wear? How do they conduct themselves? Do they ever bathe? Majorities of people love to belong and belonging means conformity. Those who do not conform to society's norms will appear to the majority to be radical, unreasonable, threatening, and evil.

Salem did not burn witches because they fit in. If you broadcast imagery depicting greens as weird and alien, you won't need editorial comment. Just make the image stick and the public will take care of the rest.

A second group of people is a less vulnerable wing of the greens, but they are active environmentalists and they pose yet another threat. This group is composed of two types. The first type includes individuals from our own ranks, many of them raised in the Midwest. These are gentlemen who are truly among the best and the brightest. Some sail yachts and become CEOs and some win appointment to Cabinet posts. But they all have one thing in common: They were all misguided in their youth. They lacked proper supervision, climbed trees, and read books like *Bambi* and

The Sand County Almanac. Hands off these fellows. Don't alienate them. They belong to the club and they are going to do whatever they like and all you can do is make tasteful jokes about their eccentricities. Fortunately, there aren't many of this type left and the damage they inflict through preservation and conservation can always be dozed over when their influence wanes, when bigger dollars and better lowyers undermine easements they arranged, or when they pass on. The second type is more dangerous but easier to deal with. These are middle class people who feel either guilty about their prosperity or resentful of others who want to express the same prosperity too close to their back yards. These types are more inclined to belong to the Sierra Club than to groups like Earth First!, and they cannot be simply characterized as crackpots. However, their principal threat is legal action in misguided efforts to affect public policy, so the best way to neutralize them is to demonstrate in the court system who has deeper pockets and more influence.

Dealing with greens is no different from dealing with corporate warriors or anyone else. When bark comes to bite, the bigger dog always wins.

GROSS DOMESTIC PRODUCT   One of the few human events that will bring tears to your eyes is news that the GDP exceeded the best-reported quarterly projections. GDP is the nation's report card and it grades our productivity. Bask in positive results but never let them lull you into complacency, and watch them closely for warning signs. Complacency is a slippery slope, and a sliding GDP, unchallenged, can accelerate toward recession before you know it. Be ever vigilant. And always react immediately to a slumping GDP. Do your part. Do whatever you must to drive your employees to higher levels of productivity. Use layoffs to get rid of dead wood if you must, and any time GDP slumps for two consecutive quarters, it is mandatory that you rewrite your fundamental business plan.

On the other hand, a glowing GDP should be cause for celebration. Educate consumers to appreciate the deep significance of a winning GDP in their lives. It is not just a number. It is a grade. GDP is a measure of personal worth, the worth of the workers whose effort or lack of effort helped create the number; the worth of consumers whose spending or lack of spending helped create the number; the worth of the nation at large, whose care or lack of caring contributed to the number.

In the same way that a religious person who meets the highest standards of behavior achieves a state of religious grace, good workers and consumers, as well as CEOs, can achieve a state of economic grace. Join together with friends and workers to celebrate the light of a robust and growing GDP confident that you have done all you can to ensure a comfortable future. Like Christians waiting for The Rapture, we are all in this together.

That is, most of us are. In 1972, Jigme Singye Wangchuk, still an adolescent, and the fourth King of Bhutan, slapped the face of the world economy when he proposed that his nation's standard of worth would be known henceforth as, "Gross National Happiness." His idea consisted of four tenets: 1. Development based on equality and sustainability. 2. The preservation and promotion of cultural values. 3. The establishment of good government. And 4. Conservation of the natural environment. What have we here, a Buddhist Shangri-La?

The arrogance of this proposal is as monumental as the Himalayan Mountains on which this tiny, landlocked, and isolated nation rests. The United Nations did not even recognize the sovereignty of this peanut of a country until 1971, and the Chinese even today claim part of it. One might argue that this quaint and backward idea of Gross National Happiness fits a country in which cutting down a tree, any tree, is a crime, and that it is therefore a laughable idea. But I am not laughing. This notion challenges The Grand Economy. It undermines the view of the classical economists that contentment results from consumer spending and acquisition. It belittles the fact that joy can be measured quantitatively and exactly by levels of consumption. Furthermore, this idea did not die stillborn. Its supporters actually have hosted international conferences on GNH. They met in Japan in November, 2006. The idea seems to be growing.

I am deeply concerned. *Deeply concerned.* What would happen to The Grand Economy if everyone thought of happiness as an end in itself, as something reachable by means other than productivity and consumption? All meaningful economic activity could grind to a halt! Not since the rise of Communism has our way of life faced a greater threat. On an ideological level, this assault against the free market system amounts to verbal terrorism, and it could prove as damaging to our economic well being as biological, chemical, or nuclear attack. Clearly, if use of this linguistic weapon of mass destruction is allowed to expand, Bhutan could become a threat to our national security. I believe that economic sanctions combined with decisive military intervention could neutralize this threat. If it grows any stronger, I would urge each of you to call upon the President to seek support among our allies to monitor this thing and to prepare for immediate action before this maverick nation poisons the minds of consumers and workers worldwide. The awful truth is that if we cannot defeat this dangerous idea of happiness in Bhutan, we will end up fighting it in the streets of New York, Los Angeles, and Denver.

GROWTH   Everything depends on growth. Without growth, continuous increases in production, sales, profits, and income would be impossible. There are two kinds of growth you need to understand.

Linear growth, or real increases in population, markets, and production facilities, has carried our economy from its earliest beginnings until now. It will continue to add profitability for a few decades to come. As populations begin to exceed the carrying capacity of the improved land base, however, and as other factors, like diminishing resources, cost of energy, waste abatement, and deserts in Minnesota, make tangible expansion impractical, CEOs will increasingly depend on something I call, "circular growth."

Picture a pond. Imagine a child throwing stone after stone into the pond. Each stone produces a wave that radiates outward in all directions across the pond. Each time the child throws a new stone, the impact creates a new wave. Theoretically, given an infinite number of stones, there is no end to the number of waves the child can produce. From the point of view of economics, each wave represents a kind of growth.

Think of each wave as a new product. The same production and marketing facilities, slightly altered, can introduce an endless stream of products to the same consumer base over and over and over again. The result of this hyperactivity is a kind of simulated growth as each product defines a new market and reaps new income from the same consumers.

Clearly, circular growth depends on two important factors: Product development and consumer education. Calculate what consumers want or what they can be stimulated to want, and then produce it. But production and marketing are only half the story. Since the accelerating stream of products is meant for a static consumer base with static income, consumers must be educated to increase the percentage of their income reserved for discretionary purchases and decrease the percentage of their income reserved for necessities and savings. Put another way, they must be educated to view the endless stream of products *as necessities*. To facilitate circular growth, part of your strategy as a CEO must be to help keep the cost of base line products, such as computers, cheeseburgers, and all terrain vehicles, at relatively stable levels, as much as that is possible, while preserving their profitability with advanced technologies and production methods. Another part of your strategy must be to keep consumers employed for the duration of their lives, and another part is to find ways to extend ever-expanding credit to masses without accelerating risk. These strategies will free up and actually increase the flow of discretionary income. They should also stimulate production of new products which will have the effect of squeezing new capital out of target markets just as linear growth takes capital out of all markets. In other words, babies can still eat baby food, but they should also be able to play with recreational lasers.

Now let's look again at the other side of the equation. In addition to supply side strategies for growth, the demand side still offers challenges. One of the biggest and potentially most rewarding challenges of the future will be to convert non-participating populations into viable consumers. You are faced with the task, for example, of educating hundreds of millions of potential consumers in Moslem and other third world nations currently hostile to Western economies. How do you get a yogi, a Sufi, a shaman, and a mullah to dig rap and play *Grand Theft Auto*? At present, the majority of these people are content to have food on the table and a goat in the stable. Plus there are vast populations in rural China, urban India, Mexico and Latin America, Africa, and backwoods regions all over the world that must meet higher standards of living before they can even be educated. Long before you can sell them video games, it will be an arduous process just to habituate them to new necessities, such as the curling iron, Sponge Bob

Square Pants, and the weight loss, buttocks-busting, body-sculpting beautification machine available for three equal payments of only $49.99 each, shipping extra. No challenge will be more necessary or more rewarding, and none will contribute more to needed growth. True, only the deepest sense of dedication will accomplish these goals. But think about it. Half the planet is still out of the race. That means you could double worldwide markets in your lifetime without even touching the supply side. Add in supply side tinkering and markets could quadruple. Add population growth, up to the point of diminishing returns, and you have to start factoring. Think about it long enough and you will conclude, as I have concluded, that there is no practical limit whatsoever to economic growth.

GUARANTEES   Foolish and anachronistic, consumer guarantees are a thing of the past. Why give away what you don't have to? The fact is there are no guarantees either in life or in business. The road of life is pitted with potholes. Consumers need to learn how to dodge them.

The Limited Warranty has replaced the Guarantee. The Limited Warranty also looks good so include it in your marketing package. It is a beautiful document of several dozen pages written in the finest, most elegant legalese, conceived to protect consumers while being fair to business. For example, let's say that some wild and crazy corporation designs household toasters to explode like shrapnel bombs the first time they are used. If a toaster works correctly, it will wipe out the entire family, including the cat and the hamster. Just for the fun of it, like the games kids play on their computers. If the toaster functions correctly and everyone within thirty yards of the toaster dies or is seriously mutilated, then the machine operated correctly and the Limited Warranty does not kick in. On the other hand, if the toaster fails to explode, then the consumer may return the defective toaster to the vendor, as long as she kept her receipt, and exchange it for a new one, because total malfunction is covered.

Other problems, like switches that appear to be defective but in fact have been abused by the owner and cause the electrocution of a grandmother, are not covered. After total malfunction, problems covered under the terms of a typical Limited Warranty for products not designed to explode are manufacturing defects resulting in critical illness, loss of important body parts, or death during the first five days of use. The moment responsibility is established, the company is obligated to repair or replace the product in an expeditious manner, or refund its purchase price. In return for this blanket protection, when accepting the Limited Warranty, the consumer waives all rights and agrees to relieve the company of any liability whatsoever. Another one of those win-win situations.

Comprehensive as The Limited Warranty is, however, the best protection the consumer can find is the Service Contract. That is the name of the game today. For about three-quarters of the cost of the product, the consumer can purchase total protection for an entire year against any problem that cannot be traced to misuse or abuse of the product. And, what is more, the Service Contract can be renewed every year. Surprisingly, a significant percentage of consumers actually buy service contracts year after year. They think of it as insurance. I think of it as a kind of tough love. A friend of mine in the home appliance business described his Service Contracts in this way: "My contracts let me hang the same housewives, moms, girlymen, and working gals by their heels every year, year after year, and skin them alive, and every year each one of them sleeps better at night knowing that we are there to protect her. Because we care." His metaphor might be a little extreme, but his point is well taken. If a business is going to assume all the risk for replacing and repairing a product during its normal wear, then that business should be entitled to an offsetting reward. The fact is that when administered correctly, Service Contracts are one of the most profitable sales anyone can make in any business. The key is the administration. Do a number in the small print of your Service Contracts and train personnel to recognize the many abuses consumers inflict on perfectly good products, and I guarantee that you will print some big numbers on your balance sheet. That is the only guarantee you will ever need.

Forget guarantees. Throw in Limited Warranties. But sell and keep selling those service contracts. And why not? Aren't corporations in the business of providing service?

"My contracts let me hang the same housewives, moms, girlymen,
and working gals by their heels every year, year after year, and skin
them alive, and every year each one of them sleeps better at night
knowing that we are there to protect her. Because we care." p. 181

HACKERS   Who are the lowest vermin in the human food chain? If you look just below cannibalistic pedophile serial killers and arsonists who burn down nursing homes with gasoline soaked kittens, you will find them: Hackers.

Hackers are the cockroaches in your salad. They conspire in secret, ignore the law, spit on ethics, laugh at precedent, and give the finger to good taste merely to prove that they can get by with it. Even worse, they steal. Every time a hacker pirates a CD, a DVD, a game, or proprietary software, he or she is taking profits away from the owner of the copyright, the corporation that owns the copyright holder, and the stockholders who own the corporation. Then, in most cases, they don't even profit from their actions. They give the stuff away! This behavior undermines markets and threatens price stabilities. It also violates security. Hackers function without authorization, without oversight, without regulation, and without any scrutiny whatsoever. They act as if they were registered corporations doing real business when in fact they are no more than hoodlums. Few of them ever suffer prosecution or punishment because most of them are minors, foreigners, or clever enough to stay one step ahead of authority.

We have laws governing use and production of illegal drugs, laws that provide for mandatory sentences and the seizure of personal property. We have RICO laws governing conspiratorial crime. We have prisons set up for Enemies of Freedom who will never talk to a lowyer and never see a courtroom. We have precedents for trying minors as adults. We have surveillance rules that give law enforcement a blank check. Why not extend these uses of law to hackers? I think hackers are such a great threat to our way of life that they should all be rooted out. Prosecute them as adults if they are minors, and seize their parents' assets so you can return some capital to the victims they have harmed. If they are foreigners, on American soil or off, apprehend them and subject them to extraordinary rendition. If they are citizens, try them under laws governing organized crime. Put some of these pretty young fellows into prisons with the mainstream populations and they will quickly learn to repent, and they will serve as an example to others of what can happen to a happy-go-lucky fourteen year old thug who thinks he can run afoul of real business and get by with it.

Meanwhile, until authority is properly applied to these characters, hire them at minimum wage as interns and put them to work. Try to pick their brains and harness their enthusiasm for productive ends, like gathering industrial intelligence and undermining your competitors. Why waste talent?

THE HANDSHAKE   When you meet someone, you will have only one chance to shape that person's first and most persistent impression of the kind of person you really are: Your handshake. If it is cold, damp, and limp, you will come off as a weak, fishy, unworthy character who deserves to be avoided, exploited, or forgotten. Someone who can be walked on. On the other hand, if your handshake is warm, dry, firm, and vigorous, you will come off as a self-confident, aggressive, powerful person, a man to be reckoned with. Someone who *does* the walking. Always make that first impression count.

Naturally, you will intend to provide your best handshake every time you extend your hand. But if you don't extend it correctly, you run a great risk of sabotaging your own best efforts. We have all had it happen. You are distracted, trying to take the measure of the person you are about to meet. Without thinking, you lift your hand and extend it toward him – and disaster strikes! You miscalculated the angle of contact between the two hands, and before you know it, he has grasped your fingers from the knuckles to the nails and missed your palm altogether. In near panic, you realize that your fingers have no strength and no leverage and so you try to apply pressure against the back of his hand with your thumb, but nothing you can do will save the day. He squeezes your fingers as he would shake a washrag and your opportunity is lost for all time.

There is only one way to shake hands. Practice it until your technique is automatic and unfailing. Hold all five fingers together at your side as if you intended to make a salute. Briskly, raise your hand until your forearm is parallel to the ground and forms a right angle with your upper arm. Keep your fingers tight and the plane of your palm vertical, at exactly 90 degrees to the surface of the ground. Now extend your hand toward the other person, and as you do so, rotate your fingers counter-clockwise until your palm is parallel to the ground. Spread your thumb away from your index finger as far as you can. Finally, as contact is immanent, rotate your hand counterclockwise an additional 45 degrees so your little finger is the highest part of your hand. This is a fail-safe formation. As you make contact with the other person's hand, wherever first contact is made, your hands will of necessity glide smartly together until the webs between their thumbs and forefingers touch. At this point you can rotate your hand smartly in a clockwise direction and close, and each of you will have an honest grasp on the other's full hand. Now squeeze until you have equalized the other person's pressure or gained a slight advantage. Look the other person squarely in the eyes and offer your verbal greeting.

Properly executed, this maneuver will ensure that, during those all-important greetings between men, you will always be master of the situation.

HANDS-ON MANAGEMENT   Manage by delegation until things fall apart. Then do it yourself. Grit your teeth. Put aside all your personal needs. Cancel your holiday. Give up your family. Square those broad shoulders. Prepare to show them how it's done. Then jump in and micromanage hands-on, or should I say, fists-on, until the morons get it right. When they are back on track, ride off into the sunset in a blaze of glory and give them one glance over your shoulder so they will remember: If they screw it up again, like the Terminator, you'll be back.

HEALING   During feasts celebrating victories over their enemies, Vikings liked to drag in a captive warrior, flay the flesh off his torso, pry open his ribs, and lift up his lungs like wings of a butterfly. All this while he was still alive and more or less conscious. They didn't have desserts back then.

Today we have desserts. However, that has not completely stopped us from committing barbarous acts, even in polite society. At cocktail parties, for example, it is not uncommon to witness one person inflict insults on another person's delicate sensibility. Any way you look at it life is still a bitch.

The solution to the Viking barbarity was to drink more beer and bring in more captives. Our solution is to undergo healing.

Idealists, feminists, counselors, and New Age gurus promise us that we will have a change in consciousness and fix the world once we experience healing. This is a very nice idea. It also boosts book sales, lecture tours, and seminars in Northern California. Once we are all healed, we won't be mean to each other any more and our yellow brick road will glisten.

However, while I do not advocate grotesque tortures, I fear that if we heal too much we might dull our edge in competition against Islam, the Chinese, the Russians, and each other. Instead of healing, I propose dealing. Stop whining. Get over it. Go out and spill someone else's financial blood to heal your net worth. Then, if you like, be civilized about it. Express your sensitivity and send a nice bouquet of fish heads to your prey.

We are what we are.

HEALTH   According to Amiel, a nineteenth-century almost-ran, "Health is the first of all liberties." I think this fellow had it almost right. Wealth, of course, is the first of all liberties, and it promotes good health, the second of all liberties, because it allows you to live well, feel secure, and have access to the finest inaccessible medical care on earth.

Besides making lots of money, there are a few other things you can do to increase the odds that you will have good health. Limit your smoking to an occasional Cuban cigar after an exceptional meal taken with exceptional company at a four star restaurant. Drink regularly, but in moderation. Exercise daily. Sleep soundly at least six hours per night. Learn to stay relaxed. Eat well and intelligently. Take vitamins. Don't worry. Have a comprehensive physical examination at Mayo's every year. Breathe deeply. Take time out of your busy schedule once monthly to fondle the contents of your home safes and safety deposit boxes, and to recalculate your net worth. If you do all this, and your genes are average or better, chances are good that you will live the full span of life and will remain healthy enough to enjoy your wealth.

As for the rest of the liberties, they are hardly worth mentioning when you have the first two.

HEALTH INSURANCE   Like all forms of insurance, health insurance is a game of probabilities pitting the informed, who have actuaries and an effective lobby, against the uninformed, who don't. Here's how it works. As an underwriter, you calculate the likelihood of different classes of consumers, who fit certain profiles, falling into ill health or dying. You factor in their probable medical expenses; then you throw in about ten percent gray sky to cover your margin of error, and you do both in a regulatory environment designed by your lobbyists. At that point you can set your premiums at a competitive level, sell your product, and invest. When the bond market is robust, discount your premiums and rake in new customers. When it is pitiful, double your premiums and blame the high cost on greedy doctors, irresponsible patients, cutthroat lowyers, and exorbitant jury awards in malpractice suits. If you have done all this with excruciating care, then health insurance, like all forms of insurance, is like playing poker with a table of drunks and your own deck. The really fun part is that when players get sick and needy, they look you, the dealer, as an angel of mercy.

If you are shopping for a hot market sector, cruise insurance companies. They dictate America's health care system from top to bottom. They define the rules of the game, provide the deck, stack the deck, deal the cards, win every hand, and pocket extraordinary profits for themselves – and for investors.

That deck, by the way, has five aces. Think about this: Has any heir ever requested a refund on a monthly health insurance premium the same month the insured dies? It shouldn't matter if she did, because in your contract, the insured purchases a month's insurance if he purchases a day, win, lose, or draw, and if the insured dies on the first day following premium due date, you get at least a twenty-nine day risk-free bonus. So you win twice. You collect robust premiums for years, invest the net, and pocket the surplus; and when the consumer dies, you keep the change. Of course the change won't always be enough to pay the dearly departed's final health care expenses, but when you cost average over the life of the policy and force big enough co-payments plus provider discounts, you make out like a bandit nine times out of ten.

I focus on health insurance because we are standing on the threshold of an unprecedented opportunity. It is called the Baby Boomers. This enormous generation, somewhat more health conscious and better educated than previous generations, has begun its golden years. Boomers are a captive market used to paying high prices for health care and facing an under funded Medicare system. They will be eager to buy tailored health insurance products. Plus there is no reason to believe that the rate of return on them will be any lower than on any other group. Odds are it will be higher. Unfortunately it won't be as high as it might have been. Baby Boomers might eat more tofu than lard and live longer, but they are still a porky group and they will have some complications from heart disease, stroke, diabetes, and various cancers, though not as many as their parents' generation. What really guarantees their profitability are higher margins on higher rates. Since there are two of them for every one in previous generations insurance companies will be able to virtually double their volume at higher rates. Do you think it might be time to invest in a rock, or buy one of your own? There is still time.

HERO, JOHNNY   No one I know has entirely forgiven Johnny Hero for his infamous *faux pas*. For those unfamiliar with history, the man, CEO Johnny Hero, announced publicly that he would accept only one dollar as salary for an entire fiscal year while his company, Mudster Motors, got back on its financial feet. Fortunately for him, his earnings in the years preceding and following the Year of the Dollar Debacle were sufficient to sustain him and his family, and to maintain his social position, though I doubt that the public relations value of his actions will ever overcome the frightening expectations they established in the minds of the public for the rest of us. The example he let loose for the whole world to see lingers like a toothache. Was he mad? What else could explain such erratic behavior? We'll give him the benefit of the doubt and assume that he was overburdened with concern for his company and temporarily lost his reason. In any case, never follow his example and try to erase it from memory.

HIERARCHY   Everything is organized into hierarchies, like football polls, with the best on top and the hopeful at the bottom. Those who reside at the top of hierarchies like them, though some get bored with the view and become champions of those beneath them. Those who dwell at the bottom of hierarchies dislike them, though to the extent that they think they can improve their position, those at the bottom can actually be more loyal to the idea of hierarchy than some of those at the very top. Figure that! It's a confusing world.

Simplify. Clear things up. Be loyal to your position atop the social hierarchy and let others worry about themselves.

THE HOMELAND   During the first two centuries of our existence, the United States was merely a nation. Today it is a Homeland. Like the Russian Motherland and the German Fatherland, the American Homeland brings to mind a unified people bound together by unquestioned loyalty, tribal identity, deep abiding traditions, and love for its sacred soil reaching back into the ages for millennia. How did this miraculous transformation occur, after only a little more than two centuries, for three hundred million immigrants and descendants of immigrants? Perhaps the concept was borrowed from the native inhabitants who had occupied the land for thousands of years before they were encouraged to move on, die, or settle in concentration camps. Whatever its origins, Homeland is obviously a compelling wrap for a political package. It is not particularly useful to business, however, though you might be able to trot it out now and then, while it is fashionable, as an aid to selling flags, guns, fireworks, camouflage jackets, and films about heroic soldiers killing foreigners.

Beyond that, I do not suggest widespread use of the concept since it is a distraction. In the same way that religious enthusiasts are mesmerized by the prospect of imminent rapture, Homeland enthusiasts are intoxicated by chauvinism. Sooner or later, they will turn all their attention to interpreting The Constitution and shooting Mexicans instead of focusing on their jobs and their next purchase of a pickup truck. Why encourage them? You can support your Homeland without flaunting it and flouting sales. Don't banner the Homeland.

In fact, as a general rule, whenever masses of people are distracted by passionate feelings for anything larger than their wallets, marshal your communications networks to put them back on track. For example, push vacation escapes to tropical beachfront resorts. This will satisfy their yearning for a transcendent experience, plus reward them with visions of *pina coladas* and beautiful people wearing thongs. Or hammer away at regional and personal tastes that make people feel at home, stuff like polka music, fried chicken, lip-gloss, unsolved murders, and pills guaranteed to shrink belly fat.

What's the bottom line here? Keep politics out of business, and keep consumers focused on their mission. However, that doesn't mean that the idea of a homeland is entirely counter productive. *Au contraire.* The idea of a homeland does provide instant enemies of the state, such as foreigners, terrorists and illegal immigrants. That is not a bad diversion to keep in the background. If the villagers decide to light their torches and go on a rampage, better they chase down an al-Qaeda operative or a wetback than one of us.

HOMOSEXUALITY This is a tricky subject that can be a real drag at times. For example, if you discover that your Chief Financial Officer is gay, do you call him a "bitch!" when he challenges you, or do you treat him like a lady? If you discover that your wife is having an affair with her female yoga instructor, do you send her back to her psychiatrist in Geneva or do you join the two of them for canapés at *Lez Grenouilles*, pick up the tab, and hope to get lucky? These are theoretical questions, but they underscore the trickiness of the issue.

We are not moralists, but men and women of the world. So what does the world tell us? It tells us that all kinds of people, whether left, right, top, or bottom, are gay. For example, at one time the leading fundraiser for the most conservative wing of the Republican National Party was a flaming faerie. I have it on unreliable authority that one of my own nephews is gay, though I have never seen him wear panty hose. Some of my best friends are gay. Then there is the famous case of former FBI Chief and hunter of communists, J. Edgar Hoover. No one was quite sure about J. Edgar Hoover, but the man could out-dress Marilyn Monroe. Some members of San Francisco's *Rive Gauche*, the exclusive club for rich, powerful, world leaders, like The Henry, The Duck, The Alan, The Dick[16], and me, The Binal, dress in drag and dance the can-can in order to humiliate ourselves and amuse the rest of the club. It's a kind of initiation renewal ceremony, but it doesn't mean that we are gay. I suppose it doesn't mean that we aren't gay either. We *looked* gay, that's all. Some experts estimate that as many as one in twenty consumers is homosexual, and another three in twenty look or act gay. The point is who knows and who cares? What businessman can afford to alienate an entire market share?

As a businessman, I reach the conclusion that there is nothing right or wrong with homosexuality. Gay money spends as quickly as straight money. Some argue that the only practical impediment to a wholesale acceptance of gays is that once accepted, they come out and expect the same rights and privileges as straight people, including married couples, and suddenly your health insurance costs, pension liabilities, and other expenses might rise. On the other hand, protracted lawsuits or bad publicity accusing you of discrimination won't fringe the panties on your bottom line either. So I suggest taking a practical approach right down the middle of the avenue. That is, express tolerance for gays in public, but express it with a wink in private. That way, you might risk your butt a little, but at least you can protect it in your club's locker room. Make no definitive statements one way or the other, but bend over toward public opinion, whatever that might be at the moment, and try to stay uninvolved. If enough gay employees demand benefits similar to those given to straight married employees, get behind

16 At *Rive Gauche* everyone gains The Nickname, even prominent politicians.

them and give them what they want. What's the difference? True, I wouldn't go out of my way to hire an entire fag battalion – why ask for trouble? But at the same time, I would not in any way inhibit the career of a promising employee who happened to be a hard-charging bull dyke or a troll queen in a garter belt. Why throw the babe out with the bath water? In other words, be practical and don't get buggered down in social ideologies.

If fate decides to test you and you find out that you have a gay child who resists therapy, then support him or her as you would a straight child and defend the child against criticism. It is, after all, *your* child. The Dick had one when he was king of the hill, and he had no problem keeping his social position. What's good for The Dick should be good enough for the rest of America. My best advice is stay calm, stay cool, and stand behind your kid. Just keep it under wraps until it grows up.

In the event that you happen to *be* gay, don't prance. Develop body language that portrays you as a psychotic NFL linebacker. In a perfect world, only your business prowess would draw attention to you. In the real world, however, people look for signs. Don't be afraid to give them some. In addition to the linebacker thing, throw out some scary imagery about hand to hand combat and steak Tatar. Make vague references to karate. And by all means, drop the suggestion that if you really wanted to, you could wrestle control of General Motors, skin the market, buy India, ride a bull, *and* satisfy nine voracious nymphomaniacs in a hot tub. All on your lunch hour.

HONESTY   Always appear to tell the truth, even when your truth counters perceived realities. Honesty is one of those virtues, like volunteerism and flossing, that is taught to children, university students, religious enthusiasts, and other naïve people despite the fact – or perhaps because of it – that most human beings are less than honest most of the time. Children lie. Students cheat. Homophobic Baptist evangelist crusaders in the war on drugs hang out in Denver so they can shoot up and sodomize male prostitutes. Only the Oracle of Delphi never lied. Still, society touts honesty and expects it and it is always shocked when people are caught lying; the more public the person, the greater the shock. Take the case of

President Clinton, for example. Millions of people, who always told the truth about their private sexual habits, became disgusted with Clinton for lying about his sexual habits. That is because Clinton was in the public eye. Society expects more from people in the spotlight, unless, of course, those people are dealing with National Security instead of personal pleasure, in which case lying might be viewed as a form a leadership or a diplomatic tool. When not faced with a national emergency, however, the public wants heroic human icons to tell fairy tales and they want the fairy tales to be true. Come to think of it, they want the same thing when faced with a national emergency. Honesty is confusing. The important thing to remember is that the public wants to be insulated from brutal or unseemly realities except when working, watching movies, viewing television, reading newspapers, cheering sports contests, playing computer games, eating out, attending out of town conventions, attending local conventions, or going to family reunions. The trick is to seem honest without seeming unseemly.

For best results, in the same way that your legal department reviews all policy statements before they become part of your public code, I suggest that you have your public relations department review all your public proclamations before they reach the public. They will review your words for perceived honesty as well as for the usual compatibility with poll results and positive psychometrics. They will test your words on focus groups. By the time your PR people finish with your profundities, they will spin into the public mind like a dose of Prozac, and you won't have to waste time pondering complicated philosophical questions.

On the other hand, honesty presumes that you can answer the complicated philosophical question, "What is truth?" Let's make it easy: Truth is a form of reality needed at any particular moment. American historians tell a truth about the Russian Revolution, but that story will always differ from the truth that Russian historians tell. Truth, like a verdict in any courtroom, is whatever can be successfully argued in a particular time and place. Honesty, therefore, is the clear and convincing portrayal of the best argument devised to present a point of view.

With this perspective in mind, I admonish you at all times to be scrupulously honest in all your dealings.

HOW YOU PLAY THE GAME   People who don't understand competition think that if you play hard and stick to the rules, you should get a trophy. You know the saying, "It's not whether you win or lose, but how you play the game." Guess what? The bottom line is the same whether you played until you puked and behaved like Mr. nice guy, or took naps in the huddle, smoked cigarettes at half time, and stomped on your opponent's face. A loser is a loser, and a winner is a winner. End of story.

Fortunately, for smart people anyway, this idea of how you play the game is rapidly becoming obsolete. Smart people have discovered that the only way to get ahead is to win, and if the established rules stop you from winning, then you damn well better make up your own rules. For example, try putting thumbtacks in the jockstrap of your best-performing teammate and eye drops in the other team's Gatorade. The second strategy will help you win the game, and the first will clear the way for you to win the Most Valuable Player award.

Does that mean that you should not promote the "how you play the game" myth? Of course not. It's one of those old aphorisms that sounds too good to give up. It is also useful. The more people there are who subscribe to it, the more vulnerable they are, and the more vulnerable they are, the easier for you to grind them into the turf. For example, performance enhancing drugs work best for you when your competitors follow the rules and don't take them.

As a general rule, you should promote all ideas that help people turn themselves into losers. The more suckers there are in the pond, the better the fishing.

HUMANITIES   Many liberal arts colleges and most universities offer a broad range of majors in the humanities: History, English, Musicology, Art History, Philosophy, Religion and so on. When graduates in these areas enter the corporate workforce, often after failing to find a career in their chosen field, they appear to be bright, articulate, energetic, innovative, and interesting. Some are, but don't be misled by the rest. A sizeable number of them are malcontents and they will make terrible employees. They are skeptical of authority, far too interested in outside activities, seemingly immune from team behavior, often times liberal, moralistic, and idealistic, and they talk too much. Most of them yearn for other careers reserved for only the best connected in their fields, such as philosopher, historian, theologian, curator, or best-selling writer, and they will have at best only a shallow commitment to commerce in any form. Particularly guard against the humanities ABD (all but dissertation), typically a smart individual with a maverick outlook who failed to complete his or her advanced degree after spending years working for it. Virtually all of these people share a set of values at odds with the corporate world. They tend to be individualistic dreamers with little toughness, less discipline, and even less ambition. For hiring purposes, stick to MBAs, economics or accounting majors, business majors with strong specialties in administration, marketing, or advertising, communications majors, and when necessary, lowyers.

What about the social sciences? Since they are not real sciences and they focus on the human condition, I have always considered them a footnote to the humanities. Think of them in the same light, though their students can be more useful. For example, you will find some practical talent among students of psychology, sociology, and anthropology. They will have plenty of work to do in your advertising and marketing research departments. However, screen them with a fine-toothed comb for oddball notions, socialist tendencies, and other eccentricities at odds with the corporation's goals. If any of them spent a semester studying in a country like Guatemala, for example, grill them like fish and find out if they were involved in "worker organization," "agrarian reform," "village development," or had anything to do with rain forests, peasants, or hemp. Grill them hard, though you can often spot the misfits by the way they dress and wear their hair.

There is nothing wrong with a first rate career in the humanities, though career opportunities are severely limited. If you have children who want to go that route, at first discourage them and if they persist, then support them and use your influence to ensure that your offspring will receive the finest training in the country and will have the best connections possible to help them succeed. The publication by a major New York publisher in 2002 of a first novel, a non-exploding blockbuster written by a Harvard bound high school senior from a well-connected family, illustrates exactly how networking with friends and relatives can perform career miracles. In a world of peril and fierce competition, a little privilege can go a long way. Never hesitate to use it, even if you have to build a new wing onto your alma mater's business school.

"In a world of peril and fierce competition, a little privilege can go a long way. Never hesitate to use it, even if you have to build a new wing onto your alma mater's business school." p. 195

ICBMS Just as in a cathedral, one still speaks with reverence when one discusses Big Boo. She was the flagship of corporate America for many years and I am still more than willing to look to Intergalactic Corporate Behemoth Management Systems for guidance. My only complaint is that she has lowered her standards for dress code. I never would have believed that I would see a tieless employee in her hallowed halls but I have seen it firsthand and been shocked. It is not my place to criticize ICBMS however, any more than it was the layman's place to criticize the Vatican when it first allowed the vernacular Mass. Only time will measure the wisdom of such a grave decision.

IMAGE The vast majority of people would rather own a faceted and polished coprolite than the Hope Diamond in its original condition. Image might not be everything, but it is the most apparent thing. Therefore, it is everything that matters.

IMF, WTO, NAFTA, ETC. Yes, these are our babies. Yes they were hatched in conspiratorial zeal within The Club for personal benefit. And yes, they are designed to pave the way for multinational corporations bent on dominating world markets. I call it, "enlightened self-interest." Keep the ball rolling, and do what you can to discredit the hippies, the losers, the communists, the greens, and the Luddites who routinely protest but who have no plan for future development of the world, for consolidation of its resources, or for productive exploitation of its workers and consumers. International trade agreements will benefit the rich whose efforts, in turn, will benefit the other ninety-nine-and-a-half-percent. Why mince words? Masses need leaders and leaders need incentives.

INCENTIVES When you design your employment contract be certain to include incentive-based rewards. Inevitably, your board will demand that some of those rewards be tied to performance. Try to define performance in such a way that your incentive package will come your way regardless of events beyond your control. And press for incentives that recognize your efforts despite performance. You need to be taken care of, whatever the circumstances, and there is no way that you alone can be held personally responsible for growth, profits, stock value, *and* every little hint of illegal activity by misguided underlings . Perfect your negotiation skills and your contract will be as good as insurance. Remember: For top executives, just as for top athletes and actors, big rewards lock in big talent and ensure loyalty and motivation. Little rewards exist for little people.

Keep that in mind when setting incentives for employees. Carve nothing in stone. You must maintain control. You are always better off using the old carrot and stick approach. When little employees fail to meet the goals you have set for them, whack them with a stick. When they meet the incentives you have established, give them a nibble of the carrot. For employees, big punishment is the only punishment while big rewards would only induce complacency. Little rewards sharpen appetites.

Sharks and sardines might swim in the same water, but there should be no question about who owns the ocean.

INCOME An old friend of mine who does business out of Singapore confessed to me while we were flying to Scotland to play golf: "You know, C.B., nothing in the world smells as good as new money. Once, many years ago, I ordered ten thousand freshly printed one-hundred dollar bills from my bank. I was still single then. I took the money home for one night, threw it into the air over my bed like confetti, and took off all my clothes. And then I rolled on it – like a dog on a dead fish."

That's what I call, *joie de vivre*. What makes it possible? How do you acquire enough wealth to have that kind of joy?

Money flowing into your pocket is called "income." When the inflow exceeds the outflow, you gain positive net worth. Grow your net worth enough and you gain wealth. Therefore, the first key to wealth is to have high and accelerating income. All that should be self-evident.

The question is: How do you turn that key? Think about income this way. If X represents all the world's income and Y represents all the world's spending, then X=Y. Every dollar of income to someone represents a dollar of expenditure from someone else. In order to grow your net worth, and ultimately gain wealth, you must induce other people to spend more than they keep and to spend it in your direction. In other words, you must provide them, in the goods or services you sell, with non-financial rewards that make up the difference between what they spend and the value they perceive. Or you must provide them with a share of your financial rewards lower than your share. That added value, monetary or non-monetary, is your profit margin and your key to sustaining more income than expenditure, and thus to attaining a growing net worth and in time, wealth.

The choices are simple. Everyone in the world can spend all their income and achieve a base net worth of zero. Or some can spend more than their income to buy added value while others can manufacture added value and make more income than they spend. The primary incentive to this dynamic is credit over time. Nine tenths of people are consumers. They can enjoy added values they covet on the installment plan. One tenth of people own capital. They can create those values, make credit available, and enjoy robust incomes.

The second main key to this dynamic is appreciation. Spend your surplus money on things that will grow in perceived value, such as stocks, real estate, diamonds, and paintings by Renoir, rather than on things that depreciate in value, such as recreational vehicles, snowmobiles, and pickup trucks. Appreciation is income waiting to happen, and like income, it adds to your net worth and to your wealth.

The final main key to this dynamic is sound judgment. What gives you more kicks, a shiny new truck, trips to Las Vegas, and unpaid dental bills, or a Lucian Freud you got for 60K that you could auction at Christie's for 3.5

million two decades later? What turns you on more, a collection agency, or a balance sheet so unbalanced that you need a vault to store the black?

Income is like the melting glaciers above the headwaters of the Columbia River. It creates a few little streams that grow into a river that draws everything in the neighborhood to itself until it leads to an ocean. At that point, it becomes an American Dream others can only view in wonder.

When you get to that point, like my friend from Singapore, you can afford an occasional eccentricity as long as you don't post it on You Tube.

INCOME GAP   The richest twenty percent of Americans today command eighty percent of the nation's wealth and are paid half of the nation's income. At the other end of the curve, sixty percent of Americans own less than ten percent of the nation's wealth and are paid about twenty-five percent of its income. Alarmists call this an "income gap." I call it democracy in action.

People vote their political judgment on candidates who set policies. And people vote their dollars on goods and services and on the people who provide goods and services. In other words, American consumers select the economy they want and they select the people they want to run the economy. They are like shareholders voting for a board of directors to oversee their life styles. Consumers understand that the best and the brightest will guide them to their American Dream more efficiently than any other force.

Furthermore, when measured in absolute terms, are the lowest sixty percent really so bad off? The average home size has tripled in the last century. More people own their own homes than ever before. Who doesn't own a television set or a DVD player? And what is net worth compared to the happiness in people's lives when they can visit Disneyworld, eat pizza whenever they want, watch the Super bowl, and collect social security? Our economy evolves progress. Progress generates investment. Investment creates opportunity. And opportunity means more progress. On the other hand, if you divided up the nation's wealth equally among all consumers, the majority of it would be wasted on frivolities and poorly planned schemes. Americans are smarter than that. They understand that when they send capital to people who know how to manage it, we are all better off.

Has it occurred to anyone to measure gaps in ability and achievement? The problem with winning is that winners win. That puts them at the front of the line. They didn't get there because of some sinister plot. They got there because they play the right game and they play it better than others. Wealth follows success. People who have a problem with that need to try a little harder. If such people can find their way to the head of the line, they will quickly change their tune. And their alarm about the so-called income gap will evaporate. But even if they never make the front of the line, they are still okay. Look at the dynamics. Line up one hundred people. The one guy in front takes twenty percent of everything. The other ninety-nine people still get to divide up the remaining eighty percent using a regressive algorithm in which share balances decline as success, or position in line, declines. What's wrong with that? If the only incentive to get in line was an equal share, or one percent, why would anyone bother to elbow his way forward and hold his ground?

Contests create winners and losers. Winners lead the pack. Whom would you rather follow?

INDIVIDUALISM   The rest of the world sometimes characterizes business, the way it is practiced in the United States, as "Cowboy Capitalism." I agree, and I like the characterization. America is a land of individuals and individualists. One man or woman, any man or woman, can dream any dream he or she chooses and can work to fulfill that dream. The operative attitude here is, "I am an individual and I will take care of myself. You do the same."

Don't misunderstand. Individualism does not mean that I would not help a crippled old curmudgeon to cross a street through busy traffic. Of course I would, particularly if I were not late for a board meeting with my private equity group. All individualism means is that I will cross that street under my own power, whether I help someone else or not. Meanwhile, if I offer others less fortunate than I jobs so they can learn how to take care of themselves, all the better for everyone. Maybe that ill-tempered old man couldn't afford a wheel chair and with a job, now he can. Maybe his sight was poor and now, with a job, he can afford glasses thanks to his company's generous health insurance plan. Independence breeds dignity. When you lose independence and have to lean on others, you lose dignity and become depressed.

In America, our economy demands independence. Every person is expected to think for himself. Every person is expected to look out for himself. And if every person did exactly that then no one would have to sap strength from anyone else. Only an idiot would turn help down when in need. But what kind of person *asks* for help? Never ask for help. And never offer it unless you have locked in a cut of the action for yourself, even if that cut is only sentimentality. That is how we play the game. Every person has the same opportunity to look out for himself. How well he does it is up to him.

Am I my brother's keeper? Hell no! I am my brother's competitor and I will eat before him if I can. If he is not clever enough to find his own apple, then I won't let him starve. I'll throw him the core of my apple and burp contentedly. Next time around he might find the first apple. Or someone else might have it, or someone else. As we compete and hone our skills and become shrewder, we all survive better and prosper more. When you beat a competitor down, you don't deprive him. You help train him to compete better and harder the next time.

Only derelicts lose out entirely. I support organizations like The Salvation Army to keep our derelicts alive and off the streets. They will never compete and so they are largely irrelevant. But they are human beings too and their plight fills me with pity. I feel sorry for them and I wish them well, as long as they don't block my doorway.

INFORMATION   Information is the ocean that will keep your ship afloat. Direct its content, ebb, and flow like Mother Nature.

In the modern world we can honestly say that information about your company is whatever you direct it to be – if you exercise proper control. Of course there will be alternative bits of information from sources outside your influence or control, but they will be feeble and will appeal only to a small sector of consumers. Factual information, misinformation, disinformation, no information, spin, sophistry, plausible deniability, and something I like to call "credible incredulity,"[17] which comes in particularly handy during an oil spill, a nuclear accident, a toxic leak, or allegations of illegal activity, all are tools you can use to set the shape and flow of information so it will help you. These are only the most obvious tools. The experts in your communications department will know many more.

The Information Age is all about conditioning and selection. Condition consumers to tune in what you want them to tune in and to tune out everything else. Then select content and feed it to them in an entertaining, engaging package that is irresistible. Condition and select; condition and select. It is a lifetime commitment. If you master it well, you can sail on your ocean with ease. Whoever controls information controls the world.

INITIATION   Every family, every social or professional organization worth joining, and every corporation should have a formal or informal initiation to test and indoctrinate its new members, and to renew the loyalties of established members. This is an age old proven method of validating one person's desire to belong to a larger group, and it is nearly foolproof. Until an individual has been willing to suffer hideous pain and humiliation in front of a select group of his peers, he cannot be trusted to substitute that group's judgment for his own. Furthermore, you haven't lived until you have seen a five star general, a retired Secretary of State, and Chairmen from three of the world's largest oil companies doing the can-can in fishnet stockings and garter belts at a *Rive Gauche* smoker. Nor have you lived Real Life if you have not heard a man destined to be elected President of the United States in thirty-five years confess his adolescent sexual kinks to a Grins and Ghouls Society inquisition.

---

17 Credible Incredulity is part of the "I did nothing wrong; I'm better than that" approach. Here's an example. Imagine a news conference with R. Tomane Company. An aggressive reporter asks a difficult question about dozens of deaths in a company town and similar risks throughout the country. The spokesman replies: "You actually question whether a company of our stature would allegedly poison thousands of citizens with an alleged toxin from our malignite mine if we knew beforehand that the alleged material was alleged to be deadly?" Pregnant silence. Barely audible snort while head shakes in disbelief. Suggestion of moisture in the eyes. Hint of a world-weary smile. "Next question, please."

Clubs like the ones we belong to provide formal settings for initiation and renewal. In a corporate setting however, your use of initiation obviously will have to be more subtle and less structured than a fraternity hazing, a *Rive Gauche* party, a *Ghouls* interview, or even, say, a Shriners' membership initiation. Giving a freshman executive an impossible assignment is always good. So is any assignment that pits loyalty to you against company policy, good taste, or the law. It won't take long to identify those you can trust.

Individuals who balk at initiation, on the other hand, are lone wolf mavericks and you would be wise to blackball them for life. If a person is not smart enough to walk a gauntlet to reach a lifetime of opportunity, even though it might cause pain or embarrassment, why give that person a second chance?

INNOVATION   Without innovation there is only stagnation. Technology is the drive shaft that empowers The Grand Economy. Technology *is* innovation.

Here is a rule of thumb to follow. Calculate consumers' reasonable expectation for the longevity of a product. This is the Should Time. The product should last that long. Divide that time by two and you will know when consumers think they will actually need to replace the product. This is the Need Time. Divide Need Time by three and you will have approximately the mean time lapsed between the purchase of a product and the purchase of the new and improved product, the one replete with irresistible innovations. In sum, consumers think like this: *Our widget is only four years old, but it ought to last twenty-five years. If we could afford a better one in eight or ten years, we might think about it, but we're happy. Wait a minute. Wow! Look at that new widget. It looks so much better, it's amazing. I suppose we could always charge it.* For these consumers, it takes about four years to take a product for granted, to consider it old fashioned, and to desire the new and improved product.

This is merely a variation of Moore's Law applied to general marketing. Innovation builds on itself and it becomes an irresistible itch that nearly every consumer will scratch.

INSIDER TRADING   One of the great perks of being a CEO is the knowledge you have of your company (and a few other companies) that other people do not have. Only a fool would waste this knowledge. I have known CEOs so competent at this game that they play the public and their own stockholders like violins, all the while raking in profits that, in the long run, are truly obscene. And I have known CEOs who ought to learn a new game, like Scrabble, because they just don't have what it takes to skin the market and survive. O.G. Waxum, former CEO of Dimclone, for example, was a wonderful man, a good CEO, and an inspiration to Boy and Girl Scouts everywhere. As an insider trader, however, he absolutely sucked. He could have saved his hide and probably no one would have known the difference. Instead, he chose to be a good guy and share his inside information with friends and family so they could save their hides too. Remember, when you think it's time to pull an end run around insider trading laws, try not to tell your grapevine or to run a full-page ad in the *Wall Street Journal*.

Other CEOs, like Jimmy de Taco, former chief at QuickieComm, played the market brilliantly, cashing out before his company's stock plummeted from dozens of dollars to dozens of cents. But since the other investors and employees ended up with a small pile of doo-doo, they complained. A jury finally decided that those secret contracts, which de Taco had promised would save the company and which he publicized as he cleverly unloaded his stock, were actually negotiated inside an alien space ship instead of the Pentagon and therefore belonged to a different dimension, so they sent de Taco to jail. It was all just part of that confusing, wacky, roller coaster world we call Wall Street. Never ride the roller coaster when you have aliens in your pocket. Wall Street thinks aliens are indiscreet.

On the other hand, if you and your plan are perfectly discreet, go for it. Start out small and test the water. Don't try to pull a grandiose coup that will bankrupt any investors. Normally the SEC doesn't look too closely at these matters as long as they are small and hobby-like. But there is nothing like a suicide or two to arouse their interest. Go for that one sweet killing only when in serious need of capital, and only when you are already contemplating retirement. Otherwise, pick away as you can on a modest scale, year after year, and, as you compound these additional earnings, you can double your lifetime income by the time you retire.

If the SEC does investigate you, have your defenses already in order, and don't worry. Odds are, the most they will do is slap your wrist, extract a promise from you not to be a bad boy again, and bar you from trading for a few months. By the time you are geared up and ready to hobby again, the world will have forgotten all about your bad behavior and your alcoholism, your childhood abuse, the sadistic lies your enemies broadcast in their bitter attempt to embarrass you – or whatever other scenario your spin doctors concocted to defend you.

INTEGRITY   Integrity means never having to say you're sorry even when you should be. That's what folks mean when they say, "Be true to yourself." So, boys and girls, go out there and be true to yourself. Stand up for integrity as you would stand up for the Pledge of Allegiance. And when you do, remember Bucky Leize, former CEO of Endrun, a man blessed with more integrity than any CEO I have ever known. Before his untimely death, while he was vacationing in his resort compound waiting to be sentenced, he never once said that he was sorry. He remained one hundred percent true to himself right to the end. Here's to you, Bucky. You were an inspiration, and I promise that your legacy will live on.

Integrity. It's what we do best.

INTERESTS   Looking and acting like a Renaissance man probably has great public relations value, and, with the right work on your image, you might be able to pull it off. However, when it comes to actual interests, I strongly recommend that you have none. Focus on your business. Outside interests all take time, energy, and loyalty that you cannot spare. As CEO of a major corporation, your business is corporate business and personal net worth. Everything else is meaningless distraction.

INTIMIDATION   There are two kinds of people in this world, caretakers and takers. Caretakers need to hoe the garden and clean up footprints left by others, usually without a second thought about the thundering herd at their backs. Caretakers get trampled or get thirty seconds of applause at a banquet. Everything else belongs to takers.

If you plan to become a CEO, you already know where you stand: You are a taker. But don't let that fact lull you into complacency. Just as there are degrees of religious people, from Saints to Easter Sunday-only churchgoers, there are different degrees of takers. They all share one motivation in common: They want. However, people who want do not necessarily know how to take efficiently, and if they did know, most of them wouldn't have the stomach for it. Among takers, all want; many reach; but very few grab firmly enough to bring home the goods time after time. What is the difference between them? What is the secret to turning your desire into fulfillment? What gives you the courage to face down those who want to keep what you want to take?

The secret to becoming a world-class taker is in one word: Intimidation. Takers who want buy. Takers who reach negotiate. Takers who grab and keep intimidate.

How do you develop top intimidation skills? First, become emotionally detached from your prey. Think like a hawk. Either you eat or you die. The life of the thing you eat means nothing. It is dinner, period. Second, enjoy the kill. Your prey would have cut your throat if given the chance, but you got there first. Like winning an Olympic dash, successful intimidation makes you the champion and makes everyone else a loser. Finally, recalculate your assets after the kill. You are bigger and stronger now. Your worth has grown. You are better off than before. You have helped yourself. And you have become just a little more skilled at intimidation. You are the alpha hawk, the killer with the best score. You are soaring at the top of your game.

Here is a practical hint to help you when you deal one on one, something I learned years ago that I call, "the touching moment." Let's say that you are taking lunch with your prey. You have already assumed that he, like every other person you meet, is both your enemy and your asset. You have already sized him up for strengths, weaknesses, and mortal vulnerabilities

– everyone has one or two. You have identified his particular soft spots. He had a successful and hard-nosed father whom he feared and never pleased. He seems to lack confidence in relationships so he needs friendship. From the get go, be warm and welcoming. Relax. Smile. Make light of yourself. Then, at just the right moment, reach out and touch. A hearty pat on the shoulder followed by an intimate squeeze, or a warm, unexpected hand-shake with your right hand and a meaningful grip of his forearm with your left will inform him, as it would any reasonable person, that you accept him and you mean to be his friend and his comrade, if not his protector. In this way, you lull your prey into a state of relaxed confidence so that without a shred of resistance you can then reach down his throat and tear out his living heart with a rip of intimidation. The military calls it shock and awe, and at that moment, when your prey lies prostrate and bleeding on the floor in a state of confusion and terror, your prey becomes your asset and your enemy becomes your property, because at that moment, whatever it is that you want from him, you now own.

As you become really top notch at intimidation you will discover that you face no or very little meaningful resistance to taking whatever you want. Most people, even other CEOs, would rather lose an arm than try to face down a tough and seasoned corporate warrior in eye-to-eye, word-to-word combat. Consider a parallel example involving a public figure with whom you should be familiar. During his forty years as a high profile col-lege basketball coach, Cy Coburn, practiced near perfect intimidation skills on and off the court. Did anyone ever see one student, one athlete, one assistant coach, fan, official, or reporter ever stand up to him? Even after he ripped that walker from the grip of a crippled nun so he could throw it at the opposition cheer squad's seven year old cheery mascot, Little Daisy, who suffered from Down's Syndrome, when Little Daisy skipped onto the court during play with only thirty seconds remaining and Cy's team up by twenty six points to retrieve stray pom-pom fluff so no player would slip and injure himself? No, no one stood up – except to demand that they throw the little bitch out. People impressed by intimidation know that it is safer to support the intimidator than to risk his personal attention.

People who intimidate get what they want. If they don't get what they want, they get the last word and turn it into a bullet. Only later, when they are away from competition, can they lighten up and do normal things like make a peanut butter sandwich or stuff the cat into a microwave for thirty seconds of discipline. The point is that in every situation, someone is going to declare himself boss of the playground. Do you want to take orders or give orders? Do you want to be the alpha dog or the cat in the microwave?

A word to the wise: When it comes to hiring domestic staff, be sure to choose only caretakers to serve your meals, tend your grounds, and wash the Ferraris. You'll have to spend less time at home looking over your shoulder. On the other hand, when selecting your executive team, choose only takers and only those already adept at intimidation. The real work of the world is theirs and if they have the right skills the worthless piss ants will grease the wheels of your career and leave you time for golf. Does it get any better than that?

INVESTORS   Now and then you will have cause to evaluate potential investors for what benefit they might bring to you and your company. Some are worth wooing while others aren't worth the bother. Most will be easily impressed by anyone else's advice, particularly about IPOs and limited partnerships, so keep an inventory of both and, always reluctantly, offer plenty of innuendo that seems confidential. If you are seriously seeking investors, spend your time only on those I refer to as TPs, or Thoroughbred Pigeons. Leave the rest to your quarterly reports, your PR people, and your closers.

TPs are folks, almost always men, who have just enough assets to make them dream about having real wealth, but not nearly enough assets, toughness, or drive to make that dream even remotely possible. These men are plungers, anxious to make the big killing to make up for lost ground and their losses of the past. They are mildly desperate, fearful that they have been left behind, and they would sell their daughters into slavery for a chance to win a fortune. If you find them before they find Las Vegas, Atlantic City, or penny stocks, then you will have the opportunity to put their money to better use than gaming tables and gold mines. You will not find any group of people more amenable. You can separate them from their money more easily than you can eat an omelet. Furthermore, their losses will not devastate them. They are used to losing. Deep down inside they want to lose. So they will endure any loss and use it as motivation to hunt for the next big killing. And their former assets will be left in hands – yours -- that will manage them with loving care. In a sense, in these situations, everyone wins, and there is no easier way to pad your net worth.

"If you are seriously seeking investors, spend your time only on those I refer to as TPs, or Thoroughbred Pigeons." p. 209

JOB SECURITY Job security is an idea from the past that forced corporations to spend enormous sums on unneeded personnel, even in hard times. In the modern economy, both workers and executives need to be nimble and quick to react, because corporations cannot afford the luxury of promoting job security. For workers, job security today means being ready to learn new skills for lower pay and move on in a hurry. For CEOs, job security means securing a front end package of severance benefits and bulletproof rewards, unrelated to performance, which will carry you through rough times at or above your customary level of earnings until the next gig. Remember, "God helps them who help themselves." So help yourself when you sign on and at every subsequent opportunity any way you can. It's an uncertain world.

*"For CEOs, job security means securing a front end package
of severance benefits and bulletproof rewards, unrelated to
performance, which will carry you through rough times at or above
your customary level of earnings until the next gig." p. 211*

K STREET   K Street is the center in Washington, D.C. of the fourth branch of government of The United States, The Lobby. While we're counting, note that some people think that K Street is a Fifth Estate or a Sixth Column. Both opinions are extreme. The first is overly generous and the second is alarmist.

I suggest that you take a more moderate view. Think of the entire Federal Government as a Bentley. A nice, solid, shiny, sleek, well-appointed Bentley. K Street is merely the chauffer. A chauffer has the power to drive, and that is considerable power, but it never has the power to decide. As you can see at once, everything depends upon who is riding in the back seat.

So long as you have one, never give up your place.

KICKING THE DOG   Is it right to kick the dog? This is one of those questions that must be asked.

Clearly, you should never kick the dog in public, in front of your children, or when your wife, your mother-in-law, or your mother is in the room. Neither should you kick the dog merely out of rage because, let's say, it ate your Gucci's or peed on your new Persian rug. A good CEO does not require anger management.

On the other hand, if you are meeting at home with an associate or an adversary who has some sensitivity to canines and you want to impress him or her with just how tough you can be, you might want to invite the dog to join you. He will be happy to be included and one solid boot to the little beastie might just convey the message you intend. If you think that you will follow this practice or make it a habit, I suggest a very small, annoying dog, such as a miniature poodle or a Bichon Frisé. His light weight will mean less resistance. His behavior will always deserve punishment, and one swift kick to his ribs will send him flying like a furry missile. With anything larger than a border collie, you could risk injury to your foot. A larger dog might also turn on you and its greater mass could seriously impair your distance and accuracy. Keep the critter football-sized.

For best results, as in any endeavor, you must practice, practice, practice.

A KILLING   Three or four times in your lifetime you will create or stumble into opportunities to realize returns of a thousand percent and more in a short time span. These are true potential Killings and they occur so rarely that each one deserves total scrutiny. Most also carry big risks. Nearly all will demand lengthy analysis and convoluted advice by your attorneys who will always tell you what you want to hear if they have any chance at all of winning or of delaying *ad infinitum* the civil or criminal actions that are likely to follow. In other words, if your lowyers' advice is not what you want to hear, walk away from the deal and wait for another one to come along. On the other hand, if their advice is music to your ears and everything else is green lights, then go for it. The returns on such deals are so hard to find and so outweigh the risks that to not go for it would be truly criminal. Remember: No one ever got filthy rich by conventional means.

Most such deals involve newly invented financial instruments, natural resources, real estate, foreign governments, foreigners acting outside their governments, associates with whom you might not ordinarily associate, or commodities for which normal marketing channels are unreasonably closed. When you spot or conceive of such opportunities, think of them as a hobby. While the risks might be bearable for an occasional walk on the wild side, they are unthinkably high and stressful for what would in all likelihood be a brief career. In other words, be smart. Jump in. Jump out. Move on quickly and count your money. Count your blessings and get back to work. The moon will rise again another night.

On the other hand, once in a rare while a gifted individual can engineer a killing so large that it becomes a career worth pursuing, albeit a brief one. Hack Grubb, former analyst for Fortressbanks, was one such individual. His enthusiastic research opinions on Winpoo Telecom and other telecommunication stocks during the late '90s helped stimulate investor interest so thoroughly that when the telecom bubble burst, these investors lost around *two trillion dollars*. Fortressbanks, meanwhile, cleared around *a billion dollars* in banking fees at the same time. When NASD attacked Mr. Grubb, he offered his resignation to Fortressbanks and they accepted it, providing him, in return, with a severance package worth thirty-two million dollars, around half his reported earnings for the last two years of his career. Wouldn't ordinary people consider that a pretty good win on a lotto ticket? Good job, Hack, and you weren't even a CEO. Better job, Fortressbanks. I call that a killing, with a capital C.

If you find a situation this wired, one in which you can manipulate an entire market, and with this great an imbalance between risk and reward, I recommend that you jump in with both feet. Screw the consequences.

A KOZDUMSKI   For those of you who have not done your homework, Pluto Kozdumski, former CEO of Fido, was indicted for, among other things, spending company money on himself. His alleged misdeeds, supposedly totaling more than half a billion dollars, included the purchase of a toenail clipper for seventeen thousand dollars. Now and forever the obvious acquisition of a trivial personal trinket using what the public regards as a large sum of company money will be known as, "A Kozdumski." While I can reassure you that Mr. Kozdumski was completely innocent of any wrong doing morally or legally, his alleged shopping sprees and his penchant for occasional saturnalia were, from a public relations point of view, gaffes. Never commit a Kozdumski.

Furthermore, the absurdity of this particular Kozdumski should be obvious. I have checked out the markets and I can tell you first hand that you can purchase a perfectly functional toenail clipper for less than $7,000.00. For what he paid for his toenail clipper, Pluto could have purchased an equally nice toenail clipper, plus a serviceable electric eyelash curler for his dog, and have had enough change left over for a small diamond Rolex to impress a fashion model.

What was he thinking?

"I have checked out the markets and I can tell you first hand that you can purchase a perfectly functional toenail clipper for less than $7,000.00." p.216

LABOR   All successful manufacturing is made up of four primary activities: The cheap acquisition of resources, the effective application of production, superior marketing, and the elimination of governmental controls. The second of these activities, the effective application of production, can be effective only when the cost of labor has been reduced to the absolute minimum possible.

We all remember Henry Ford because he disliked Jews and overpaid his assembly line workers -- five dollars a day[18] -- so they could go out and buy Fords. Those were simpler times. Today, we live in a multinational economy where bigotry is impolite and exorbitant wages are scrofulous. Business leaders at the vanguard understand that it is essential to reduce domestic labor costs to those of a typical developing nation, and to raise gradually foreign labor costs in third world countries to a high fraction of the same level. (It goes without saying that labor unions have become ineffective in most sectors, and should in time become extinct.) If marketing does its job correctly, workers will find a way to buy needed goods like their claw hammers, their garden hoes, and designer pajamas for their Shar Peis. It follows that if a worker can find a way to buy a cell phone or a fifteen inch high definition digital TV with Super Sound while making ten or even three dollars a day, why pay him or her ten or even three dollars an

---

18 Most skilled laborers in developing and Third World countries make less today than Ford's workers made a century ago. This illustrates the important principle of economies of scale. A vast pool of needy labor creates the same efficiencies as vast production or farming facilities. Whoever coined the term "overpopulation" approached economics from the wrong end.

hour? And what about Ford's idea? Let's say that under his plan, a thousand workers could each save up for seven or eight years then buy a Ford. Under the modern umbrella, ten million workers with steady and higher paying jobs can each finance the purchase of an automobile today and have it nearly paid off in seven or eight years. With interest. Which scheme is better? The answer is obvious to any holder of capital, and we haven't even begun to discuss the numerous additional advantages of owning paper – origination fees on installment contracts, preparation fees, late fees, rising variable rates, no-interest monthlies with mandatory annual balloon payments, and even foreclosure, repossession, and resale. Managed correctly, labor is a valuable and profitable resource.

Unless, of course, *you are* the labor. In the real world, labor, the trading of one's time and muscle for capital to do someone else's bidding, is the living of last resort. No one in his or her right mind who could do better would ever resort to labor. Those who make up the pool of labor are followers at best and it is up to the CEO to lead them. As the average real costs of labor continue to decline worldwide, and to even out between nations, the CEO of a multinational corporation will have unprecedented opportunities to lead an unaccomplished rabble upward into a global market economy based solidly on realistic wages, easy credit, accelerating profits, and the ability to consume. Where it will all end one can only guess, but use of the word "Utopia" does not sound entirely inappropriate. We live in a wonderful era.

LEADERSHIP   Followers are those who cannot decide whether to dribble or shoot. They need to be told. Leaders are those who tell them. As a leader, always take charge and always be decisive even if, privately, you flip a coin to make your decision. The only thing that matters is that others think you have all the right answers. Leadership is the ability to move people from point A to point B without hesitation and then *always* to recognize that point B was the right destination.

LEARNING   The majority of what you learned in prep school, college, and graduate school is useless in the real world. Bits of it will apply. For instance, charts and graphs and technical methods of analysis will help you snow your associates at the mid-management level. Concepts like risk sharing will help you get through negotiations. Your association with a large number of assholes in graduate school will help you in your ability to read adversaries. For the most part, however, you will learn as you work in the real world, and if you fail to learn quickly, particularly from your mistakes, you won't make it. Learning is like swimming in the ocean. It can be a lifelong proposition as long as you don't get eaten and you inhale only what you need to survive.

Beware. Sinister academic forces will try to induce you to inhale what you don't need. Sooner or later, when you attend humanities classes or tune into your local public radio station, you will be forced to endure some professor expounding about The Life of the Mind, Enlightenment, and the dreaded Unexamined Life. This is the other kind of learning, the non-practical kind, which its proponents think anchors civilization more than paychecks and peanut butter. The ministers of this learning, particularly those born prior to 1960, typically single out people like us as examples of The Enemy. We are philistines and pirates. After all, we live by our wits. We celebrate greed and rape the countryside while ordinary people read Wordsworth and frolic in meadows of daisies. Pay no attention to this ranting. Most of it comes from thinly disguised envy since most of these folks are lucky to make two hundred thousand a year at the peak of their careers.

English departments in liberal arts universities are the worst. On top of being poorly (but adequately) paid and overlooked by their society, about a third of these professors have the added burden of being failed writers. Many of them distrust anything to do with money, sports, the military, fraternal organizations, and, most of all, business. In other words, they are skeptical of real success and of aggressive people who band together to take what they want without guilt or punishment. If you are still an undergraduate student, be extremely wary of these characters and learn how to deal with them. Some of them will do everything possible to discredit you simply for who and what you are and what you wish to achieve. If you should become the object of this kind of intellectual discrimination, either pull a first rate snow job and convert to the Life of the Mind for a semester, or deliver a fatal blow to your adversary by actually writing a first rate essay. Or if you don't have the time or ability for that, try recycling an old essay selected from your fraternity's archives written by that alumnus who won a Rhodes scholarship a few years back. If all your efforts fail and you are still the object of persecution, figure out a way to turn your adversary into a ball of raging self-mutilation because all of these characters measure their net worth in angst, not dollars, and that makes them easier targets than that cottontail you found in the crosshairs of your .458 while hunting moose in Wyoming.

History departments are better, but you have to be careful how you take history. According to Scooter the Oracle of Gilchrest[19], who died prematurely while snorkeling in the company of sharks off the Great Barrier Reef, it was a famous Mexican guitarist who said that if you don't learn from the past, you are condemned to repeat it. Scooter assured me that this explains why today we have jazz, rock and roll, and rap instead of more big band swing.

As you know, this idea of learning from history is widely quoted. I take it to mean that you can easily learn from history how to locate established routes that work. Halcyon Law, for example, is a well worn path to success. Others take this idea to mean that established routes lead to predictable disasters, such as being eaten by sharks when snorkeling in shark infested waters. The only problem with this latter interpretation is that it leads some impressionable students to the conclusions that *all* habits are bad and that every generation should start a revolution just to escape them. Thoughts like these spawn sophomore identity crises and radical campus politics.

Clearly, not all habits are bad. Most of them are traditions, the products of natural selection operating in society over long periods of time. How can such traditions be bad? One can swim safely with dolphins, for

---

19 As an undergraduate, I spent my Halcyon days at Gilchrest House. Codington Gilchrest Emory III, nicknamed Scooter, was revered as "Scooter The Oracle of Gilchrest" because he answered all questions. A complex lad with an ancient pedigree and a rebellious streak, Scooter majored in history, women's studies, and sailing. He graduated Halcyon Law, took the helm of his family's investment banking firm, and won accolades for his acumen before succumbing to sharks in Australian waters. Not a day passes during which I fail to remember at least one of his proclamations.

example, or sell old term papers for a profit. And you can do these things confidently because they have been done before. Throwing out the past every generation, just because it didn't work perfectly, would be disastrous. Can you imagine having to stop and reflect every time we need to invade a country to keep control of its resources or its strategic location? International relations could grind to a halt. In addition, breaking with tradition makes people crazy. Most people most of the time respect tradition. They take a quick glimpse at the past and say, "Good, let's do that." Of the remaining few who push change, only one in one hundred will revolutionize something and win a Nobel Prize. The other ninety-nine will get burned at the stake.

Granted, maybe once in a while, if you have the time to analyze every mote like a true intellectual, history will show you what went wrong. Most of the time for most of the people, however, a Polaroid of history will show you precedents which relieve you of the need to break ranks and think new thoughts. History reveals beaten paths and if nothing else it should demonstrate to you that blazing new paths can be an invitation to homicide – yours. So give history a chance. Then if you come up with a better idea be shrewd enough to market it so that it doesn't seem outlandish. After all, in the real world, whether you learn your lessons from pet rocks or Petrarch, everything you do comes down to salesmanship.

I advocate learning. Learning is essential. I also advocate learning what you need to know, not what some pathetic hiding under the ivy thinks you ought to know, and certainly not what some malcontent on a soap box thinks you need to know. Choose your mentors with care. If you inadvertently choose one who thinks you are the devil, then do unto him what he wants to do unto you only do it harder. If you get mesmerized by a reincarnation of Che Guevara, amuse yourself until your shrinking trust fund casts a shadow over your future, then get back to work on your career. You can always reminisce to grandchildren about that wild fortnight you spent in *la résistance*. Finally, if you pick a helpful mentor, as you should, then learn all you can without making villagers restive. Just remember to filter whatever you learn through a sieve of pragmatism. Civilization might not improve as a result of your learning. It might not even survive. But the economy will always survive and if you learn how to use what works for your personal and professional advantage, the chances are good that you too will survive. At that point, your place in the world should feel less like the main course at a barbecue and more like a hand in an old glove.

Practical learning from past experience clearly advises us to not swim with actual sharks and not to rock boats without a return that outshines risk by leaps. The fact that my old chum Scooter considered the shark infested waters of the Great Barrier Reef a trifle, when compared to Wall Street, certainly does not indicate flawed perception, but it does reveal a small but important gap in his learning. Scooter failed to understand the subtle difference between corporate and corporal appetites, something precedent teaches eagerly. The great whites of Wall Street eat only exposed testicles, faint hearts, wallets, widows, orphans, cripples, gamers, players, pensioners, first timers, last timers, suburban moms, priests, medicine men, and puppies, while those of the Great Barrier Reef are indiscriminate. Perhaps Scooter took his "Mexican guitarist" a bit too lightly and as a result, he gave up the whole enchilada.

If you learn enough history to follow old trade routes, the past will teach you one lesson that is irrefutable: Forgiveness is not part of the plan. However successful you become, you cannot make the same fatal mistake more than once.

LENDING   Borrow whenever you must or whenever the projected return exceeds the cost of money by a light year or two, but never give up anything to acquire the loan. Borrow only when your books say that you don't need to and only when the lender will think that he is privileged to give you his money.

Lending is another matter. If you are not in the business of lending money, then you can follow your own rules. People will come to you because you have money. They will always be desperate, having been turned down by mainstream sources. Nine out of ten of their ventures will be doomed, so study the venture with great care. Look for that one venture that is hotter than even its inventor imagines. When you find it, consider lending.

Lending Rule Number One Through One Hundred: Never lend a dime without taking equity in return. If it's a pretty good idea, and the supplicant is about to become your son-in-law, then be satisfied with a minority share and a vote. If it's a great idea and the supplicant is anyone other than a future son in law, then act annoyed and uninterested, settle for fifty-one percent, and promise to stay out of the way and to let the supplicant run his venture as he pleases because you don't have time to mess with it anyway. If the venture fails, write it off. If it looks promising, get rid of the founder and run it right.

It's not a bad thing to have people come begging for money when you yourself have all that you could ever spend and more. Anyone can buy a New Mexico cattle ranch or a Pacific island. But who, without supplicants, can buy a good idea dirt cheap at the ground level? Lending can be a license to steal; only it's not really theft because you actually put your own capital at risk. You deserve fifty-one percent or more. When you see nothing but blue sky, take what you deserve and run with it.

LEVERAGE   Puts, calls, and other instruments on Wall Street and in commodities markets are clear examples of the principle of leverage and how it can work for you. A small investment placed on a field with unknown outcomes is all you can lose when you lose, but it will expand geometrically when you win.

Less obvious are types of leverage used in human relations. You will come out better in every endeavor in your life if, before you act, you devise a clear strategy with options, all of them incorporating leverage. Just how badly does your son want that ski trip to Switzerland? Perhaps enough to dump that tawdry little tattooed princess he's been dating. Precisely what is your Chief Operating Officer willing to risk to help you gain the upper hand with your board and your stockholders? Maybe a few stock options will stimulate his added loyalty. Reward and punishment play as large a role between individuals as between competing companies, and when used properly, the leverage they offer will help you get what you want out of friends, family, and associates as efficiently as a crowbar under a rock.

Conducting any human encounter without leverage is like waging war without arms. Always take an edge. Get the goods on people. Know your enemies' weaknesses better than they. Know their appetites, their fears, and their hot buttons better than they. If you deal with people correctly, you can pop them straight out of their seats with a single word. That's leverage.

On the other hand, never confuse leverage with the illusion of leverage, which is the primary lure of gambling. Casino gambling, for example, is not gambling at all. It is one of life's greatest certainties: The house wins, and that's the end of the story. But the games offer illusions of leverage. Bet one hundred dollars on number twenty-one on a double zero roulette wheel. Watch it hit and win thirty-five hundred dollars. Leverage? No, sucker bait. For every ninety-five dollars you win, the house wins one hundred, a fast road to your bankruptcy. If gambling interests you, buy the track, buy the casino, or buy the book, and then sit back and count the donations. That's big leverage. With zero risk.

Any way you look at it, living without leverage gives other people an advantage. For example, it means that you will always pay the asking price for a hotel room, a new Lexus for one of the kids, or a boomer dot com company. Apply leverage and you will give yourself the advantage. Expect every leveraged deal to add at least an additional twenty percent across the board. Compound that twenty percent plus return year after year and by the time you retire it will add at least a third to your net worth.

LIABILITY   Remember taking a stroll down a country lane in New England in autumn? Think of those colorful autumn leaves as liabilities. Wherever we go, whatever we do every CEO and every corporation with deep pockets wades through liabilities.

Most civil actions are frivolous and gratuitous. Most are brought by avaricious people looking for a windfall in the form of a settlement that is cheaper and less embarrassing to a corporation than a trial. In some cases they are correct and they will walk away with some pocket change. But no CEO can afford a reputation as a patsy. Therefore, most actions brought against you or your company require a counter suit or other effective means of discouraging litigants.

Keep a lowyer in your pocket. Not just any lowyer. This lowyer must be a litigator, a maniac, a fanatic, an attack dog, and a raging young man with the personality of a pit bull and the will of a falling boulder. He needs to know a few good, discreet private investigators, a scary looking thug or two, half a dozen law enforcement friends, at least one important judge, a cooperative prostitute, a drug dealing gang member, two soldiers of fortune, and a gay club owner. If your hound can't get the goods on someone intent on suing you with a crew like that, and you decide that you cannot settle with this person, then turn your dog loose in the courts and let him fight to the death. If the plaintiff wins in court, he will have gone through worse than hell to do it. If he loses, he will make the same journey. Either way, you win.

In the unlikely case of criminal liability, what can I say? The best way to avoid problems with laws is to remove or change the laws. Keep deregulating and keep pressure on congress to pass more legislation like the Private Securities Litigation Reform Act of 1995, the Securities Litigation Uniform Standards Act of 1998, and the more recent Standard Securities Uniform Private Litigation Settlement Reform and Wall Street Bingo Protection Act, all of which deflect liability back to the responsible party, the individual who made poor investment decisions and now wants to blame someone else. You can't be responsible for other people's stupidity.

Years ago, at my company's annual stockholders' meeting, I did my job and presented the most positive view of my company that I realistically could. My view couldn't have been too far off because I cleared more than one hundred million dollars selling some of my company shares the next few days. Nevertheless, a few months later, I received an email from a disgruntled stock buyer who had lost his life's savings on our shares. "How can you live with yourself? I believed every word you said!" he whined. Number one, I don't control the markets. Number two, does any individual who is reading this book base life affecting decisions on what someone else says in a public speech? And number three, what kind of masochist doesn't diversify? People who burn themselves always want to thank someone else for their pain. Ignore them. Legislate them into the dungeon where they belong. Life is too short to baby-sit morons, particularly when they can't prove liability.

LIBERAL   Like most people, I could write volumes about political philosophies, but is there anything left to write that you haven't already read? Let me make one brief comment here that gets to the heart of the matter, and then move on.

The world is filled with individuals who describe themselves as liberals or progressives. They will tell you that people are more important than money. Of course people are more important than money. Everyone knows that. The thing is that without money, people cannot express their importance. That is the real difference between liberals and us. We put the horse of capital before the cart of importance. That way we stay in the race and have something to celebrate when the race is over. They cook the horse to feed the people in their cart then complain that the race is not fair because they have no way to move their cart. My question is: Why did you let so many strangers in the cart in the first place? Why not support the right of ordinary people to walk until they learn how to cross the finish line on their own? How much importance will they gain in someone else's cart anyway? Once they learn how to finish the race on their own, they can go out and buy all the horses they want and do whatever they want with them.

Forget political philosophy. Make money. Express your importance. Encourage others to do the same. The more money you have, the more importance you can express, and the same goes for anyone. It's a no-brainer.

THE LIFEBOAT   When things turn sour, remember that a good captain always stays with the sinking ship until the very last moment. Contrary to popular opinion, you don't stay to save the crew and the passengers. They can take care of themselves. And you don't stay because you are in love with the ship. Ships are a dime a dozen. Speaking metaphorically, you stay until everyone else is gone so you can grab the lockbox, get the hell out on your private lifeboat, and paddle for The Cayman Islands.

If people want to think that you are a hero, as they define a hero, encourage them to do so. However, when your ship is about to sink make sure that you become a hero to yourself. That kind of heroism has to be planned. That is, you must *have* a lockbox that you can take. It should be part of your Golden Parachute, the unofficial part, and it should always be full.

THE LIST   You win or lose by your planned achievements, and the best way to keep score is to keep a list of your daily goals so you can strike them off and count them up at the end of each day. Whether you organize your daily tasks on a yellow legal pad or in an electronic notebook, you will quickly learn that every CEO lives or dies by The List. There is no feeling better at the end of a work day or even a vacation day than the warm fuzzy feeling you get when you look at The List and can no longer read it because every entry has lines drawn through it.

Some people might be surprised to find items like "sex" on your list. Don't let others' surprise deter you. You live a busy life filled with distractions, and every essential activity must be listed. Truth is, even when it comes to the "sex" listing, there is no consensus among CEOs as to which feels better, the activity listed or crossing it off the list.

As you gain more experience you will understand that the nature of the task is irrelevant. What matters is crossing it off The List. In other words, keep score whatever you score and you'll never doubt your ability to win.

LISTENING   Never heed others. You are the leader so the buck stops with you. Therefore, you should be the only person others take seriously and actually listen to. If you heed others, and by that I mean that if you take others' advice and give them credit for good ideas, then all you will do is undermine your own position as the best and the brightest.

That said, obviously you'll want to monitor everyone around you with ears like radar, and that includes using clandestine methods, such as in-office video cameras and intensive monitoring of employees' personal email and other uses of their computers. Not only will you glean some of your best ideas from the careless, eager proclamations of others, which you can subsequently develop and claim as your own, you will also be able to keep your finger on the pulse of your immediate office, your management team, and selected divisions of your companies. You will learn more by listening than by any other activity. Plus, you must always appear to be a good listener since others expect to have your ear and if they think they have it, they will be more candid, less guarded, and more vulnerable to your manipulation.

LOBBYING   In Washington, D.C., the ratio of paid lobbyists to elected representatives is approximately 63:1 and growing. More than half of those lobbyists work for corporations. Many of us think that K Street, not Pennsylvania Avenue, is the real center of government in The United States.

Lobbyists are the grease that lubricates the wheels of government. As an extension of his employer, each corporate lobbyist in Washington, D.C. and in every state capitol represents the millions of consumers who vote their opinions with their dollars on goods and services each corporation provides. I can't help but believe that 34,000 hard working lobbyists on K Street better represent the will of the people than a mere 535 senators and congressmen milling around Pennsylvania Avenue. The same has to be true in all fifty state capitols and in local governments. Without lobbying, governments would grind to a standstill and the will of consumers, and of those corporate officers who oversee consumers' market choices, would go unheeded. With lobbying, trained professionals are able to influence government, draft legislation, and define policies on behalf of corporate executives who work on behalf of their customers. Was there ever a better example of democracy in action?

If there were a Golden Finger Award for being first in influence, I would nominate the pharmaceutical industry. Continuously setting new, high standards for the rest of us to shoot for, pharmaceuticals annually spend two hundred million dollars or more lobbying congress. At the same time, they maintain a low lobby to campaign-contribution dollar ratio of nearly nine to one, demonstrating that you obviously get a much bigger bang for your buck from a lobby than from a handful of legislators you helped to elect. Pharmaceuticals employ their own congress: More than one lobbyist for each elected representative and senator. As a result, they beat back efforts to regulate their industry. They maintain a highly profitable pricing structure for their proprietary drugs. They streamline the testing and evaluation process for hot new products. They defeat all efforts to make cheap, generic drugs more available to the public more quickly. They prohibit purchase of prescription drugs from unclean foreign nations, like Mexico and Canada. (For all we know foreign pills contain DDT and rat poison.) The pharmaceuticals suppress notions that manufacturers should

*"If there were a Golden Finger Award for being first in influence,
I would nominate the pharmaceutical industry."*

trim profits for indigents. They stimulate sales with lucrative kickbacks for doctors who distribute free samples of new wonder drugs to treat diagnosed diseases, side effects from other drugs, and terrifying conditions like sore rotator cuffs, imperfect HDL scores, indigestion, and used lungs. These samples introduce many patients to the need for life-long prescriptions. And finally, pharmaceutical companies maintain their brilliant leadership in advertising, which stimulates many consumers to demand only the best and the newest when it comes to pills.

What is the end result of all this effort? Yearly profits in recent years have soared to new records in an industry with already obscene margins. Not only that, they are able to pay for all their lobbyists *and* their massive public advertising, which was not allowed when their industry was regulated, with ease simply by working together, by raising prices of their products, and in some cases by prohibiting discounts and requiring vendors to purchase quantities sufficient to see them through several millennia of national emergencies. They can fund serious new R&D for mass market products and still bring home the bacon; only the slab is much larger than in days past, a true testament to the efficacy of deregulation and the stiff competition that follows. Even major setbacks, such as the occasional miracle drug rushed to market that turns patients' heart muscles into spaghetti, have not seriously damaged the bottom lines or the prospects of most drug companies. Kudos, gentlemen.

Pharmaceuticals have raised the bar and they have demonstrated that the benefits of massive lobbying are well worth the high cost. It is shameful to realize that those of us in other industries who have been slackers in this area have allowed congress and public interest groups to bully us merely because our own lobbies are inadequate. My recommendation is to spend as much as you can afford on state and federal lobbying efforts, then add ten percent, and keep it up until your sector is on a par with the drug companies. Who else, other than your own paid lobbyist, is going to look out for your best interests?

In the future, if CEOs in all industries do their job, we can look forward to a world in which there are a hundred or more active, aggressive lobbyists for every candidate who runs for public office. Then and only then will the bullying stop and will each industry be able to write its own legislation. In a world teeming with individuals who don't understand the free market system, many people would rather tear companies down in the interests of socialism than encourage a pharmaceutical to develop a pill for cancer. And some would rather attack an auto manufacturer in the name of "the environment" than encourage it to design what the market demands: A battle tank that is sleek as a Maserati, accelerates from zero to sixty in 4.4 seconds, corners like a hydroplane, offers more cargo space than a C-130, and still gets 12 miles per gallon. Hire enough lobbyists to write enough legislation and you will neutralize the uninformed and the radical fringe without having to use pit bulls.

Lobbying represents a partnership between the public and private sectors working together for the betterment of all. America is good for lobbyists. Lobbyists are good for America.

LONG TERM   Whatever happens a year or more out from the present is called, "long term". Don't worry about it until you have to.

LOVE   Love is a pleasant enough disease and if you must suffer it, do so during the college years while sailing The Vineyard or paddling The Charles with a wicker basket inevitably filled with *pain de Provence*, apples, Brie, and a bottle of Beaujolais Nouveau. Just be sure to get it out of your system. It is a dangerous and disorienting condition that has no relevance to a meaningful career.

LOYALTY   Demand absolute loyalty from your staff, every employee, every associate and ally, and your family. You won't get it, but demanding it will establish just cause for those dark days when you must excommunicate or eviscerate those who betray you.

As to your own behavior, remember that loyalty is the first of all duties. That is a simple enough maxim, but you will understand the true meaning of loyalty only after you have answered the question, "Loyalty to whom?"

Your first loyalty must be to yourself. You cannot function properly until you have taken good care of your financial and social needs. Self-loyalty also extends to your decisions. You cannot function effectively if you equivocate like "a reasonable man." Never doubt yourself. Never entertain alternatives to your best judgment once your best judgment is known. You must be right to be effective, even in the face of massive evidence or widespread opinion contradicting your judgment.

Your second loyalty must be to those who help you gain and maintain your wealth and power. This is a simple matter of following The Golden Rule. Treat your friends and mentors as you would want them to treat you if you had helped them get rich and become CEOs and Chairmen of boards. We belong to a small tribe and, if you will forgive the double entendre, our ability to hold power depends on our bonds.

Our ability to forge and maintain strong bonds, in turn, depends on our ability to have the goods on each other. Expect to share all of your most intimate secrets with your most intimate friends, just as you will learn theirs, as a kind of insurance policy devoted to mutual preservation. Secret clubs and societies provide an excellent venue for this kind of bonding.

The meat in this chestnut is this: Require loyalty from those you need; extend loyalty to yourself, your closest allies, and your class. All other allegiances should be temporary and pragmatic.

LYING   There are two kinds of lies, those our enemies tell, and those we tell. The former are sins, judged by the authority of the Ninth Commandment and occasionally by the authority of civil or criminal courts. The latter are useful forms of communication judged by their effectiveness. When speaking honestly, we might call them spin, propaganda, sophistry,

equivocation, dissembling, half-truths, rhetoric, slant, or bullshit. For example, when President Clinton said he did not have sex when a young
woman gave him fellatio in The White House, his enemies claimed that he
was lying on the speculation that oral sex is a form of sex in general. The
President, on the other hand, argued that since his and the young lady's
genitals had never met, what they had was not really sex, but something
more like baseball. His fielding wasn't much better in the Paula Jones de-
position, so Republicans claimed that he was a liar and impeached him.
The Democrats claimed that he used spin ineffectively and tried to apply
more spin, but they could never get their curve balls over the plate. Their
arguments were limp.

Now look at what can happen to a really firm argument. President
George W. Bush and his Republican Congress wanted to save us rich folks
from inheritance taxes, one of the best ideas to come out of the White
house in decades. Since inheritance taxes don't impact ninety-five percent
of the population, and since repealing them would likely increase a majority of people's taxes to make up the shortfall in revenues, the President
and his advisors guessed that this legislation would be a hard sell. Then a
communications genius came up with the term, "The Death Tax." Does
anyone think it is fair to tax death? Initial public support was overwhelming. Democrats claimed that The Death Tax was a lie, but every time they
mentioned it, they enhanced its effectiveness. Clearly this Republican pitch
was in the strike zone.

When *we* tell lies we do not recognize them as lies and we do not
moralize about them. We market them. We are not interested in truth.
We are interested in results. When *others* hear our lies, they recognize them
as such. If they are our friends, they shrug. If they are our enemies, they
declare them immoral and demand to know the truth so help us God. And
this is precisely how we treat our enemies when they lie.

So the moral of this story is simple. If you own a mine and you are
convinced that it contains gold, but you can't get to the gold without some
capital, salt the mine, publicize the discovery as a rocket to Rodeo Drive,
pin the whole project to a sexy symbol, and then sell shares. A little convincing fool's gold in the shape of a beautiful and fabulously rich actress
stepping out of her stretch limousine to shop at appointment only stores

wearing a Chanel couture suit might not tell the whole story, but it makes for snappy images, and sometimes that's all you need to turn a tricky situation into a winner. Like the ad men say, "don't sell the cigarette; sell The Marlboro Man." Or the diva. In other words, say what works and say it with irresistible conviction. If it is not one hundred percent accurate, you can scold yourself all the way to the bank.

Lose any moral queasiness you might have about lying. A few sexy distortions will always get your point across better than a dissertation or a sermon and they will keep your audience awake. Lying is universal. Everyone does it, and everyone expects it. It is a tool we live by. In fact, sometimes, it is a tool we yearn for. President Jimmy Carter could not tell a lie, even about lusting in his heart. Even when the entire nation was praying that he would, *please, just this once, tell a lie!* The bottom line is that we are all going to tell a few whoppers, and whoever tells them best will rule. Your task, as for any other requirement of your job, is to become the best at what you do.

"Lose any moral queasiness you might have about lying. A few sexy distortions will always get your point across better than a dissertation or a sermon and they will keep your audience awake." p. 233

MANAGEMENT   Corporate management is more than a means of directing corporate entities. It is a worldview and a life discipline, like Islam and science.

For corporations to function at peak efficiency now and in the future, management must extend a paternal hand over the entire globe. Corporate need will determine how oceans and forests are utilized. Corporate vision will define the marketplace and regulate what goods and services reach whom. Corporate communications will guide consumers and help them define their thoughts, their values, and their financial practices. And corporate influence will refine government policies. At every step of the way consumer choices will be registered in a closed feedback loop and corporate policies will be adjusted accordingly. This will work like voting, only more efficiently. It is Adam Smith's "invisible hand" at work.

To reach and maintain this peak efficiency, corporate CEOs must be willing to invest substantial capital not only in traditional areas such as research and development, market research, and sales analysis, but also in all areas of communications from simple jingles in advertising to methods of lobbying to entire media broadcast systems. Trust me. I promise you that the degree of worldwide homogeneity that will ultimately result from these efforts will bring corporations across the threshold to management of this planet and its inhabitants. Think of this process as just another takeover. Your goal is to gain and keep controlling interest in Earth, Inc., and then to load your board of directors with qualified individuals with whom you can work.

I look forward to the day when national governments dispatch lobbyists to influence corporate management and policies. Actually, that day has already begun.

MANIFEST DESTINY　　Anyone who has ever worked in an office has one overriding faith: Someone somewhere has a plan. This faith keeps bands of office workers everywhere from attacking their supervisors with staple removers.

But is there a plan?

This is one of those eternal questions that must be asked, and I am happy to inform you that I can answer the question. Yes, boys and girls, there is a plan and it covers all the bases. It is called, "Manifest Destiny."

Today, the world is linking together to form a single, gigantic, free market economy. This Grand Economy is not entirely the result of a central plan hatched in a boardroom filled with cigar smoke. In the long run, plans like that never work. Permit me to elaborate.

For the purpose of our discussion, let's lump all central plans hatched by committees into a single category called, "intelligent design." All intelligent designs are rational plans, drafted by reasonable people who have convinced themselves that if you want to map an entire field of corn you need to look only at a handful of kernels. The most notorious example of an intelligent design was Soviet communism. In the palm of Joseph Stalin, a ruthless politician with an ambitious axe to grind, kernels from rational thinkers like Marx and Lenin became a national and even an international blueprint. The result was a highly successful system of enforcement. Between the KGB, gulags, psychiatric prisons, executions, civil war, and pre-scientific agricultural plans, twenty to thirty million Soviet citizens died at the hands of their own government, and the system it promoted ultimately collapsed. That wasn't what the idealists had in mind. But this is the fate of all intelligent designs. They require enforcement to stay in business. And sooner or later, the designers can't see the cornfield for the colonels.

The other side of the coin is called "manifest destiny." In general, that means that things eventually work out as they should. Specifically, it means that American free market democracy will dominate the world. Manifest destiny does not result from central planning. It results from the momentum of history. It is the inevitable outcome of the way things are.[20] You could say it is the result of evolution and natural selection. Why?

Basic human urges, such as greed, altruism, flight, fighting, faith, reason, domination, obedience, and the desire to breathe while swimming under water, all compete for success in the game of survival and prosperity. Some do better than others. After centuries of sorting through these urges, people gravitate toward those that help them most and they discard those that help them least. In economic activity, the result of this process is the emergence of free market democracy, and its momentum, like its successes, makes it virtually inevitable.

People who understand this process do what we can to nurse it along and accelerate its outcome because we must, just as the railroaders, the copper kings, the cattle barons, the buffalo hunters, and the Indian fighters on the Western frontier did what they had to do, and our government does what it has to do when it tinkers with other countries or bombs them into proper allegiance. We are following our manifest destiny. Why wouldn't we go along with the inevitable? Marshall Matt Dillon of *Gunsmoke* said it all: "A man does what he has to."

So does a nation. Manifest Destiny is the business of America.

MANNERS   Everyone belongs to a tribe. Manners are the social habits approved by the tribe. If you violate your code of manners then you violate the terms of membership in your tribe and you make yourself vulnerable to criticism, scorn, ridicule, and even ostracism. Imagine what could happen to you, for example, if you misused the cocktail fork at a formal dinner hosted by the British Embassy, or wore Birkenstocks and a sweatshirt to a black tie soiree in Hong Kong.

---

20 The deterministic element in Marx's dialectical materialism was the right idea with the wrong outcome. Economics is the main force in history, but laissez faire capitalism has emerged as the winner.

Rock musicians and comedians who have achieved celebrity status are the only people granted exemptions to manners. Rock musicians are exempt because they are, by profession, bad boys and girls, and requiring them to display the good manners of a host's tribe would be the same as requiring them to violate the rude behavior required by their tribe. One would be disappointed to see a rock and roll rebel elevate his pinky finger at just the appropriate moment. Comedians gain exemption because it is their duty to make fun of all standards, including manners, so a comedian can do well wearing sneakers with a tuxedo. Unless you want to draw attention to yourself as a rebel or a satirist, follow the rules with skill. Why is that important?

Manners create a level playing field and thereby the pretext that we all play by the same rules. Upon that field and within that pretext, the only thing that differentiates one individual from another is skill. For example, while looking and acting like every other penguin at a black tie party, how skillfully can one negotiate a trade deal, an interest rate, a piece of legislation, controlling interest in one's next acquisition, or the assassination of a recalcitrant leftist president of a small, resource-laden country?

How these things happen doesn't really matter to anyone so long as one demonstrates one's allegiance to the tribe by wearing a black tie and using the cocktail fork correctly.

The bottom line on manners is simple: You have to mingle to do business, but if you don't have manners, you won't be invited to the party.

MANTRAS   First developed by Vedic Hindus as a way to achieve pinpoint concentration on a single thought, or absence of thought, without interference from anything else, the reciting of mantras was later borrowed by Buddhists, Jains, Sikhs, and advertising gurus. How do mantras work? They follow the principle that if you recite a phrase long enough, and tune out everything else, then you will achieve a state of deep consciousness in which the mantra guides your entire being and you become one with that part of the universe described by the mantra. Here are two examples of mantras that have guided entire nations.

When you hike the Himalayas in Nepal, you will find mantras carved onto stones scattered along your pathway. The most common one, when recited, sounds like "Om mani padme hum." It refers to the compassionate aspect of the Buddha, and it might be translated as, "I salute the god within you." Here is another example. When I was a kid, I hiked part of The Appalachian Trail and I found mantras printed on little pieces of paper scattered along my pathway. The most common one was, "L.S.M.F.T." This translates as, "Lucky Strike Means Fine Tobacco."

Today, with modern communications, you don't have to hike to find mantras. They are scattered everywhere. Here are some examples: "We bring good things to light;" "the liberal press;" "a mind is a terrible thing to waste;" "The War on Drugs;" "The War on Terror;" and "Can you hear me now?"

As deep, rhythmic, unchallenged assertions that define the universe, mantras bypass judgment and go directly to that part of the brain that also produces dogma. Therefore, people who recite their mantras learn to prefer reaction over thought and skepticism. Clearly, those who teach mantras know how to get the job done.

If enlightenment is the true path of civilization and mantras serve as beacons to light the way, then you had better hire the brightest ad agency money can buy so you can get there first with the most and stuff your competition.

MARKETING   Marketing is the defining feature of civilization today. Imagine my surprise when a young intern once asked me, "How important is marketing?" I responded by asking, "How important in a slow deflationary spiral would a non-callable ten year treasury bond be at one point under prime?" Since he could not answer either question, I cancelled the program and recommended him to my competition.

How important is marketing? Three generations ago, the best product in the world could sit on a shelf because of poor marketing. Today you can put crud in a can, turn on your marketing department, and sell millions of pallets of it.

Whenever one of my vice presidents in charge of marketing needed to be revved up, I would call him into my office, remind him that I was a history buff, and give him the following brief lesson. Catherine the Great, Empress of Russia, was a voracious woman who knew exactly what she wanted. Think of her as the embodiment of greed. How does such an empress obtain what she wants and at the same time preserve some small measure of decorum in her court? She delegates – and picks just the right man for the job. A man who can deliver. According to legend, Grigori Alexandrovich Potemkin, her former lover, friend, and confidant, knew how to obtain and deliver exactly the young men the Empress wanted time and again. He performed an essential service, kept the Empress satisfied, and maybe kept himself from being devoured by wolves.

After explaining all of that I would look directly at my vice president and ask him, "Now I want to ask you, in the strictest confidence, have you ever known a woman like that?" To a man, every vice president to whom I posed this question answered in exactly the same way. After a brief and uncomfortable hesitation, his face betrayed some doubt but then he smiled and replied, "Uh…sure. Of course. I…."

At that point I would interrupt him and say: "Then you understand greed and how unpleasant things can get when it is not gratified." After he nodded in the affirmative, I concluded the interview with this: "I am like Catherine the Great, Charles, only I am greedy for revenues. I listen to the Board and the stockholders and they are greedy for revenues. New revenues. Lots of new revenues. Now, put that genius to work and ramp it up; we have a lot of ground to make up. I am counting on you. Just this morning I reassured the Board that you are a good man and you *will* deliver."

Boys and girls, I am here to reassure you that from every corner of the globe, whether in products, politics, or propaganda, marketing people are delivering like never before. Their work is revolutionizing human civilization.

When I was a kid, I faced boredom every morning at the breakfast table: Oatmeal and fruit. Farina and fruit. Barley and fruit. I was so bored I actually considered barbecuing Dolly Tenzin, my Lhasa Apso, for breakfast. Then came one of the greatest marketing inventions in history: The pop-up tart. Once again, my life had meaning.

Today, that kind of revolution occurs daily as marketing geniuses consider whether to send a new product to market or to the dumpster. Analyzing mountains of data from past sales, computers can establish profiles for success and failure in the marketplace with more than ninety percent accuracy. Many products and ideas that snobs once dismissed as clichés are today recognized as market superstars destined to produce mass sales, and just as many weird turkeys that intellectuals and critics once defended as "provocative" are today recognized as losers destined for the alley. Products that have exact quantifiable characteristics present in best sellers of the past will pass directly through the computer sieve, and products that don't have them will get the brush. Risk could become a relic of the past. Before you know it, the only films you will ever see in big theaters will be star-laden blockbusters. The only books you will ever have to wade through in big book stores will be blockbuster best sellers. And the only music that industry producers release will be best selling cuts on the *Billboard* top ten charts. Consumers will never again have to waste their money on anything but a sure winner.

You think this is not revolutionary? Consider how music history might have changed if marketing gurus had been in charge during the first decades of the twentieth century. Imagine the heartache Igor Stravinsky could have saved himself if only he had been influenced by first rate marketing criteria before he composed *Sacre du Printemps*. He never would have composed *Sacre du Printemps*. He would have composed *Glow Worm* instead. Its premiere would have won him roses and some nice royalties instead of a riot. Imagine how Arnold Schoenberg's life would have changed. He might have found a real job writing lyrics for *Sweethearts* and then John Cage could have done arrangements for the Nitty Gritty Dirt Band and won accolades from three hundred thousand fans at the Missouri State Fairgrounds and today composers everywhere would have fat 401-Ks and Nashville mansions and live appearances on *The Tonight Show*.

Now all of that can become a reality as marketing criteria take the mystery out of success. No longer does marketing just tinker and plan and make educated guesses. Today it thrives on certainties. It unleashes the magic and the power of supply and demand. Marketing is the procurer that delivers the right goods to the empire of greed, and in return, the emperor and the empire's stockholders gain satisfaction, vice presidents of marketing gain their careers, and consumers everywhere gain those perfectly processed popup pastries they so enjoy.

MARKETS   The primary directive of any multinational corporation must be to grow your markets. Be prepared to expend enormous quantities of time, human resources, creative energies, and money to accomplish the directive. There are four principal ways to grow markets.

1. Develop new and underdeveloped marketplaces. As a new marketplace, the Internet offers almost infinite possibilities, though at present it is still defining itself and will not offer high or even reasonable profits for most until methods become more standardized, Internet use becomes almost universal, and the Internet itself becomes more compatible with corporate needs.

Underdeveloped marketplaces certainly include emerging and third world nations. Work to break down their indigenous cultures, introduce them to free market capitalism and world markets, and gradually replace their indigenous cultures with elements of Western popular culture and democracy.

2. Develop for proven markets new products and services that will not compete directly with existing products and services. Recent gains in the pet logistics industry are a perfect example of how existing markets can be expanded with new products and services as humans are trained to respond to their pets in the same ways that they respond to their spouses, their children, their lovers, their favorite celebrities, and the Pope. Pet clothing, pet daycare, pet massage and analysis, pet costumes and costume birthday parties, pet jewelry, gourmet pet foods, pet prams, and other anthropomorphic pet accessories of all kinds have been injected into the marketplace with robust results and without entirely forcing other priorities, such as food for babies and medicine for old people, out of the marketplace.

3. Reduce consumer savings and increase the percentage of consumer income earmarked for spending. This can best be accomplished by keeping interest rates low and simultaneously by offering increased lines of credit, new credit cards, quick secured financing, second and third mortgages, fast

payroll loans, and other easy ways to put disposable cash into consumers' hands. The kicker here is to hedge added risk and catch part of your profits up front with service fees, harsh late payment penalties timed so they are almost inevitable, high interest rates on cash advances and past due balances, extreme rates for consumers with poor credit histories, and add-on target marketing that uses customer profiles and preferences to intensify product reach and to stimulate impulse buying immediately after the loan is processed.

4. Grow the consumer base. Work to increase world population, particularly indigenous populations in economically viable regions that already have robust birth rates. Obviously these people like to breed so they should have no problem breeding more. This offers a long-term solution to the problem of stagnating markets, and one that will also require long-range planning to ensure sufficient per-capita incomes. Though it might seem like promoting wood to woodchucks, for quick results that will add a guaranteed jump to world population immediately, promote more babies in India, China, and Utah. At the same time, lay groundwork for future development of economies that will sustain more and more babies in Islamic, impoverished Southeast Asian, and marginal South and Central American countries, and establish inroad beachheads throughout sub-Saharan Africa, where current birth rates are terrific but are undermined by disease, poverty, and dismemberment. As these economies reach minimal proficiency, accelerate development quickly. If you can keep their indigenous populations pacified, disarmed, and inoculated, they should be able to breed effectively and add big numbers to the world base.

How you choose to grow markets matters less than your success in expanding the markets you choose. The point is that, like oxygen and favorable interest rates, market growth is an absolute necessity.

MEANING   Meaning is like the weather. Everyone talks about it, but no one does anything about it. The truth of the matter is that people don't want meaning in their lives. They want money in the bank. Money will buy all the meaning most people can handle.

MEDIA   I cannot remember a time in years past when you could enter any person's private domain and tell him or her what to think and what to think about without getting slapped up side the head. Today, people open their doors and pay you to come in by subscribing to communications and marketing vehicles, such as cable and satellite television, satellite radio, cell phones, iPhones, and the Internet.

Information and communications media provide power. Ideally, you should own radio and television stations in major markets, film and video producers, a print media conglomerate that controls newspapers, magazines, and book publishers, and you should establish a growing presence on the Internet and in personal communications and entertainment networks. In addition, it doesn't hurt to sponsor some public radio and television programs to counter your critics. For example, if you manufacture chemicals or own nuclear power facilities, sponsor a nature show about baby animals or a conservation show about sacred forests. If you have manufacturing or assembly plants in third world countries, sponsor shows sympathetic to hungry masses in Africa. If you are in pharmaceuticals, sponsor shows about curing AIDS or other epidemics. Be creative and sensitive. Consumers automatically assume that the sponsors of such programs are humanitarian in general and activists for the specific topic. Who are consumers going to believe, strident business haters, or corporations that spend millions to help wretched masses and trees?

Media control the thoughts of the world. Whoever controls the media has the minds of consumers in his pocket. If for some reason you cannot or won't own these facilities, then make alliances with those who do. At the very least, use massive advertising.

If you become directly involved in media, be certain to have your producers at all levels continue to shorten the attention span of their audiences by shortening the sound bites and image bites used to carry information. As consumers adapt to nanoscopic segments of time packed with information, you will be able to educate them more efficiently and more fully to become more reactive and useful consumers and you will be able effectively to eliminate their ability to question, to think, to contemplate, or to be skeptical. This process has already become astonishingly efficient, but there is always room for improvement.

MEDIOCRITY   Back in 1970, Senator Roman Hruska, Republican from Nebraska, gave us the final word on mediocrity. President Nixon had nominated Judge G. Harrold Carswell to fill an opening on the Supreme Court. The Senate was debating the nomination. Opponents claimed that Judge Carswell was a mediocre choice. Rising to the occasion, Senator Hruska, a Carswell supporter, asserted that, "There are a lot of mediocre judges and people and lawyers. They are entitled to a little representation, aren't they? We can't have all Brandeises, Frankfurters and Cardozos." Mediocrity deserves representation too, a principle that is as integral to our democracy as crackers are to soup.

In fact, you can count on mediocrity. It is here to stay. However, that doesn't mean you have to tolerate it in your life or in your business. In fact, the world does offer some talent. The trick is to recognize it. Take a prospect for your management team golfing. Is he content to three-putt to a bogie or a double bogie all afternoon? Or is he driven to make or break par? What kind of car does he drive? What does he order for lunch? What does he wear? How does he use the language? What schools do his kids attend? Measure his conversation. Does he tell all and bore, or does he suggest and entice? Does he fake it? Is he clumsy and oafish, or does he spar with agility, good humor, and wit? Is his demeanor sluggish, beaten down, or apologetic? Or does he face you as if you were equals? Useful talent nearly always speaks for itself. When it doesn't, try to measure the individual's eccentricities. Sometimes the brightest bulbs don't react to normal switches, but they will burn like the sun over the right projects.

However, I will give Senator Hruska his due. While you never want to let mediocrity creep into your life, it is invigorating now and then to seek it out so you can measure yourself against it. Take a stroll through a supermarket, a mall, or a box store where you will have no choice but to mingle with mediocrity. Listen and watch. Not only will you walk away amused, you will better understand your place in life and why keeping it is all that matters.

MEETINGS When in doubt, call a meeting. Meetings are always good because the primary purpose of a meeting is to validate the person who called the meeting; namely, you.

Meetings have added benefits as well. They allow underlings to brainstorm, which allows you either to listen to their spontaneous, half-baked opinions which will elevate yours, or to troll for real thoughts if you are having one of those days when you just don't have any of your own. In the latter case, you can cull wheat from chaff, develop the idea, rightfully appropriate it, and issue a decision that reinforces your position as the brains of the operation.

Meetings also make underlings feel like a useful part of management, which is important for their self-esteem. In addition, meetings are more fun than doing actual work. Meetings allow you to humiliate targeted idiots and to validate staff members whose stock currently trades high in your estimation. Most of all, meetings allow you to dictate your wishes in a way that will make your staff feel that you are not a dictator because they were part of the process. And finally, meetings allow for good theater. You can shock, inspire, terrify, or otherwise motivate your captive audience in such a way that their reactions will reverberate down through the ranks with almost perfect effect. The net result will be to raise the level of fear and awe in which others hold you, and to do it from a setting where everyone started out feeling equal to everyone else. In other words, whatever else they might accomplish, meetings reaffirm for participants the nature of the world in which they live and their places in it.

MILITARY RETIREES That well-oiled machine that President Eisenhower identified as "the military-industrial complex" has created some of our greatest fortunes. There is no reason to believe that it will do any less in the future. To get and keep on the inside track, you will need to hire retired senior military officers, bird colonels and up. Give them spacious offices, lots of obedient secretaries, and showy perks like permanent lunch reservations at five star restaurants and a new black Hummer, and most of them will give you absolute dog-like loyalty in return. Then mine their connections and use them to guide you through the government labyrinths and you will enjoy contracts heaped upon contracts and unquestioned cost overruns that can go on almost forever.

Pretend to take seriously your corps of officers' gratuitous and often arrogant observations about the apparent lack of discipline in your organization, and vow, by God, to get right on it which, of course, you won't. These people are useful keys to lucrative doors and nothing more. Generally speaking, as long as you feed their hungry egos with plenty of glitz, glitter, compliments, and apparent respect, you won't have to endure them socially or allow them into your home. And that will be fine with them. Their world is different from yours and they prefer to stay in the structure of its weird shadows, thank God.

MILITARY SERVICE   If you can afford a stable, then you can afford to hire someone to shovel out the shit. The same can be said of military service. The military is a nice place for people who need unpleasant work, are happy to have it, and want to call themselves "professionals" or "heroes." It's no place for a person who has means and real prospects.

I suppose in some circumstances it can't hurt you to have military service on your resume, particularly if you plan some day to run for president, like Don Quickoats. Obviously, you will want to choose the safest venue, as he did. Pick the Air National Guard, the National Guard, or the Coast Guard, and serve through a reserve program if possible, though with the precedent set by the war in Iraq, the guards and the reserves aren't now much better than regular active duty. Then there are the academies. An academy appointment offers instant prestige in return for absolute control of your life for many years. Pay the price if you are gung-ho to become Chairman of the Joint Chiefs of Staff or you are terminally insecure and need a quick and lasting fix. Otherwise, express your patriotism by betting on the annual Army-Navy game.

My best advice is to avoid all military service and particularly to avoid active military duty at all costs. You are a white collar warrior, not a blue collar one, and no one who will have an ounce of influence on your career will expect you to take the military seriously. In fact, if you did serve in the active military, some people who matter might question either your connections or your judgment. How many influential people or their sons or daughters, have served in the active military? The numbers are not overwhelming.

Services you perform in The Grand Economy will be much more valuable than anything you could ever do militarily. Besides, time spent in the military is time wasted. Anything useful that you might actually learn in the military you can learn more efficiently by reading von Clausewitz or playing squash. Plus, military service will expose you to vulgar people and you might risk forming bad social habits. Finally, you might get hurt, maimed, or killed. Military service is for those with limited resources, few connections, no better prospects, and questionable survival skills. Why put yourself in harm's way? Like Shooter Grimm, who served as CEO of Baad-Halibut and Vice President of the United States, you have more important priorities.

MINDSHARE   Imagine if you could have surgeons implant electronic devices inside the brains of millions of consumers, then broadcast your marketing messages directly. Such devices would redefine mindshare. But I'm getting ahead of myself. What exactly is mindshare?

Mindshare is a kind of Nielson Ratings for individual consumers. To what extent is each consumer focused on your company or a specific product or service that you offer? How big is your presence in each mind? Clearly, the more you can keep consumers focused exactly where you want them focused, and the more you can intensify their focus, once it is properly aimed, the better for you. The object, of course, is to beat the competition and get more consumers to tune in to your program than to competing programs. You always want to be first in consumers' minds when they step up to the plate ready to spend their money and their credit. Look at the advantage big mindshare gives to a brand like Kleenex, for example. When someone says, "I need a kleenex," she means that she needs a facial tissue. When she goes to buy her kleenex, the odds are increased that she will, in fact, buy Kleenex.

It takes years and millions of dollars to achieve that kind of mindshare. But researchers are trying to make the process faster, easier, and cheaper, and they are meeting with some success. I think we can look forward to a day when mindshare becomes an exact quantitative science. Clearly, the human mind is malleable enough and predictable enough that we will never have to go to the expense of hiring surgeons. However, I should point out that the idea of a working nanotransmitter with feedback capability is already on the experimental drawing board and might some day become a reality for marketing. What a rave new world that would be!

THE MINORITY SHUFFLE Small businesses owned by minorities are eligible to win small federal contracts without having to win competitive bids. If a native tribe owns the business, there is no limit to the size of the government contract it can win. There is nothing to prohibit non-native corporations from going into partnership with small, tribal-owned businesses. Therefore, it is possible for big, non-native corporations, like Baad-Halibut and Wackynut Providers, to partner with tribal companies, win large non-competitive contracts that they would lose if they had to submit competitive bids, and increase their bottom lines accordingly. The trick is to stick to statute guidelines, follow government procedures, and, of course, partner with a tribal company that employs at least one person.

This situation reminds me of those almost-something-for-nothing deals that lots of people know about but very few ever exploit: Repossessed car auctions, homes foreclosed for delinquent mortgages or appropriated for back-taxes, government grants for just about anything, and law enforcement auctions for everything from unclaimed bicycles to forfeited property resulting from drug busts.

Always keep your eyes peeled for deals. How hard is it to buddy up with a tribal member to facilitate winning a few hundred million dollars in contracts that will grow your revenues? A program designed to help native tribes can also help your tribe if you are willing to hire a few lowyers and former government employees who understand the program. Then all you have to do is show up at the shindig, pick a willing partner, and dance the minority shuffle.

MISTRESSES   I do not recommend the keeping of a mistress or mistresses. First of all, the risk always exceeds the possible rewards. What's to prevent her from blackmailing you, or becoming hysterical in public, or being talked into spying on you for your enemies, or turning into a clinging, demanding pain in the ass? Clean, well-educated, high-performance prostitutes can be found easily in any major city and I guarantee that their level of skill will surpass that of any amateur, regardless of your proclivities. If you have an abundance of sexual energy then use them. Be discreet, but if you get caught, just confess that you gave in to temptation. Let the "boys will be boys" tradition take over. The majority of your peers will envy you for what you've obviously been able to get by with and anyone who matters will not only understand, they will elevate your status to a level almost as high as the level they reserve for themselves.

The fact remains that the wealthiest CEOs divert so much of their hormonal-driven energies into their work that they have little time or inclination left over for sexual dalliances. The slaughter of a hapless company during skillful arbitrage delivers more satisfaction to the conqueror than anything any legion of women could ever devise in the bedroom. On the other hand, if you are having a bad month, a quick stop at one of San Francisco's infamous dungeons[21] can purge you of self-doubt, whip you back into shape, and give you a remarkably clear view of what you want and why you want it.

MONEY   A pair of chickens and a sack of potatoes offered in barter won't get you very far these days. In the modern world, money is the lifeblood of survival. Poor people are quick to point out that you can't buy happiness with money. People of means are often the first to agree, although they usually add that money buys everything that makes people happy. Money empowers. Money buys security. Money buys time and

---

21 Similar establishments are available in New York City, Los Angeles, and several other major cities around the country and the world. If you need a complete transformation, I know of a discreet, commodious, and particularly brutal camp in the Czech Republic that requires a minimum stay of two weeks. Any member of The Club should be able to provide details on demand.

freedom from labor. It also finances shopping malls, factories, apartments, highways, and national defense, not to mention jewelry, trophy homes, sports cars, and yachts. Without money, we would not have NASA, the Mayo Clinic, wars, demolition derbies, or that quaint getaway to the Dhoni Mighili in the Maldives. Without money, we would be left with nothing but our chickens, our potatoes, and each other.

At that point, our only options would be to have a picnic, eat fried chicken and potato salad under some nasty trees, swat flies and flick ants, make love on a blanket like animals rutting, wade in a creek amid swarms of mosquitoes, sketch a landscape in the August heat, and then go home to our hovel to pull weeds, change spark plugs, make sun tea, and squeeze the budget to pay the phone bill.

Money saves people from toil, bugs, disappointment, anachronism, and exposure to dirt and grease. Clearly, money is the root of all progress.

MONOPOLY   It is sometimes painful to remember that Theodore Roosevelt was a Republican. His penchant for green, his "trust-busting" adventure, and his forays into regulation of business can only be viewed as anomalies that we would all like to forget.

In a perfect world, a CEO would be able to use all the power he gains to acquire whatever he wants. Nervous Nellies still call that monopoly. Because of Roosevelt and the tradition of nervousness he provoked, the best you can do today is an informal cartel, the results of which you would have to identify as, "market forces at work." Throw a barbecue. Invite the right people. Engage in conversation. If your goals happen by chance to coincide, then what's the harm in moving ahead, all in the same direction? You would have moved ahead in that direction anyway. The boys in oil have been doing this for years, and with sweet results. How else do you suppose Exxtort Mogul can pull in one hundred million dollars daily in profit? It would take fifty ordinary wage earners working independently their whole lives to make that one day's profit. A little mutual cooperation can make dark days look brighter.

Sometimes it's best to go it alone, and sometimes it's best to look for common interests. Just remember that whenever you lead your friends on an expedition of cooperation, go that extra mile to make the Rough Rider proud. Conserve your environment. Pack it in and pack it out. And most important of all, leave no tracks.

MOTIVATION   Like all other animals, people need to be lured or driven to get off their butts and produce. As their boss, you need to fill the lives of your employees with pain and pleasure. Keep them at a high and almost frantic state of anticipation. When they do well, reward them lavishly. For guys, put your hand on their backs and give them a pat or a meaningful squeeze; praise them in front of their rivals; take them to lunch and slip them a pair of tickets to a Nicks' game; or give them a hot stock tip. Gals are easier. Give them a big bouquet of budding red roses. It's amazing what you can get for a few buds.

When your employees screw up, on the other hand, scorn them in front of everyone and move their offices to noisy interior cubicles. Change their parking places. Warn them that their careers are stalling, and devise jokes about them that your whole staff can repeat and enjoy. They will learn quickly never to screw up again and always to give 110%.

Knowing that your staff is giving their all will help you sort them by their talents into dead wood, keepers, and race horses. Set the horses on the right tracks; keep the keepers busy; and get rid of the dead wood.

Whole libraries have been written about how to motivate personnel. Those libraries might be worth visiting if all you want to do is be friends with your employees or have an amusing lunch with your Human Resources Director. On the other hand if what you want is results, then don't bother the librarian. Beat the dog when it's bad, feed it when it's good, and never let it get close enough to bite.

MULTITASKING   How much time do employees waste on breaks, toilet trips, phone calls to the kids, computer games, online news briefs, socializing, and lunch? Why not turn waste on its head and demand not only concentration, but concentration on several tasks at once? Take a hint from computers and expect your employees to work on numerous projects at the same time. Have qualified people teach them. Multitasking is a concept that all executives and all department heads in any large corporation should push. Not everyone is able at the same time to chew gum, ride a bicycle, hum "The Battle Hymn of the Republic," and juggle three oranges. But some people are and others will never know what hidden talents they possess until you challenge them. So challenge them. Give each employee enough work with deadlines for five people and let them discover what they can do. If multitasking works out well for even half of the staff in each department, then you should see an increase in productivity. How much better is a ten-hour day when people accomplish seven tasks than an eight hour day when they accomplish two or three? Anything that improves productivity is a virtue.

"*Multitasking is a concept that all executives and all department heads in
any large corporation should push. Not everyone is able at the same time
to chew gum, ride a bicycle, hum "The Battle Hymn of the Republic,"
and juggle three oranges. But some people are and others will never know
what hidden talents they possess until you challenge them.*" p. 253

NARCISSISM   Much has been written about America's culture of narcissism, as if it were a bad thing. Ask people who sell tanning booths and plastic surgery if it is a bad thing. This debate underscores an essential philosophical question: Why argue with a trend that works?

Don't fight human nature. Exploit it. And never reject an opportunity to flatter someone who has a fat wallet. People spend most on what they most admire. Besides, if you aren't fascinated by your self, chances are that no one else will be fascinated by you either.

Enjoy mirrors. If you look at one long enough, it will always return a compliment.

NATIVE AMERICANS (OR, INDIANS)   I know almost nothing about them. I included them here to ensure cultural diversity.

NATURAL DISASTERS   If Hurricane Katrina taught us anything, it taught us that people must be prepared to take care of themselves. Yes, a few individuals, a handful of NGOs, and the governments we supposedly depend on will provide some assistance for people in trouble so long as the organizations in question do not have to give up too much. But the bottom line remains that when faced with disaster, whether natural or human caused, each individual must look out for number one or lose. My advice? Live your life and build your assets so you will always be able to survive. Can you make gut-wrenching decisions fast? Can you let someone else drown to save your life? Can you run away from your art collection and your wine cellar to keep your hide intact? Do you have the means to charter the last helicopter when everyone around you has the same intent? If you are clumsy, hesitant, and poor, chances are you might not survive even a minor disaster. But if you are rich, nimble, and ready, you can survive just about anything.

Here are a couple of hints. Always wear a loaded money belt, and always keep a survival kit in your brief case so you will have it with you 24/7. The kit should include extra batteries for your iPhone, your passport, a few spare credit cards, a comb, a tooth brush, a roll of Altoids, a month's worth of prescriptions, a couple of condoms, and a minimum of two hundred thousand American and fifty thousand Euros stashed in the built-in secret compartment. Anything less could put you at risk.

NATURAL RESOURCES   If you were strolling past the Shipwreck Bar at Kona Village and you found a Krugeraand on the black sand, wouldn't you pick it up and drop it into your pocket? Nature is like a beach after thousands of people with loose change in their pockets have spent hot days relaxing on it. Everywhere you look, if you look carefully, there is treasure. Someone is going to take it.

If your company is resource based, you need to think of yourself as the person who gets there first and takes the most. Historically, that was not the case. Early prospectors did the grunt work and made the discoveries, and capital followed the scent. The day after gold was discovered in the Homestake Mine; the day after silver was found in The Mother Lode; the day after they identified copper in The Richest Hill on Earth; and the day after the first diamond was plucked from the pastures of South Africa, the real prospectors started to move in and the discoverers got left in the dust. Discoverers were naïve, undercapitalized, and disorganized. That is no longer the case. Major resource finds today are made by large corporations ready to reap, and a second chance for tagalongs is doubtful. If you don't get there first, you won't get there.

Even if your company is not resource based, you and your firm will use natural resources. Don't be shy. The planet is large and resources are abundant. Nature does not charge rent or tax itself. It provides gifts for the taking.

On the other hand, the perception is widespread that resources are scarce or that they should be preserved rather than used. Don't be afraid to use this perception to advantage, particularly when dealing with resources that produce energy. During the summer of 2001 in the state of California, for example, a handful of shrewd individuals was able to convince the entire state, and a large part of the rest of the world, that there was an immediate energy shortage. Wherever you looked, ordinary citizens were turning down their lights and turning up the thermostats on their air conditioners. They also paid higher rates for electricity and were glad to have it. A strategy like this can add ten years' worth of plodding profits to a bottom line in a matter of weeks. Nature provides. And when you can convince people that she's going on strike, the way energy traders did in California, she also helps those who help themselves.

This strategy of helping yourself was not lost on the major oil companies. Following the lead of the California Coup, they successfully sold to the entire nation similar "short supply and big demand" strategies, revising production figures daily to account for changes in the price of gasoline. Cleverly, they threw in fears of dangerous dependence on foreign energy, catastrophic disruption due to global warming, and reduced refining capacity because a big refinery in Texas had to be shut down after a janitor discovered a cockroach in the women's bathroom. And that was the industry's newest refinery too, the one built in 1978. What were the results? While quadrupling the retail price of gasoline, they more than quadrupled their net profits without much more than a peep of protest from consumers. In doing so, they also cleared the way for future nuclear and coal development, unrestricted oil and gas exploration, subsidized alternative energy R&D, and off-the-chart earnings. What started as a fleece job on one state turned into a national energy policy. Always think BIG.

The case of California and subsequent events also underscore our most important natural resource. No, it's *not* the stuff that makes energy. Let's take a look at the obvious for a moment, since the obvious sometimes gets obscured in all the details of planning. Our greatest natural resource is the consumer, and it is one hundred percent renewable. Think about it. Millions of individuals, each with a few dollars in pocket, a few more in the bank, and a few credit cards in a purse or wallet with a few dollars credit remaining – each of these individuals, taken alone, is hardly worth a thought. But taken together they are the most important fact in nature and the most accessible source of your wealth on earth. If you could pry loose one dollar from every consumer in America, you would pocket overnight some quarter of a billion dollars in revenues. Up the price to ten dollars and throw in the rest of the developed world. Then add the developing world at a discount of nine dollars per person. Extend your campaign for three years. Has your calculator exceeded its capacity yet?

Keep the proper perspective. Get down to basics. Identify the sources of your wealth and hunt them down; turn their pockets inside out and then harvest. Nature has provided an almost unlimited and certainly growing base of human resources. The size of your take is limited only by your imagination.

NATURE   The idea that nature knows best is a primitive idea. If nature knew best, we would all die by age forty-five of ruptured appendices, untreated infections, or excruciating wounds. Nature provides resources for us to use, but beyond that it is cold, uncaring, brutal, and inhospitable. The answer to nature's shortcomings has always been technology, from the first garden tool to the home computer. However, you will encounter a small number of people, such as greens, neo-Luddites, animal rights activists, and neo-primitives, who worship nature and hate you, your technology, and everything else you stand for. Like terrorists, they are looking for their paradise: They want to annihilate you and replace you with people like themselves. Can you imagine the world's boardrooms filled with hemp shirts and vegans?

Fortunately, when they become persistent, it is easy enough to keep these people in check by limiting their access to information technology, by deploying security forces when necessary, and by making them objects of fear and ridicule. All ideas have a dangerous side, theirs included, so your main task is to make sure that no one can hear them. However, you can't yet control information channels like the Internet, so if their squawking starts to rise above the normal din, then your main task is to make sure that no one takes them seriously.

In other words, your first line of defense should be the silent treatment. Ignore them. Don't respond to their challenges. Keep them out of the media. They might just atrophy or get bored and wander away in search of better weed. If that fails, then dismember them with a media blitz aimed at character assassination. If that fails, set them up for a public demonstration, call out the police, and make it look like they started a riot. However you choose to neutralize them, just make sure that their ideas don't infiltrate the main stream in a positive light.

In the not too distant future, their ideas automatically will become anachronistic and will disappear altogether as what they refer to as "nature" shrinks to an insignificant percentage of the world and continues to shrink until it disappears altogether from common view, except for a handful of managed curiosities such as zoos, game parks, national parks, and recreational installations at theme parks.

The essential questions about nature that you must answer for yourself are: What good is a "wild and scenic river" or a "wilderness area" if you can't harness it, mine it, or charge admission and sell hot dogs, beer, and tee shirts at the other end of it? Who benefits when you lock up valuable and needed resources from any development whatsoever? Why follow the dictates of random events of nature, like hurricanes, volcanoes, and floods, when you can rely on engineering and commerce to benefit humankind? Why depend on mindless nature when you can depend on yourself and on the best technical minds in the world to construct rational solutions to every human need?

Some day, someone needs to build a chain of Natureworlds. Imagine a twenty-mile long water park with canyons and rapids beneath bluffs lined with polyester trees and big-eyed animal bots stepping out cautiously to peer at consumers who squeal with joy and splash their way to natural ecstasy and a first rate burger bar. Keep the safari open 24/7 without risk to life or health, and I'll guarantee that within a couple of generations, the only tree huggers left will be those in line with tickets in hand. And that will leave all the planet's resources to us, and to rational development.

What are the alternatives here? As I see it, we can let obstructionists take charge, in which case we will have to either engage in perpetual conflict with them, or adapt to their view, trade our Brooks Brothers suits in for banana leaves, learn how to grunt, and let nature waste its resources on its non-productive course to oblivion. Or we can take charge. We already know how to improve those parts of nature that amuse people, so lets do it, and do it in a big enough way to distract them and keep them entertained. Only then will we be able to claim, extract, and allocate natural resources efficiently. A worldwide chain of Natureworlds would not only be good for business and good for America. It would be the perfect setting for families and children to get in touch with the real primal forces that rule their lives.

NEPOTISM   I have a brother whom I never discuss except to ridicule. Years ago, I tried to set him up in business. After serving on my team for a decade, he abdicated all his responsibilities, took advantage of our stock value, sold out, and ran off to Argentina to become the gaucho potter of the pampas. The ingrate even took his 401-K.

I mention this only to remind you that if you practice nepotism you will pay a price. If your relatives have any value, they will demonstrate it on their own. If you want to work with them then, fine, treat them like any other executive material. However, I strongly recommend against putting family ties in business. If your relative is worthless, like mine, you will suffer. If your relative is worthwhile, you can never promote him often enough or high enough. And if your relative has real talent he could lure you into an ambush when you least expect it. *Et tu Brute?*

Birds of a feather fledge together and from that day forward, each one should be on his own. Enjoy your family dysfunction at weddings and funerals. You don't need it in the workplace.

Leave nepotism to politicians. They like drama.

NEWS   Everyone knows that news broadcasts have shifted from boring journalism to entertainment that keeps you right on the edge of your chair. But you might not be old enough to notice just how much the hard news segments of broadcasts, and the terminology used to present them, have shifted to business. As The Grand Economy grows and spreads, the focus of attention is increasingly commercial, and even non-business news items are depicted in business language. I remember watching a television news report on a massive heat wave and drought in the Midwest and East that caused a three hundred million dollar loss in productivity. As a post script, the reporter added that the heat wave killed more than two hundred people. Likewise, a follow-up human-interest story didn't dwell on death, suffering, medical needs, or the causes of the bad weather. Instead, it told how sales of ice cold drinks were soaring by more than twenty-six percent. Now that's perspective! And with a positive slant as well.

News today is focused on the meaningful work of the real world. National and local reporting increasingly shift emphasis away from unpleasant stories that are irrelevant to our daily needs to hot topics affecting our economy. Stories about overpopulation, world poverty, starvation, and Janjaweed militia – whoever they are -- gang-raping pregnant women then cutting open their bellies to resolve bets on the sex of the fetus just don't cut it any more next to hard news about the ill effects of parking meters on customer traffic or the positive effects of box store prices on a single mom's budget. The anchor might open with a ten minute hook about the latest celebrity arrest and close with a cute two minute story about that duckling that loves a puppy, but most of our attention, the other five minutes of hard news, is focused where it should be, on work. On the results of work. On how to invest in the economy. I am hopeful that a new generation raised on worknews will have better perspective, a more productive outlook, and more efficient habits than past generations. If so, then The Grand Economy will grow even more rapidly, and you will become part of an era that relieves us all of the burden of having to watch reports on television about the poor, sick, displaced, isolated, violated, abused, and weird, when all we really need are market reports, trend analyses, and the GDP.

Learn to exploit worknews, to profit from it, to use if for personal advantage, and to perpetuate the new work ethos for generations yet unborn.

And learn to keep an eye and an ear trained on the news. It strives to be fashionable. It is in the vanguard of language and therefore of trends, ideas, and assumptions that are in the air. If you watch and listen carefully, you will understand where we are all going and why we are all going there.

NICE GUYS   Why would anyone take an insult from a coworker and then just stand there quietly waiting for the next insult?

Even more absurd, why would anyone ever hold a door open for someone else when they could more easily walk through it first and be on their way? I can think of only three reasons for a door holder. First, someone lower in a pecking order should hold a door open for someone higher to demonstrate his acceptance of the order. For example, the CFO should hold the door open for the CEO, unless, of course, the CFO has spearheaded a forthcoming coup with a majority of the board members and he has chosen this moment to insult the CEO and assert his ascendancy. Second, anyone can hold a door open for a cripple or an old person who can't open the door herself. Who knows? One day the holder might be incapacitated. It is always a good idea to sustain a practice that you yourself might someday need. Finally, some people hold doors open for the same reason they take disrespect. They are nice guys.

What is a nice guy? How many times have you witnessed someone holding a door to an office building open at three minutes to eight o'clock while dozens of workers stream in? Half of those workers are thinking that this guy is a schmuck, a rube, a doorman out of uniform, a sucker, or maybe a tourist. Actually, the guy is just being nice. That is, he has a pathological need to be liked by others.

Nice guys I have known like to think that they are people filled with loving-kindness and are out to demonstrate their respect for the dignity of their fellow humans and for the ideal of mutual cooperation. In fact, they are profoundly insecure people in desperate need of acceptance and approval. You know the type. They are losers in the workplace because they don't have the guts to negotiate a raise or face down a more aggressive competitor. They would rather be liked. They are even losers on the highways because whenever they slow down to let others into their lane, they guarantee that they will be late for that important job interview or sales pitch. No problem. They assume that those faceless drivers they let into the stream of traffic will like them and remember them forever as harbingers of human decency, and the warm feeling they get from their good deed will easily replace that new job at twice the wage or that big commission with a bonus. As you can see, nice guys live in a fantasy world where good karma replaces good commissions and self-esteem is measured by personal sacrifice, not personal gain. If you need to be a nice guy, at least do a better job of it than other nice guys. Attach a sign to your backside that reads, "If You Like Me, Kick Me."

Or better yet keep turning your other cheek until some big dog crucifies you and you become the laughing stock of the village. At least that way people might remember you.

NOBLESSE OBLIGE   Centuries ago, an idea began in Europe that the nobility had an obligation to take care of people who couldn't or wouldn't take care of themselves. That idea has persisted up to the present day. Wherever and whenever wealth flourishes some of the wealthy establish foundations to benefit students, the poor, the homeless, the hungry, the diseased, the gifted, nature, or other pet concerns. Remember the Carnegie libraries? You don't have to remember that far back. Each year, anxious applicants and hard working geniuses look forward to celebrating grants from foundations with names like Ford, MacArthur, and Rockefeller. Even in recent years some prominent CEOs, such as Bill Gates, Ted Turner, and Warren Buffett, have earmarked billions of dollars for charitable purposes. The list is quite long.

Despite my belief that moderation should rule in all things, I tip my hat to these CEOs for giving The Club a great public relations shot in the arm. In addition, their generosity underscores our economy's efficient use of capital. Clearly, it is preferable to leave surplus capital in the hands of a few successful individuals, who can dole it out intelligently according to their personal whims, than to put it in the hands of ordinary people, who would spend it on pizza and snowmobiles, or to put it in the hands of government where allocating it would be subject to the whims of voters. Can you imagine? Instead of libraries and research laboratories, governments would be forced to provide free food, diapers, daycare, public transportation, energy, water, security, housing, tuition, and unlimited medical care to every citizen claiming need. Before you know it, every citizen would demand early retirement at age fifty plus a two week all expenses paid vacation on the Riviera at taxpayer expense to kick it off.

While noblesse oblige might be overdone, it is preferable to government handouts and the punishing taxes government would have to levy against the wealthy to sustain those handouts. Similarly noblesse oblige is preferable to the idea of broader income distribution to the masses. What do masses know about libraries and post-graduate fellowships? Always maintain control of the capital. It keeps choices in *your* hands.

Contrary to some of my friends, I see no reason to scold CEOs who choose to give away their billions. At least some of them force applicants to prove that they qualify as recipients. And you are in no way obliged to follow their example and give away your billions. Just remember that philanthropy always gets good press, so don't be shy about riding the coat tails of those who practice it. In addition to lending the odd work of art to a public museum, be sure to keep up those generous donations to the United Way. Always drop pocket change into those Salvation Army bell-ringer pots, and encourage your employees to do the same. It is the least you can do. And it certainly can't hurt if people associate you with nobility.

NONCONFORMITY   In the animal world, there is a genetic strategy called "protective coloration." Think of it as camouflage for critters. For example, deer in summer are the same color as dried grass so they blend into their backgrounds and it's hard to single them out.

The human equivalent of protective coloration is conformity and sometimes it is useful. Dress, speak, and act in an expected way, and you'll be difficult to spot. Anyone looking for success will use this protective device of conformity to advantage, mainly to not seem weird or threatening to others. Even after the successful bloodbath of a hostile takeover, the winner can appear to be just another of America's smooth, well dressed, normal businessmen, rather than the reincarnation of Attila the Hun that he truly was for a few weeks. Appearances are everything. Look like one of the crowd when you want people to take you as one of the crowd, and in our democratic world, that will protect you better than a battleship.

People who choose to appear non-conformist are often looking to draw attention to themselves because they are angry, malcontent, or just like to break rules. If that offers any advantage I don't know what it is, except it probably impresses adolescent girls and bored housewives the way James Dean did. I prefer to impress people who have money to spend and assets to invest after they have let me in their front doors filled with trust and good will because I look and act just like them.

Non-conformity, however, does have its proper place. If you want to unleash that bohemian side of your personality and get wild now and then, do it on your own time far away from your normal channels. Take a vacation to a place like Tuscany. Wear Birkenstocks, short pants, and a tee shirt. Order a glass of grappa in an outdoor café bordering a *piazza*. Then kick back and discuss *The Sun Also Rises* and *The Razor's Edge* with dissident intellectuals on sabbatical from Minnesota.

NORMS   Most people want to do that which is normal. To a rational person, of course, some norms might seem absurd. It is important to remember that in the popular culture of ordinary people, norms are norms, whether some of them are absurd or not. It is even more important to remember that absurdity is just as profitable as good sense, if not more profitable. Therefore, when you create trends to market products and services, do not hesitate to embrace the absurd. As always, advertising is the key.

Good advertising can turn weird, contradictory, and even pathological impulses into patterns of behavior that appear to consumers to be perfectly normal. For example, if you are a young man, it would be normal for you to pay two hundred and fifty dollars for the same pair of gym shoes you could buy for fifty dollars, less the logo and the endorsement of a famous athlete, so that a bigger young man can steal them from you for nothing. It would be normal to spend on an automobile that gets less than twelve miles per gallon more than your parents spent on their first home. It would be normal to eat half a pound of cheese fries with your fast food double bacon cheeseburgers while skipping the salad bar that would add too many carbs to your meal. It would be normal to pay someone thousands of dollars to suck fat out of your stomach, using a vacuum that looks like a sump pump attached to a bayonet, so that it won't bulge. And it would be normal to pay someone else even more thousands of dollars to sew bags of synthetic fat into your breasts so that they will bulge. If all these normal activities created anxiety in your family, it would be normal to give your kid Ridlin and yourself Prozac, but take your dog to a Jungian analyst. What gives? Well, manufactured norms can make an Alice-In-Wonderland world real. That world might have a few rough edges, but its bottom line is profit, so if you have to smile at absurdity, at least you can smile all the way to the bank.

What defines the norms that make up popular culture in America? When you answer that question correctly, you will also explain why you and I are rich and others only wish they were.

OFF SHORE   It is rumored that paradise might be found a mere six hundred miles off the Carolina coast. Some of our brethren have reincorporated in such places as Bermuda and there, in their world headquarters, flunkies make paper airplanes and take phone calls. If you don't like Bermuda, try The Cayman Islands or any number of other off shore havens that treat businesses fairly.

This is only one of several ways to beat back the voracious, money-grubbing tax-and-spend liberals who think that every corporation and every wealthy individual is a gravy train for pork barrel revenue and who, so far as I am concerned, will be the death of the free enterprise system in America if they are allowed to persist. While your personal income taxes may have declined from 50% to 20% during your career, they are still exorbitant. Any tax is exorbitant. Taxes, regulations, and high wages and benefits for workers have made it almost impossible to turn a fair profit at home and this situation leaves many companies no alternative except to move off shore, at least until our elected representatives get the word and shape up. Islands like Bermuda, where you can get by with paying virtually no taxes, have one great added benefit. You can take a nice, long cruise to your world headquarters with your friends in your favorite yacht, call the destination a meeting, and if you do pay any taxes, you can write off the trip.

OLIGARCHY   Oligarchy means governance by a small group of privileged insiders. When used to describe America, the term is completely misunderstood.

First of all, there are no fixed, inherited classes in America, as there still are in many nations, including Britain and even India. Second, privileged insiders come and go, and they earn their privilege by their successes. Don't you want the best and brightest people at any given moment to influence the government? Finally, consider scale and unity. How can diverse and fragmented masses of ordinary people productively influence any government? One must be selective. Stockholders at meetings make points. Boards of directors make decisions.

It is true that influence flows into our government from thousands of directions. America is a republican democracy that ensures one vote for each citizen and encourages active participation from every consumer. The doctor of philosophy and the shoe shine boy are counted as equals in our political process as they should be. However, the quality of inputs from citizens varies considerably. One citizen group might advocate stronger enforcement against drunk drivers on federally funded highways, while another might demand that all portly red headed people of Lithuanian descent should be electrocuted. Influence received must be filtered and refined before it can be used. That is why we have caucuses, committees, lobbies, boards, executives, and a cabinet. American government is run by small groups of inside experts smart enough to make rational choices, experienced enough to make deals, and small enough to make decisions on a moment's notice. They are still answerable to voters but they are seldom misled by psychopaths, unless of course they are psychopaths. Fortunately, that is not usually the case.

What is unique about democracy is that anyone can become influential enough to join one of these small groups. It is called, "upward mobility." This is The American Dream and it allows talented leaders to rise to the top like fresh, shiny Macintosh apples in a rain barrel.

The Framers of The Constitution understood that a beast without a head is far more likely than not to paddle his canoe too far down the Niagara River. America needs core leadership. And in America, leaders may rise from any circumstance and any background, however humble. You don't have to belong to a central party, a landed aristocracy, a rich old New England family, or the right fraternity at the right college in this country to rise to a position of prominence. All that can certainly help you, but it is not absolutely required. More than any other institution, business makes upward mobility possible. Academia, by contrast, rewards publishing and longevity, but it seldom pays recipients enough for them to influence anyone more important than a waiter at a pet bistro. Business, on the other hand, rewards results and it does so with hundreds of millions of dollars. Money is what matters. Where do you suppose real talent will gravitate? A poor girl or boy from a rough neighborhood can excel in business and become the CEO of a Fortune 500 company and the master of a commercial universe and build dream homes on four continents. Rising like a phoenix out of a crucible of leadership, that bright, young, aggressive winner will evolve into a seasoned CEO and will then be in a position to offer intelligent advice to a grateful government in need.

I am proud to acknowledge that in recent years, America has expanded its crucible of leadership. Since the election of Ronald Reagan to the presidency, itself a demonstration of our democratic spirit at work, the deregulation of business, the curtailment of union influence, the elimination of unfair taxes on successful people, and countless more incentives favorable to corporations and the holders of capital, have worked together to stimulate a massive transfer of wealth in the direction of success. More millionaires and billionaires have arisen in the past two and a half decades than our nation has enjoyed throughout its entire history. Everywhere you look, the most successful men and women are being rewarded for their efforts – it could happen to you just as well as to anyone else – and in turn, they invest, spend, create jobs, and strengthen our corporate economy even more. This revolution in wealth has created a larger pool of leaders than any we have ever known. Furthermore, with every election held during this period, the American people had the opportunity to express their favor or disfavor with this redistribution of wealth, and time after time, they expressed their unqualified support, culminating in the election of America's first MBA as president, who happened by chance to be the son of a living former President. Don't mistake this event for the endorsement of an elite class of rulers. It is democracy in action in the finest tradition of the Founding Fathers. It is America reaffirming the principle that young people who work hard and prove themselves eventually make the best leaders. The point is that anyone can join this club of meritocracy. If you play your cards right and prove yourself a winner, then you too one day could give away medals in the Rose Garden, sign bills, commute sentences, and take naps in the Oval Office.

So let's call this fair play, not oligarchy. And let us understand that it can only happen in democratic nations that have been liberated from autocratic oppression by market economies that offer freedom and equality to all citizens. Nations such as the U.S., Canada, Japan, Great Britain, Germany and, more recently, Russia and The People's Republic of China.

OPM   If you don't know by now what OPM stands for, put down this dictionary, go directly to your nearest college, get a degree in art education, and have a good life.

The invention of capital, or the opportunity to have "my money," coincided with the discovery of the perfect financial lever, which is the opportunity to use "other people's money" to make "my money." This answers a host of questions: Why are there so many banks and bankers? Why are there so many stocks and stockbrokers? Why are there so many money managers, investment counselors, IPOs, bond salesmen, insurance men, and real estate agents?

OPM means that you can reduce your risk to near zero, leverage a million dollars with a thousand dollars and a smile, keep outrageous profits in exchange for a modest return promised to the owner of the capital, and basically, pole-vault over the high bar using momentum generated by someone else. It is the perfect use of capital.

And you thought that it was illegal to print your own money.

OPTIMUM   Ride the optimum wave whenever you can in business and in your personal life. The more you can do so, the less others can criticize you and the more they will envy you. Go for the optimum house, the optimum car, the optimum performance, the optimum management team, the optimum vacation, the optimum suit, the optimum dog, the optimum wife....Ride high on every wave that rolls in.

It is a simple matter of choice. If you can afford anything you want, why would you not want the optimum? Why choose a flawed fifteen-carat off-color diamond when you can have a flawless ten-carat colorless D diamond for the same price?

If it is your habit to ride the optimum wave in whatever you do, those around you will admire your taste, envy your abilities, and pay attention when you speak. The optimum aura that surrounds you will elicit admiration and awe from everyone you meet. As the CEO of a great corporation from a great nation in a great economy, do the optimum and you can't help but be associated with greatness.

ORGANIZATION   The Holy Trinity of any successful enterprise is Leadership + Communication + Organization. Lack one and the enterprise will either fail or muddle. Let's take a quick look at organization. Exactly what is its aim?

It is apt that the term "organization" is used to describe both a method of doing things in an orderly structured way, and the result of that effort, an institution reflecting those values. Organization stimulates efficiency, which creates productivity, which builds profit, which makes you a success. What is true for you is true for your corporation, *The* Organization. As CEO, your job is to reorganize the world around you into a machine that produces predicted results with as little waste or distraction as possible. In essence, you re-create nature and human nature for profitable ends. You spread the word, *your word*. And you do both in a way that reduces friction from all contrary sources. Think of it this way: When organization functions as it should, like the Holy Ghost of Christianity, then you, like the God and Savior, can step forward and turn chaos into order, subsistence into profit, and doubting Thomas stockholders into faithful fanatics.

O'RILEY, BEEKEN ALI   This terrifying young man believes that he can become President of the United States of America because he has intelligence, character, candor, and principles, and because he cares. I'm not kidding.

Let's take a closer look.

O'Riley's father was an Irish Catholic immigrant intellectual and his mother was a black African Moslem foreign exchange student. He has no political legacy, no money, and no important long established family connections, other than his first cousin on his mother's side, B'ill.[22] Since no one takes B'ill seriously, his modest celebrity is not considered an asset to O'Riley's campaign.

O'Riley is polite. No one will ever mistake him for a bully, the way ordinary people often mistake vice presidents. Likewise, you can't consider him a great face man, like some presidents, because O'Riley has actual substance and because he has a wart growing out of his forehead the size of a Tootsie Roll. He is also a Christian Scientist convert who doesn't believe in plastic surgery. He does have a prayer circle working on that wart, but the wart is still there, big as life, right above his left eye. I could go on and on. The bottom line is that Beeken O'Riley at present has none of The Right Stuff to become a CEO of anything, let alone of our nation.

O'Riley reminds me of a scholarship boy I knew at boarding school from the backwoods of Idaho. I asked this fellow once, in the presence of five of my pals, to do my laundry on a Friday night because I was too busy. He actually agreed and treated us to a good laugh after he left the apartments toting two laundry bags instead of one while we headed for a party of townies at the local nursing school. I never again asked him for anything because I knew what the answer would be – I gave him that much credit. But the fellow never attempted to exact revenge, and he continued to treat me politely. What kind of young man cannot recognize his tormentors? And what kind of man fails to push back? Can you imagine what disasters would befall such a character surrounded by career politicians, lobbyists, heads of state, religious leaders, business leaders, generals, reporters, and intellectual assassins from opposing factions? Can you imagine what might happen to our nation if a person like this ever stumbled into power? This fellow should practice corporate law for a couple of decades and prove that he has what it takes to build a successful career. Before he aspires to manage the world, let him demonstrate that he can earn the hatred, enmity, and envy of colleagues and competitors by routinely beating them into rubble.

---

22 B'ill, whose full name is Kamal ben B'ill Abdul-Azim Hauif Rayhan, converted to Christianity and the American way and subsequently founded BBN, the Bullhorn Broadcast News network affiliated with thirteen public access television stations in Brooklyn. He is BBN's anchor, lead commentator, producer, director, and cameraman.

Then, if they truly despise and fear him and he can produce or raise forty million dollars at a moment's notice again and again, someone might consider him a viable candidate. Until then he is just another voice of reason spitting in the wind.

However, his popularity grows among ordinary people. One of the weaknesses of democracy is that the masses deceive themselves, particularly when they can identify a public figure as one of them only better. Don't give them latitude to deceive themselves. Provide them with more compelling deceptions. Lead them to a better candidate; one who works within established networks; one who is not afraid to listen to people who matter.

Democracy is a fine Chevrolet, but like all Chevies, it requires some tinkering to keep the wheels on and the engine running. Hire an experienced mechanic wielding a wrench to keep the machinery of state on track, not an unseasoned idealist who is liable to mean what he says when he talks about truth, justice, and the price of gasoline.

"…just another voice of reason spitting in the wind….Lead them to a better candidate; one who works within established networks; one who is not afraid to listen to people who matter." p. 273

THE PACE   Long ago, ordinary people wasted time. They called it leisure. The contemporary world has finally realized that time is money, and no one wastes money. The way we now live, I call, "The Pace," and you see it everywhere. On thoroughfares, cars race past you, cut in front of you, then slam on their brakes to avoid crashing into the line of more cars stopped at the red light. When you check out at the supermarket, the bagger has your groceries squashed and ready and the checker rolls her eyes and drums on the scale with her fingertips while the people in line behind you elbow forward and make rude comments as you fumble to force your debit card through the machine in record time. When you make a bank deposit at the drive-through window, pray that the person behind you does not drive a Hummer or you and your Honda might get dozed into a trash heap of urban road kill.

When you encounter The Pace, be of good cheer because it does not represent mass insanity. It represents an acute, unconscious awareness of the need for higher and higher productivity. Among hunter-gatherers, it was the swiftest runner who speared the antelope -- and the rest ate his dust. We have at last figured out that if we mean to compete to win, we have to pick up The Pace a notch or two every few months. And we are doing a great job of it. Even new technologies advance The Pace. Cell phones allow us to multitask. We can close a deal, comb our hair, and tell a friend about our spouse's insulting behavior while balancing our checkbook *and* weaving through a school zone to deliver the kids. Email allows us to send amusing imagery to a dozen friends simultaneously, rather than composing an interminable letter to each. But even email is slow. We can text message them instantly and get instant replies. As a result, we can invest time gained in moving faster, or in shuffling our paperless paper more quickly. That is a big gain too because, as anyone knows who has studied systems, when it comes to inputs, whether to our friends or our documents, it is the contact that counts, not the content.

The Pace saves us from waste. Stay in line and keep in step. If you don't, you will be scorned, insulted, and trampled flat as a dead squirrel.

PASSION   Passion is an affliction suffered by people who have weak character and poor discipline. It has no use in business, although I can imagine that *acting* passionately might be useful under certain circumstances, such as a motivational speech or an ass chewing.

But under normal circumstances, why be obvious?

PATERNALISM   Someone needs to evaluate meaningful social problems, weigh them against available assets, and then decide whether -- and how -- to fix them. Who should that be, incompetent government bureaucrats, lunatic revolutionists, religious fanatics, ill-informed ordinary people, self-righteous do-gooders, or extremely intelligent and highly successful international business leaders with outstanding track records?

When I was a kid, there was a T.V. show called, "Father Knows Best." It was popular and it made a point. If anyone thinks that human beings can survive longer than a day without strong leaders, they should attend a British, Italian, or South American football match when something goes wrong. The human species at large is always about thirty seconds away from panic and riot, and the only thing that keeps order is a strong leader. Someone who knows best. Naïve critics call that "Paternalism," as if ordinary people actually knew what served their own interests best. If that were the case, no one would smoke, drink to excess, gamble, drive too fast, use drugs, eat French fries, own cats, or trample their neighbor's baby while fleeing toward an exit. Furthermore, you can't count on self-appointed saviors with an ideological axe to grind. We all know where roads paved with good intentions lead, and our species has just about had enough of wackos who mean well. And governments? They don't always do a bad job, but normally, they do an inefficient and wasteful job or a job tailored to meet the needs of the party *du jour*. That brings us down to society's winners.

Two things need always to be in the hands of proven leaders, money and power; power to make decisions, and money to execute those decisions. It is a thankless job that will draw criticism, but never shy away from paternalism. A leader might not always be right, but there is no question that he always knows best. He has to know best because he controls the money, and whoever pays the bills calls the shots.

PATRIOTISM   Like many emotions that evolved through centuries of human society, patriotism is a two-sided coin. Critics are correct when they point out that patriotism is an irrational and tribal drive that can be distorted into an excuse to commit the most barbarous acts imaginable. A brief glimpse at any point in history will substantiate this view. Consider, for example, the internment during World War II of American citizens of Japanese descent. Many loyal Americans lost all their property and years of their lives. Or consider the rabid obedience to duty so widespread in the Third Reich and so contrary to any standard of civilized behavior. Never treat patriotism lightly, and never allow it to be used without thought, like a common coin.

On the other hand, the bundle of emotions that make up patriotism developed in human society for good and functional reasons. When faced with profound challenges like a natural disaster or invasion by a skillful and brutal horde, most people, strictly on their own, cannot summon enough courage to fight back. In such circumstances, most people will first choose to get out of harm's way so they can be left alone to live their lives as they wish. Patriotism is the rush of adrenalin needed to arouse people to group action and sacrifice. The Allied victory in World War II, spearheaded by America, rested on gas rations, victory gardens, and guts, all made imperative by patriotism. Don't dismiss patriotism and never trivialize it. Just use it wisely when less powerful means fail.

You might want to follow the stunning example of President George W. Bush. Following the catastrophic events of September 11, 2001, he admonished the nation to reach into their wallets, dust off their credit cards, and shop as a demonstration of their love for their country. Now there is an admonition that hits home. If Generals MacArthur, Patton, and Eisenhower had been alive, I'm sure they would have offered President Bush some kind of salute.

Our trials aren't over. They will never be over. More attacks will occur on our soil. When they do occur use the power of patriotism for ends of which you can later be proud or don't use it at all. Meanwhile, let all Gods and all citizens bless America. And to all of you whose best vision of a better world is terror, torture, mutilation, murder, and suicide I wish to repeat the succinct reply issued by General Anthony McAuliffe in Bastogne, Belgium on December 22, 1944 to a German commander demanding American surrender: Nuts.[23]

"Shop" is good, but I think "nuts" is more eloquent.

PAYBACKS   When it comes time to pay someone back, mere revenge won't do. Can you end your adversary's career? Can you humiliate him in the press, or better yet, in public, say at a dinner party? Can you help guide him toward a federal indictment? Can you ruin his marriage? Can you out him in public? Can you, by some means, cause him to be skewered on a spit and roasted over an open fire for eternity? Forget all that. When you want to inflict a real payback on someone ignore trivial revenge and hit your adversary where it hurts: In his wallet. Figure out a way to make him lose money and you will hear his screams of agony forever

PENSIONS   You have every right to expect employees to plan ahead and take responsibility for their own futures. You are an employer, not a sugar daddy.

Pensions are required only so long as other corporations offer them. If we all got together and ended them, then no one would have to put up with them any longer. Meanwhile, if you are stuck with old-fashioned pen-

---

23 If any of you whose vision is here challenged happen to be reading this and you need a translation of the idiomatic term, "nuts," I will provide the same one Colonel Harper offered the Germans when he delivered McAuliffe's reply: "Go to hell."

sions, convert to cash balance immediately and you will save millions. Or declare bankruptcy and turn your pension obligations over to the Pension Benefit Guaranty Corporation. Otherwise, I suggest that you use 401Ks instead of a traditional pension plan. Allocate contributions to your 401Ks in direct proportion to voluntary contributions made by your employees. That makes the 401Ks selective since lower paid employees can't afford to make contributions and the higher the pay scale, the greater the employee contribution, and thus the matching corporate contribution. That is as it should be. The right people get rewarded.

In time, the financial whiz kids will devise and test new ways to make retirement contributions less painful and more useful to operations without exposing the company to excessive long-term liabilities. Until then, or until we do away with the whole concept, I suggest that you follow the straight arrow approach because all retirement benefits are glass houses.

Here is one straight arrow approach that a colleague of my father practiced years ago. It might be difficult to set up today with ERISA, but otherwise I see no reason not to recommend it. As you know, pensions can buy a lot of grudging loyalty. But at what cost? And for what reason? Why do you need the loyalty of people who are about to retire? And how much pension money does a retiree need to buy an RV, discover Dollywood, and then suffer a stroke and die in the Arizona desert? Dad's colleague owned steel mills. He offered pensions to employees who retired after thirty years of service. Rather than lay off high paid employees with twenty-eight years' service and ruin their lives, he did them a favor and demoted them from their supervisory jobs to the janitorial staff. Since he based their pensions on average earnings during the last two years of employment, these transfers saved his mills millions of dollars annually, but they also kept these old employees eligible for pensions. This proved to be a classic win-win situation. Of course he had to sacrifice some employee loyalty and put up with the occasional death threat, but his retirees still had plenty of money for their reduced needs. If nothing else, this story should demonstrate to those critics of big business just how wrong they are: No, you don't have to be heartless to make money. You just have to think realistically, make tough choices and – most of all -- be willing to make sacrifices.

You will, of course, have to sacrifice your own lifestyle too when you retire. Plan ahead and lower your expectations because it is just not realistic to hope that when your productivity stops you can continue to earn what you have earned while at the top of your game. This can degenerate into a pathetic situation, because once you are over the hill, a lot of younger people would like to cut you adrift and sick the dogs on you. That's life and no one ever promised you that life would be fair, so buck up. Meanwhile, even if you were CEO of a leading corporation you will not be able to count on much from your corporate pension, something between one and ten percent of your prime time earnings. Converted to an hourly wage based on a forty hour work week, once you hit the golden years, you will be forced to settle for an annual pension of something less than two thousand dollars an hour; three if you are extremely lucky.

Considering the personal portfolios you will have put together from your earnings over the years, your pension will only provide ten percent or less of your retirement income. Of course that is peanuts compared to your needs, but what can you do? Thank God for Social Security and senior discounts.

PERFORMANCE   Never allow your board to tie your earnings to performance. There are too many variables involved and too many ways to interpret data. Besides, whether your company does well or does poorly during one quarter or one brief year is largely irrelevant. You will have worked just as hard in either case, and sometimes business conditions or your own employees can screw up your plan and there is not a lot you can do about it. You are paid to be the CEO not a miracle worker.

On the other hand, you need to tie all rewards in excess of base salaries for all of your employees below the level of management team executives strictly to performance. This will give you absolute discretion to reward those who please you and to punish those who don't. You will need that kind of control to get the most out of them and to get rid of the dead wood without having to suffer unpleasant recriminations and wrongful discharge suits.

Tying their bonuses to performance has one more advantage. When you present your budget to the board at the end of a good quarter or a truly sensational year, the vast majority of your people will receive scheduled bonuses, yet you and your team, the people who made it all happen, will not. This will look so unfair to your directors, and they will be so grateful for the company's soaring stock price, and so fearful that you and your team might accept a better offer, that even though your earnings are in no way tied to performance, you and your team *will* get substantial bonuses. Be sure to have one of your closest allies on the board have a proposal in hand just in case no one else is considerate enough to introduce it.

THE PERP WALK   There seems to be some debate as to whether or not top executives, when subject to arrest, should be handcuffed and displayed in public for the whole world to see. Rudolph Giuliani, when working as a federal prosecutor in New York City, believed that they should be treated in this way. As a result, "Perp Walk" became commonplace in our vocabulary and some of our finest Wall Street executives have suffered shame. This view implies that white collar infractions are in the same category as real crime, and that the suspect has already been convicted and sentenced – to humiliation, at the least. I think this practice is barbaric and sadistic. Shame, Mr. Giuliani, shame!

Standard police practice calls for suspects to be handcuffed for safety and security reasons, and in some high profile cases, to showcase the fine job police do to protect the public. Obviously, suspected perpetrators of violent crimes should all be handcuffed. Less obviously, so should most other suspected perpetrators. Take, for example, the happy-go-lucky musician arrested for possessing a marijuana cigarette. As a class, these fellows are notorious for their drug use and this smiling fellow could just as well be high on PCP as on pot. He might go berserk at any moment and attack the arresting officers with the strength of five men. Cuff him? Shackle him! Or consider the con man passing a counterfeit fifty-dollar bill. What led a man with enough social skills to become a con man to make or distribute bogus money? What deep-seated desperation lurks just under the surface of such a character, and in what terrifying form might it suddenly strike out? Of course, cuff him, and keep the Taser close at hand. Or what about the single mom who cashes bad checks? Could anyone be more desperate?

Imagine what hysterical madness could snap into action the moment such a person understood that her children might be taken away from her. Cuff her indeed, and be prepared to order a straight jacket. Think of the other people that all these suspected perpetrators might already have harmed by their misdeeds and you will understand the need to protect peace officers from the callous and uncaring behavior of common criminals.

You will understand that need even more after you consider the potential for violent behavior among truly hardcore criminals like murderers, arsonists, armed robbers, rapists, gang thugs, mafia enforcers, terrorists, and perpetrators of assault. What are police officers supposed to do when they pull over a speeder who gets out of his car and becomes argumentative? No profiling intended, but what if he is dark skinned or has a gold tooth or is named Ali in a neighborhood populated by street gangs or refugees from the Middle East? It would not be unreasonable to beat him into a coma with night sticks and stomp on him to make sure that he is incapacitated. At the very least he should be handcuffed and hauled away to protect the arresting officers and the public and to demonstrate in public view to other vicious criminals what will happen to them if they persist in their criminal pathology.

But cuff the CEO of an important corporation? Get real! You might *accuse* an executive of inadvertently disturbing the retirement fantasies of a few thousand employees and investors because of a lapse in somebody's judgment; or of tinkering with the quarterly P&L to maintain a positive outlook on stock values; or of profiting from the markets with information not published in the *Wall Street Journal*. A handful of avaricious fools might ruin or even take their own lives because they made ludicrous investment decisions based on sound, but perhaps not literally accurate, public relations offered by a dutiful CEO striving to save his company. Whatever. Business is complicated and not always antiseptic. But do any of these activities compare to the drive-by murder of an entire family, the rape and mutilation of a ten-year-old girl, or the suicide bombing of three boy scouts, a grandmother, and a cheerleading squad of innocent young women sipping fresh lemonade? Every CEO is at heart a gentleman. If he weren't a gentleman he wouldn't have made it this far. And no gentleman would ever create a public scene. We're talking about important people here. Successful people. Wealthy people. People who appear on the covers of *Fortune* and *Forbes* and *Time*. People who serve on the mayor's, the governor's, and the President's task forces. Men and women who serve on the boards of directors of other important corporations not to mention some of the most prestigious NGOs, galleries, symphonies, and charitable organizations in the nation. For the most part, these are people trained in the nation's finest colleges and universities. Many of them grew up while attending the nation's finest prep schools. They go to church, raise families, and in general, form the backbone of every important community in America. We're talking about graduates of Harvard, Yale, Princeton, and Stanford. We're talking about people who subscribe to *Gentlemen's Quarterly*, not *Ruffians' Weekly*! Why would you take pleasure in shaming and embarrassing and dragging away in handcuffs any such person unless you yourself suffer from repressed and deep-seated hatreds that need analysis? What is wrong with allowing an important executive facing arrest for a series of white collar infractions – even granting that some of them might technically be considered felonies -- to have lunch at his club then voluntarily to surrender himself, at a mutually convenient time, to the jurisdiction in question, with his head held high, as it should be? With dignity. With pride intact. With his staff of lowyers and spin-doctors in tow.

I don't believe that the "perp-walk" will ever be tolerated for long in America. The good people of this nation understand that corporate executives are sophisticated individuals and that we are bound to conduct business as all businessmen conduct business. The fact that an executive in a high profile corporation gets arrested for an infraction that is widely accepted as good business practice throughout the business community should not make that executive subject to embarrassment. Even the fact that a few hundred or thousand people might claim, with exaggerated drama, that their lives were ruined by that infraction, should not make that executive subject to humiliation. That would be unfair and prejudicial, almost as bad as selective prosecution. Furthermore, you cannot treat the better members of society with disdain any more than you can treat the lowest and most violent members with velvet gloves. Let the punishment fit the crime. And let the methods of apprehension and incarceration fit the nature of the suspect.

PERSONNEL   Let the term "personnel" refer to all corporate employees at middle management level and lower. Anyone higher than that has talent and you have expectations for them. Personnel fall under the direction of a human resources director, formerly known as the personnel manager. The human resources director is the least important person in the corporation. The janitors and the boy and girl in the mailroom are more important. The human resources director is why you have a boy and a girl in the mailroom, when a boy or a girl would do nicely.

I suppose that someone has to advocate fresh fruit and flossing for employees. And personnel people do take care of a whole slew of paltry details, like intramural sports activities, company get-togethers, newsletters, the contents and placement of vending machines and water coolers, ergonomics, lighting, sound levels, appropriate behavior with regard to gender, race, religion, ethnicity, size, age, and, for all I know, baldness. Plus they must field all the nagging, nitpicking, whining malaise that comes with a pack of employees. They also handle the nuts and bolts details of a few substantive issues, such as labor relations, pensions, unemployment benefits, health insurance, misbehavior and tardiness, attendance records, workman's comp claims, OSHA requirements, health screenings, holiday decorations, and the inevitable pandemic of carpel tunnel syndrome. But in general, they are eccentric, out of the loop, amateur psychologists/sociologists who always have a better way to organize workers and their tasks, and, like the people they supposedly serve, they can be replaced in a minute when they become overbearing. They are valuable and necessary in only one respect. They serve as a buffer between executives and personnel, and you'll want to waste as little time as possible with personnel.

PHILANTHROPY   People expect the rich to give away lots of money. Everybody is looking for a handout. Some billionaires comply. In my opinion, you shouldn't give away one thin dime unless you get something in return. Have a big, nice building or a university department named after you, for example. Or, like the Rockefellers, the Fords, Cecil Rhodes, and Alfred Nobel, set up a big foundation that everyone hears about for generations. If you don't, as soon as people get their hands on your cash, they will forget your name. Why give it away if no one remembers you?

Look at the case of Julius Rosenwald. Who, you ask? This is the guy who made Sears, Roebuck & Company. He also built five thousand schools in the segregated rural South so Blacks could get an education. He helped out thousands of Jews in countries that did not like them, and he gave Chicago its Museum of Science and Industry. But outside of Chicago, who remembers, or would even recognize, his name? There is no Rosenwald Museum, no Rosenwald's Israel, and no Rosenwald University in Alabama. More people have heard of Evel Knievel.

If you are inclined to be overly generous, at least put your fortune to work to build some kind of monument to your life so people will remember what a great man you were. And you were – how else did you acquire so much money? So why not give a little back to yourself when you give to others? You don't have to relinquish your image as a leader, or as the best of the best and the brightest, just because you die.

PLANNING   Nothing worthwhile happens unless it is first planned. The world we build might reflect the world we imagine, but it becomes the world we imagine only after we reconstruct it according to rational blueprints over which we have labored. Planning is the bridge that connects human imagination to reality. Without that bridge, we would be lost in a world of dreams, as naïve and useless as children

With that bridge, on the other hand, our visions become bricks and mortar and those humble edifices inspire new and more advanced visions cast in steel and concrete. Before you know it, development becomes an engine that drives itself and our visions morph into aluminum and glass and epoxies and polymers. Science becomes nanoscience. Technology evolves into robotics. Biology leaps to genetic engineering, and our brave new world is born. Why? Because we planned it. We could have planned a tulip garden, but we didn't. This is the world we have made because this plan reflects our inner being and our talents more honestly than any other possibility.

Look at the development of the assembly line. Somewhere, a couple of guys tinkering in a shop understood that if they specialized their tasks then they could produce more and do it faster. Their insight grew into a primitive assembly line and, in time, that grew into a line of robots that can be reprogrammed in a day to produce different products. They could have developed a way to think in rhymed couplets but they didn't. The end result of the plan they did choose was productivity leading to profits that those two guys in a shop would never have imagined possible. Instinctively, they chose a path to development and to wealth, not to enlightenment or ease or grace or pleasure or anything else that lures the human soul. Planning is the only pathway to progress.

Have you ever thought about bees? For as long as Homo sapiens have inhabited this planet we have depended on bees to pollinate flowering plants and trees that feed us and the animals we eat. Now, after all these centuries, bees are letting us down. They are disappearing and farmers are on the edge of panic. Are we all destined to starve? I say good riddance to the little vermin. No one planned a bee. Bees just happened, the result of chance operating through natural selection and mutations. Now we are faced with the challenge to plan something that will replace bees. Will we succeed? Of course we will. We might have to wait until the food situation is nearly critical. Then there will be sufficient profit potential in the pollination sector to motivate entrepreneurs to invent a replacement bee. Whether it will comes from nano-robotics or genetic engineering remains to be seen, but it will happen. Someone will make a lot of money in bees. Life will go on and it will be improved because we designed the replacement bee and we can therefore control it and make it more efficient.

You must plan everything you do if you intend to reach your peak performance and contribute to progress. Never take a step without first having planned it. There is no room in your life for spontaneity. Some leaders plan more quickly than others and they make decisions with lightning speed. Others deliberate. They all have one thing in common: They plan. Do not mistake agility for serendipity.

I understand that this discipline runs opposite to the message we teach consumers, which is, by and large, to plan nothing but spend on impulse. There is no contradiction in this contrast. Some of the bees build the hive and some of the bees bring home the pollen. The tasks of the two kinds of bees are different. Their abilities are different. Their training is different. Consequently their methods must be different. Besides, as our plans for consumers evolve, consumers themselves will evolve until they are more like the replacement bees and they will follow their directions as efficiently as the new little nanobots or clones follow theirs.

Like a religion, planning must be a way of life for every CEO. Artists, dreamers, and children might be satisfied with imagination alone, but planning builds the world. That's your job. You are the architects of the future.

PLAY   What children do when their parents fail to offer them sufficient supervision is play. They do aimless things that feel good and accomplish nothing. Like innocent little animals, children require direction, organization, structure, and training before they can become productive citizens. As a parent, you are required to provide all of that if you hope to reduce your risk of disappointment in your children.

Clearly the concepts of Adulthood and Play are oxymoronic. Take a few moments to relax. Daydream prior to sleep. Develop a killer backhand and a devastating putt as part of your overall recreational strategy. But if you catch yourself sketching a tree, playing a game of FreeCell, or searching for dragons in clouds, then talk to your primary care physician and get a prescription. Fire a hapless employee or find some other way to get yourself out of the funk you are in and get back up to speed. Never allow your mind to wander outside the boundaries of a previously crafted plan. Your mind is a carefully crafted tool and a highly specialized weapon. Don't waste it and don't dull it.

Aside from time you invest in holidays and in your five or six annual vacations to exotic places where recreation is part of the required agenda, play is for babies.

PLUTOCRACY   It doesn't sound very complimentary to be called a plutocrat. It is a comical, awkward, obese word. On the other hand, a spade is a spade. Part of the job of a wealthy person with plenty to lose and more to win, and a leader with plenty to offer, is to take an active, responsible part in running his country. Not directly, for most of us, but indirectly, through influence. Consider it one of the perks of the job. Congressmen, senators, cabinet members, and presidents listen to other successful leaders who have wealth, power, and prestige, as well they should. Some of those office holders come from our own ranks. I don't think a plutocracy is such a bad idea imbedded in our sometimes dysfunctional democracy. After all, it is only logical that those of us with the most to lose and the most to gain will govern best. We provide stability and direction, clear-headed and realistic thinking, tough-mindedness, experience, and common sense. Some of you, raised in the best of circumstances, already understand that America has always been a plutocracy and that the plutocrats have saved this nation more than once from foreign enemies and from itself. Enough said on that subject. The thing is that ordinary people balk at the term and the concept, so never use it. A spade might be a spade, and a club might be The Club, but we'll continue to call our game a "meritocracy" to pasteurize public perceptions of it and make it safer to digest.

POKER   The game of poker is life reduced to cards. Each player is the adversary of every other player. Nice people lose. The best players would like to cut the throats of all the other players. Those who win want more. Those who win most want all. And the outcome of the game depends on equal parts of capital, chance, guile, balls, and bluff. If you can win at poker you can win at life, and if you can win at life, you have the right stuff for business.

POLICY   A large multinational corporation has more assets, more responsibilities, and more influence than many small countries. Just like a country, a corporation needs to have a set of policies that describe its expectations; terms under which it will deal with others; its requirements for maintaining facilities in foreign countries; how it will react to threats from foreign government intrusions, civil unrest, natural disaster, and direct attack from terrorists; how it will react, or not, to community problems unrelated to its operations; how it will react, or not, to community problems supposedly related to its operations; abatement procedures for off-plant fuel, chemical, and toxic substance spills; emergency evacuation and relocation procedures for on-site employees; its perceived views in relation to host countries' politics, religions, and social and legal practices; and anything else deemed important for one country when dealing with another country. You should also provide to your employees a confidential manual describing how to deal with the host country's customs, languages, social practices, and accepted business practices, and a confidential memo or statement of policy that might be compared to the military's "rules of engagement." In other words, you need to spell out exactly how you can treat your hosts in the pursuit of company profits.

Whenever dealing with host nations' governments, you will be best served if you think of yourself as the ruler of a superior nation. You can dictate much of what you want. Normally your threats will be heeded. Whenever you remain firm and deny a host's demands, most of the time you will come off looking like a respected and mighty enemy -- who happens to enrich local economies. On the other hand, if you use sufficient tact, whenever you have to bend toward the host's needs, you can come off looking like a benign, enlightened, still powerful friend. When negotiating with a more or less stable government from a position of strength, it is difficult to lose so long as you have a well-reasoned set of policies and you remember – and act like it -- that if it weren't for you and your corporation, the host country could revert in a minute to a tribe of primitive troglodytes.

If you craft your policies correctly, your presence in foreign lands should lead to sound symbiotic relationships: The foreigners provide natural resources, cheap labor, ready markets, and quaint customs; you provide jobs and civilization.

POLITICAL PARTIES   Realistically, The United States has only two political parties: Representatives of consumer voting districts elected to public office, and representatives of private interests hired as lobbyists. If you include congressional staffers, each party has roughly the same number of people working on legislation at any given time, though in recent years, lobbyists have gained a recognizable majority and their advantage increases yearly. Among elected representatives, historic distinctions between two factions, the Republicans and the Democrats, hardly deserve mention. Today, these factions are united into a single party composed of the Republicans, who defend and promote a conservative ideology, and the Democrats, who criticize but publicly emulate it to curry favor with voters.

As the CEO of an important corporation, part of your job is to make laws favorable to your interests. You can accomplish that goal by purchasing influence either directly with elected representatives or indirectly through your lobby. The latter method is cheaper than the former. It is also more reliable, involves less risk, avoids public scrutiny, and deflects criticism. On the other hand, a congressman in your pocket can serve as your expediter more effectively than your lobbyists whenever you need quick results. I advise you to be actively involved with your representatives and your lobbyists. And I recommend that you contribute to both parties. It's only fair.

POLITICS   Every state exists as a social contract between the citizens of the state and its government. Deciding how a government should execute the terms of that contract is the art of politics. Those who engage in politics, either directly or indirectly, share one common motive: Self-interest. Politics is much like a smorgasbord banquet. Those nearest the table will eat first and most. Those who wait to be served will be thrown scraps. It is the duty of every CEO to eat first and eat well; that is, to gain and use as much political influence as you can for personal and corporate benefit.

How is that accomplished? How does one gain political influence in our government? One buys it. We live under a wonderful system of government designed by The Framers specifically to accommodate citizens of means, and politicians are commodities, much like extracted natural resources, available to the highest bidder. That is not to say that you can own every politician. You can't. Occasionally, consumers elect politicians who are not for sale. Two examples come to mind. Both are folk legends from one of my adopted home states, Montana: former Congressman Pat Williams and former Senate Majority Leader and Ambassador to Japan, Mike Mansfield. Both were teachers, both had populist leanings, both believed that their principles should guide them, and both are no longer in service. Don't waste your time on characters like these. Invest in people you can understand, real politicians most of whom are ambitious lowyers dedicated to their careers, to retaining power, and to making money. But even they are not a sure thing. In the end, politicians are answerable to an electorate and regardless of how well you groom and pamper them, they can turn maverick for the survival of their careers.

Nevertheless, today politicians need large quantities of capital to gain and keep their seats. You can have profound influence over most politicians simply by financing their campaigns, contributing to their support groups, stroking their egos, inundating them with gifts, and wining, dining, and entertaining them and leading them on junkets to their favorite vacation spots around the world, all in the name of development, diplomacy, and fact-finding. This is where it pays to have a spacious lodge in a resort such as Aspen or a villa in an out of the way place like Tuscany.

Be vigorous and ever vigilant toward your politicians. Make them feel as if you genuinely like them and as if they are part of your inner circle of closest friends. Expect them to represent your interests in direct proportion to the size of your investment in them. A few dozen well-placed politicians, or even bureaucrats for that matter, can do more for you and for your corporation than the greatest inventors and the shrewdest MBAs. Ideally, pick careerists who come from modest middle or upper-middle class backgrounds. Those with working class, teaching, or agrarian backgrounds tend to have issues and loyalties that will interfere with their expected performance and hence with their loyalty to you. Those from comfortable backgrounds will be difficult to impress and many will have armchair causes – trees, whales, AIDS, pregnant orphans, what have you – that tap their loyalties. Give me a hungry, naïve, upwardly mobile, lowyer or technocrat in awe of his or her office and I'll soon give you back a reliable resource loyal as a lapdog.

A word of caution. Buy as many politicians and upper-level bureaucrats as you can afford, but appear to follow the rules as much as you must. An enemy or a do-gooder will always be waiting in your shadow to club you with the law. But then, as we all know, there are a hundred ways to circumvent absurd restrictions. Keep your puppies well fed and happy. Just don't be obvious about it.

POLLUTION   Waste is a by-product of all business enterprises, just as fecal matter is a by-product of all human digestion. I do not know of anyone who has proposed to make fecal matter illegal. All communities accept fecal matter as a perfectly natural phenomenon and they contribute their resources to fix fecal matter so it is no longer offensive or dangerous. They build sewers and sewage treatment plants. Why is the same understanding and assistance not offered to corporations accused of polluting? These are businesses that provide payroll to a community; that support retired workers and those active workers who require medical care; that fill the coffers of United Way, the Red Cross, the Boy and Girl Scouts, the YMCA, Habitat for Humanity, and all the other beneficial service organizations that support communities. Who hosts community picnics in the town park? Who supports the local baseball farm team? Who contributes huge amounts to the local tax coffers? Who takes up a collection for the retired, impoverished widow who needs cornea surgery?

Pollution is a community problem, an inevitable and natural result of prosperity in action, and any effort by radical, anti-business groups, to transfer that responsibility to corporations themselves, must be met head on with fierce and entrenched opposition. Most people will understand your position. They will want to keep their jobs in their communities.

POPULATION   I once heard a self-proclaimed population expert claim that every major problem on the planet could be traced to over-population. Normally, I don't beg, but in this case, I beg to differ. I can trace every one of those same problems to a combination of poor planning, inadequate technology, lack of development, and too many cats.[24]

If you have one hundred people on an island, and the island, as is, can feed only fifty, you can throw up your hands, give up, and say that your island is overpopulated. Or, if one of us happened to be there, we could say, "Let's organize the means of production and develop a market system that delivers twice the food." I guarantee that in no time at all, we'll develop systems and technologies to feed our masses and still swim away with a net profit of nineteen percent or more.

Most deprivation is caused by poor productivity and most of that is the result of inadequate technology. Plan, invest, develop, boost productivity, invent new technologies, and deprivation will vanish. In fact, once you set a viable economy into motion, it will feed upon itself enough to grow and encompass whole populations otherwise earmarked for despair. In time, even that population could double and double again and, in a sound economy, flourish.

In a sense, every CEO is a missionary spreading the good news that population is not a negative, but a positive asset for growth. Furthermore, corporations can accomplish with relative ease the same humanitarian goals that churches, the U.N., and a host of other NGOs struggle to accomplish. It is not out of the question in the future, once enough people understand how economics works, that CEOs of major multinational corporations will be nominated to receive Nobel Prizes. Certainly, a full belly and a disposable income will do more for the wretched masses than all the ministering of all the self-appointed angels flitting through history. The Nobel Committee will eventually acknowledge that reality as populations accelerate, cities balloon to thirty and forty million inhabitants, technologies advance

---

24 Do the math. There are at least a billion to a billion and a half house cats on earth. During its lifetime, each cat will kill hundreds or thousands of rodents and birds. Poor people could eat their cats, but they would increase their nutritional intake geometrically if they ate the rodents and birds instead. But they can't. The cat ate them. To maximize efficiency, boil the cat, eat the stew, then go to work on the mice, chipmunks, buntings and warblers.

in response, and people everywhere are able to keep rice in their bowls, cats in their kettles, tortillas on their skillets, goats in their kitchens, and credit cards in their shiny new wallets.

Compassion is nice and charity feels good. Results, on the other hand, can feed hungry babies and teach adults how to feed themselves while adding substance to a corporate bottom line. After all, the larger the labor force, the lower the cost of labor and the higher the number of employed. Population is not the enemy. It is the energy that builds economies.

PORTFOLIO   What is a portfolio, really? To a fine artist, a portfolio is the orderly collection of his life's work and struggles. It is his soul depicted on paper or canvas in all the colors of the palette. The same can be said for people of money. To a very wealthy person[25] a portfolio also depicts his or her soul, and though the depiction is monochrome, it includes all shades of green. The fine portfolio also works together in its diversity and its balance like a fine symphony. And a complete portfolio is like an eiderdown pillow on which you can rest your tired head at night, knowing that God is in his heaven, and all's right with the economy. With your economy, anyway, which is all that really matters. Relax in your bed. Listen to the music. Let your portfolio surround you, comfort you, and protect you like a big green womb.

POSITIONING   Everything you do and every decision you make; every directive you sign and every memo you email; every order you bark and every word you utter is a position. A CEO is like a thoroughbred racehorse jockeying for advantage at just the right moment, and every move you make as a CEO will be noticed, studied, analyzed, and acted upon by your underlings, your investors, your enemies, and the press. Always think position. Realize that every waking moment you possess is an opportunity to improve your position. The race to wealth is relentless. You must be equally relentless.

---

25 With the exception of The Man from Omaha. Frankly, I don't know what a portfolio means to people like him. Why build a portfolio just to give it away? Life is a mystery.

On the other hand, if the time should come that you find yourself in a hopeless position and you cannot devise a graceful way out, then bail fast and save your ass. Never try to repair a hopeless position. Cut your losses as quickly as you can, learn from your mistakes, and then re-position. Next time around, ask yourself: How many ways can I approach this investor or that target company to get what I want? Like the *Kama Sutra*, you should have at least six positions in mind so you can exploit every opportunity for maximum benefit.

POWER   With his show, "The Prairie Home Companion," Garrison Keillor made a career on public radio as a spokesman for shy people. He made them seem amusing. However, you will not find any of them in corporate boardrooms, and you will find few running successful businesses of any kind. The world's work is reserved for aggressive people who enjoy using power. As for top executive positions in large corporations, only the most aggressive need apply, and of those applicants, only the five or ten percent with the greatest appetite for power will climb the summits.

By nature men are warriors. Warriors love power because the more power they wield, the better they can do their job. This world does in fact belong to the meat-eaters. It tolerates fruit-gatherers and biscuit-makers only so long as they stay out of the way and live in the shadows of what others build. Make the choice: Either Powdermilk Biscuits, public radio, a Piper Cub, and a green car that runs like a vacuum cleaner, or blood rare steak, your box on Super bowl Sunday, a Gulfstream G-200, and a vintage 1964 Shelby Cobra 427, no seatbelts. Life is about action. Speed. Risk. Dominance. Glory. It is about taking what you want and beating back your enemies. I am here to tell you that if you act with muscle at all times you will climb over the spent bodies of your competitors and make it to the top.

Here's to all you gentle shy folks. You do make us smile. And you make a fine staircase.

THE PRESIDENCY   I have always thought that Texas and Wyoming produced more men with the right stuff than other states. From earliest days, both states have been dominated by cattle and oil men who were tough, decisive, hardheaded, hard drinking, shoot-from-the-hip businessmen who don't tolerate nonsense and who understand the importance of power, money, property, loyalty, strong leadership, and free enterprise on steroids. George W. Bush and Dick Cheney confirmed my belief. However, recent events have caused me to alter my view. Neither place holds a candle to our newest state.

When the state of Grace was admitted to the union as our 51st state, who would have believed that it would give us a president *and* vice-president? Whoever orchestrated the merger of these two men, President Don Quickoats and Vice President Shooter Grimm, two United Universal Pentecostal Full Baptist Methodist Evangelicals, loaded with personal ambition and optimism, was brilliant.

Both leaders are top drawer members of The Club and tireless supporters of free market trade, a strong monetary policy, an even stronger military policy, and backyard barbecue. Quickoats inherited his membership from his family, its broad network of influential friends, and its solid name-recognition, while Grimm earned his, all on his own after a shaky start, as the archetypal self-made CEO. In other words, one man brought old money, good looks, and family connections to the table, while the other brought actual skills and attitude. Thus these two men melded together two dominant traditions in American culture, symbolized by their experiences at Wigglesworth University.   Quickoats was the classic front man, the New England born preppy insider gliding through on a gentleman's C and his trust fund, president of his fraternity, and tapped by the august Grins and Ghouls Society. Grimm was the outsider with true grit, the rugged individualist and scholarship boy from Humble City, Grace who snubbed the snobs, boycotted glee clubs, wounded a descendant of Increase Mather whom he mistook for a duck, and got expelled for his efforts. One was raised in the silver spoon bounty of The American Dream; the other forced hard-charging merit down the dream's throat until it let him in, by God. Yet despite their differences, both men have a few things in common that make them a good match. Both men drank like fish when they were younger and both admitted to sniffing insect repellant, though neither inhaled deeply. Neither served in the active military; both were driven by a secret compulsion to play with Legos; and both held an almost fanatical allegiance to Roadrunner cartoons. Could anyone come up with a better pair to look out for three hundred million Americans and lead the most powerful nation in history through the labyrinths of international relations than Quickoats and Grimm?

Technically, Quickoats became the fortieth-something President of The United States. In reality, he became the nation's first CEO, and Vice President Grimm became its first Chairman of the Board. The rest of the directors were tapped from party stalwarts; Quickoats family friends; the secretarial pool of the Grace Chamber of Commerce; OPEC (the Organization of the Petroleum Exporting Countries); the NAACP (National Association for the Advancement of Corporate Profits;)[26] and, of course, major campaign contributors keeping an eye on their investment. Quickoats and Grimm were brilliant. It was no small task to reorganize the executive branch and do business as a corporation. None of their reforms was new to Washington politics, but Quickoats and Grimm advanced several of them farther than any previous administration, and advanced some of them almost to the point of true corporate efficiency. Let's take a look at their record.

Secrecy. No corporation can make sound decisions with an open door to enemies, the press, the public, and any half-wit ne'er-do-well with a bur under his saddle. Quickoats and Grimm succeeded in draping the executive branch at all levels with a long-needed cloak of secrecy, which allowed them to take advice from trusted friends, to ignore everyone else, and to make decisions compatible with their business plan, the top secret "Yearly Unified Government Operations Strategy," (YUGOS.)

Both men also appointed themselves to honorary membership on the White House janitorial staff, which placed them under the Janitorial Branch of our government. In turn, this membership superseded their membership in the Executive Branch. Since janitors are not allowed to

26 Not to be confused with the NAACP (National Association for the Advancement of Colored People). This White House didn't belong to this NAACP. However, some of their best friends were PCCPs (politically correct colored people.) For example, Fortissima Squash was appointed to the cabinet as Secretary of Public Relations for Unresolved Conundrums Excluding International Terror and Unilateral Peace (SPRUCEITUP).

know national secrets, and since they are not required to keep records and turn over archives even if they did know anything relevant to national business, both men – as janitors -- were automatically exempt from the normal reporting requirements expected of normal White House executives. This helped them preserve the integrity of their private meetings and discussions. I say kudos, gentlemen. Anything that contributes to integrity in government must be considered a memorable achievement.

Accounting. By applying corporate accounting standards to national finances and to statistics, they were able to support the value of their stock and sustain the confidence of their shareholders through many troubled times. For example, although the national bottom line moved swiftly from a huge surplus to the largest deficit in history, and the nation's trade deficit broke record after record, extraordinary write-offs, future profits, job creation, low unemployment, rising productivity, falling labor costs, and a host of other deeply significant factors combined like a baseball team to whip doom and gloom and hit the nation's corporate report card out of the park. Furthermore, despite astronomical increases in the prices of energy and food, not to mention core indicators like education, health care, and drugs, inflation rates for working people as calculated by accepted reorganized accounting standards remained negligible. And while worker productivity soared, labor costs plummeted, leading to a robust GDP with record setting profits for corporations, particularly in the energy and finance sectors. The result was a robust corporate economy with outstanding future prospects. Finally, by treating the war in Iraq, inherited from George W. Bush and Dick Cheney, as an off the books, offshore limited partnership, the two plus billion dollar official weekly price tag did not figure into the national budget deficit. Using widely accepted mark to market accounting procedures, future gains projected from the war were counted as present profits. That is as it should be. Depending on its outcome, the war can always be deducted later as a write off when earnings are restated, but for now, it counts as an asset.

Finance. Modern finance is like modern physics, where new dimensions and new entities are always on the table, things like time and virtual particles that have to be plugged into equations. Line items adding up to trillion dollar deficits don't look good on a standard profit and loss statement until you realize that certain losses are only virtual because the time line that measures them is limited. What about re-capitalization, robust bond sales, buy-backs, and future increases in revenues? Plenty of variables, not measurable in the present, produce new revenue streams that quickly transform virtual losses into real profits. What you need is confidence in the plan, not carping, and Quickoats and Grimm demanded that confidence.

In addition, they were masters at using creative financing and OPM to capitalize government just as corporations do daily. For example, American corporations are moving to take over Chinese markets, a factor that will lead to enormous growth in our GDP. Meanwhile, who is financing our government while we expand our markets? Who is buying U.S. Treasury Bonds for modest returns at a record pace? Thanks, PRC. If it weren't for customers like you, we might have to restate earnings monthly.

The result is that America runs smoothly under virtual deficit spending that will be ameliorated over time, as capital freed for investment stimulates growth and growth provides new revenue. Deficits and future deficits that appear unsustainable today, particularly in Social Security and Medicare, will become minor budget items in tomorrow's panacea. Quickoats and Shooter were able to do all this *and* cut federal taxes for heavy hitters, who represent future investment and growth, because they understood finance.

Communications. Corporations are the masters of communications, and Quickoats and Grimm brought that mastery to government in ways that stunned even the most advanced Washington spin-doctors. No administration in history ever exercised tighter control over imagery, information, and public appearances, and none ever used greater skill in attempting to dictate public opinion by employing all the tools of communications, information technology, and product promotion. Even cereal box people could take a lesson from Quickoats and Grimm.

Executive Authority. Both men concentrated power in themselves in order to facilitate efficient decision-making and keep the nation on the right track. They refused to listen to naysayers and they eviscerated anyone who publicly disagreed with them, including, for example, the formidable former Secretary of State, B. G. Brassley, America's first and only nine star general. They also disemboweled the less formidable Hart Goodman, a career diplomat who suggested in a *Realist* op-ed story that Quickoats and

Grimm had exaggerated the threat posed by that notorious terrorist organization, "Islamic Women for Peace, Tranquility and Automatic Dishwashers," as an excuse to threaten Iran with nuclear holocaust. The actual
vivisection was applied to Goodman's wife, Plumb Dandee Pahlavi, who
was a CIA undercover mole in the fanatical Iranian group. One day, while
arranging for a clandestine shipment of automatic dishwashers to Teheran,
she was dragged from her apartment and stoned. Mysteriously, someone
had outed her, though later investigation proved that it was definitely not
Biff Loupy, another stalwart Wigglesworth man, or R. S. Putin, the college dropout and self-made advisor to presidents, both of whom served as
White House *councilieri*.

More important was Quickoats's use of "signing statements," a practice he picked up from George W. Bush and expanded modestly. Often fa-
cilitating a compromise between parties to get legislation passed, Quickoats
would sign the ensuing bill into law ceremoniously in the company of
Congressmen, Senators, and the press. Then, after everyone went home
satisfied, he would privately annotate the bill, outlining which parts should
become law and which not. During his first six months in office, Quickoats
never exercised his veto, which would have led to heightened debate and
inefficient decision-making, but he penned more than seven hundred and
fifty thousand signing statements *after* signing three hundred and two bills
into law. This allowed him to supersede an inefficient congress and keep
the nation on track with his business plan, YUGOS, and it turned his administrative policies into laws of the land.

Quickoats's uses of administrative law, through executive branch ap-
pointive offices, were equally decisive in hundreds of instances throughout
the nation. For example, by changing the definition of elemental mercury
from a "toxic metal" to a "funny liquid," his Environmental Protection
Agency succeeded in reducing pollution significantly throughout America,
since toxic metals pollute and funny liquids don't. Experts are currently
working on a new project to provide clearer definitions for Cadmium,
Lead, Arsenic, and Polonium-210 (project CLAP).

At one time or another, most of us have been heard to mutter, "If
my business did things the way government does, I'd go broke in a week."

Quickoats lanced that idea and turned it on its head. He forced government to do things the way business does, with unregulated executive authority, and look at what he achieved.

The Grand Economy. By recognizing and promoting, in every aspect of American life, the machinery of supply and demand; the inherent goodness of the free enterprise system re-tooled to fit corporations and then supercharged; globalization; the model of the corporation as a template for all human activities; the value of privatization and deregulation; the usefulness of networking with close, loyal, like-minded friends; the necessity for winner-take-all competition; the wisdom of rewarding those who win competitive battles so they can successfully manage the nation's capital for the good of all; and the nearly-impossible-dream of transforming Middle-East tribal sheiks into Rotarians, Quickoats and Grimm advanced the cause of The Grand Economy almost as much as Ronald Reagan and George W. Bush, and more than their predecessors, George Herbert Walker Bush and Bill Clinton, both of whom did a creditable job of their own during their turns in office.

Individualism and personal responsibility. The cornerstone of all free enterprise is individualism, the idea that each individual and every corporation is capable of taking care of number one, *should* be responsible for taking care of number one, and, most importantly, is free to take care of number one without interference from government. This nation was made great by people who pulled themselves up by their own bootstraps, or by people who had loyal, talented, and well-connected family friends to help them pull when their own tugging got them nowhere but stuck. That is The American Way. More than any administration in our history, Quickoats and Shooter advanced the cause of bootstraps. By eliminating, reducing, or opposing government welfare subsidies, such as block grants to states, funding for failing public schools, giveaways to retarded and crippled citizens who are perfectly able to work, excessive benefits to veterans, subsidies for students, money-losing clinics for Indians, birth control and abortion for the promiscuous, Social Security for old people funded entirely by the government, and dozens of other wasteful programs and half-baked notions left over from the welfare state mentality that dominated America from the election of Franklin D. Roosevelt through the demise of Lyndon B. Johnson, Quickoats and Shooter forced America's consumers to take responsibility and stop sponging off Big Brother. This tough love aspect of their administration will have tremendous benefits for the long term, as people and states get back on track, shed the idea that someone somewhere owes them a living, and start organizing bake sales to fund needed programs and maintain the nation's infrastructure.

Aggressiveness. The tone of the Quickoats-Grimm administration, particularly the personality of Shooter Grimm, did more than any administration in our history to emphasize the single most important character trait required to compete successfully: Aggressiveness. Flat-out, in your face, no bullshit, I'm-going-to-get-there-first aggressiveness. Winners push. Shy people get pushed aside. If you can't promote yourself and bully others, then you'd better become a Buddhist monk in Nepal because our real world no longer has room for pussies. Consumers followed enthusiastically this change of tone both in their businesses and in their personal lives. Throughout America, people today are driving, speaking, arguing, preaching, working, buying, selling, and shooting each other with more rapture and more spontaneous, joyful aggression than I have seen in my lifetime, an observation that warms my heart and gives me hope.

Loyalty. Quickoats-Grimm required loyalty. For example, the selective suspension of some secondary civil liberties, such as *habeas corpus,* privacy, and free speech, requires trust in your leaders, and trust is loyalty. Americans came up with an amazing amount of loyalty in response to The Glorious Heroic Homeland Act and other administrative actions in the ongoing War on Terror. But loyalty is more than a response. It is a way of life. A successful plan succeeds only when all on board are rowing in the same direction in synch. Enemies of this kind of loyalty are enemies of the state, and while their voices may be heard, the speakers also need to be pilloried and stoned as traitors. The best way to do that is to let the public do it. For example, carefully depict an enemy, such as the hysterical mother of a dead soldier who insists on criticizing national policies that killed her son, so that depiction will invite a buzz. In short order, selected loyal citizens, news networks, commentators, talk show hosts, and think tank gurus will amplify that buzz until public opinion catches fire. Before you know it, virtual volunteer vigilance committees all over the nation will round up the offender like a trout for a fish fry and pack her off to town squares to face justice in courts of selected public opinion. Sometimes disloyalty hits closer to home. For example, it you hired a secretary of state who, just because he is a genius, thinks that his ideas are better than yours, then you must try to ignore him, undermine him, or demote him to errand boy. If all that fails, fire him and call it retirement. As a CEO, how long would you employ an independent minded executive who is smarter than you? Just long enough to replace him, if you're shrewd. Running a country is no different and Quickoats and Grimm understood that.

Loyalty also cuts both ways, and Quickoats-Grimm were absolutely amazing in their tenacious support of their most loyal soldiers, men like Attorney General Niño Cabana, and like Secretary of Defense, Louis Fourtinski, who had a sunny disposition but no skill whatsoever as a leader of military leaders. However, he was a brilliant spokesman and government insider, and he displayed, often under extreme duress, more loyalty to his masters than a poodle. That loyalty was returned in aces until voters spoke and the administration had to clear the way for images of a new administration, a new war policy, a new military, and new yellow brick road.

Idealism. Evil lurks in this world like a demonic windmill on the horizon, ready to cut to ribbons anyone who approaches. Only a true crusader could attack that evil with the fury of three-hundred-Spartans-times-a-thousand and stay the course until all that evil is exterminated from the world and replaced by good. Quickoats took on this quest. Sometimes it was lonely with only his sidekick Grimm and the prime minister of Togo to cheer him on. There is nothing more to say except, God's speed, Don.

In summary, Don Quickoats will be remembered as a pioneer. His life's great success was getting into the White House, our first MBA with a minor in BBQ, and our first real CEO with janitorial credentials. Ambitious CEOs of the future will take note. Once elected, his most memorable achievement was pushing his agenda. He contributed measurably to the advancement of The Grand Economy and corporate profits. As for his leadership and his administrative abilities, of course, he will not be lionized. Tragically, I think that Mr. Quickoats thought of the Presidency as a venue in which he could finally make his bones on his own, without assistance from his dad or his dad's friends.[27] However, he wasn't any better as a CEO in the White House than he was in Mucho Gusto or any of his other ventures. He will not be remembered as a pretty good CEO, or even as one of nation's best marksmen, like his Vice President, Shooter Grimm. But that is immaterial. Mr. Quickoats will always be admired by ordinary citizens for his unwavering support of baseball, his friends, and barbecued ribs. Future historians will remember him as a pioneer in the quest to incorporate America; as a heroic idealist on a mission to destroy evil; and as one of the truly great face men America has ever produced. His jaw was nearly flawless.

PRODUCTION   Nature produces nothing. It merely provides. Only human beings produce. Production is the creation, according to a rational plan, of an artifact that does not exist in nature. It is this value-added aspect of production that makes it so important and so valuable. Nature provides rocks, but only we can produce a *Pet* Rock. Nature provides gold, but only we can produce a fine tennis bracelet. Nature provides sunsets and big horn sheep, but only we can produce a television commercial that uses them to sell stuff. Production is the re-assembly of nature into stuff interesting or useful to human beings, and the more advanced the economy, the more complicated the stuff it produces.

As we re-make nature to suit our needs and desires, we create a new world of complex stuff which in time will replace and improve the old world of simple nature. Production is, therefore, a God-like function. In the beginning there was light, thanks to Thomas Edison and his stuff, the light bulb. And from there we advanced. Year by year as we adapt to this new world of stuff and discard the old world of dirt and trees, we become more acutely aware of the importance of production in our lives. The truth of the matter is that production, along with the stuff it produces, is our lives. Go forward and produce and let production multiply until it

---

27 Whatever advice the President received, his use of it was minimal. We can say with certainty that Quickoats achieved his goal of making his own bed. It wasn't as comfortable as he had imagined, but it featured nice trim and it gave him a place to lie.

takes over the minds and hearts of people everywhere. The sooner primitive and underdeveloped peoples get on board, the better. The future is already scripted, like the plot of an entertaining movie, so let's teach them to crave stuff, love production, and depend upon both. In time, because of your efforts, they will become more and more productive until one day, while visiting one of your production facilities in Peru, Bangladesh, Viet Nam, or the Marianas, after you carefully inspect the stuff they make, interpret their final production reports for a given quarter, and crunch their numbers, you will be able to stand as tall as Andrew Carnegie, inhale with pride, and pronounce them, "efficient." Let me tell you, it doesn't get any better than that.

PRODUCTIVITY   The Industrial Revolution gave us an amazing gift: The machine, and with it, the concepts of efficiency and productivity. Since the invention of the machine, the mechanical model has increasingly become the standard for all industry, all business, and life itself. Today, the idea of productivity allows us to quantify human utility and measure it exactly.

Yesterday, people measured the success or failure of their lives in nebulous terms like "happiness," or "good times," that are so subjective as to be meaningless, even childish. Today, in the same way that the dollar in America has become the sole measure of all value, productivity has become the sole standard by which to judge the usefulness of a human life. Even line workers, after spending half a Sunday on a couch watching football, will comment, "I have got to do something more productive." Watch them get up and mow the lawn and wash the car. These people have found something a lot more substantive and measurable than so called "good times."

I am amazed at how much productivity we can get out of young MBAs fresh out of graduate school and striving to earn their spurs. Young people used to spend half their lives cruising bars with friends, dancing, dating, and playing softball. Not any more. Some of these new folks work eighteen hours a day seven days a week and sleep on the floor under their desks. They don't even ask for vacation time. It's enough to bring tears to your eyes. Plus, think of how the human species has benefited from the productivity model. Every night, as people prepare for sleep, they can look back on their day and literally count their worth by the number of reports they completed, the number of meetings they attended, and the number of solutions they generated. You couldn't do that back in the Gay Nineties, for example, when it was enough to take a joy ride in a carriage, eat home made ice cream at a picnic, and paddle a canoe with some girl down a lazy, meandering river. We have progressed to the point that many ordinary people, even single mothers, work two or even three jobs to keep their productivity levels high. Let me tell you, nothing is more rewarding than to feel a pat on the shoulder, as you are starting the back nine, from a fellow CEO who asks, "How do you get so much productivity out of your marketing people?" He might as well have told you that you had won an Oscar.

I salute productivity, but I also know that we have not yet reached anywhere near our potential. Given another half century, perhaps we will reach maximum productivity, and if we do, of course, then we'll have to turn many of our tasks over to robots and supercomputers who will raise the bar of efficiency to new levels. Dare we dream of a world in which there is no limit to productivity, a world in which human fulfillment increases with every generation as each of us becomes more productive than anyone in the past has ever been? Dream on, I say. Dream on until your dreams have been replaced by a final accounting that lifts human productivity to the almost supernatural level of a Cray computer.

PROFIT   An apple picked from a wild tree is only an apple. Someone eats the apple and the food is metabolized and that is that. A jar of applesauce, however, is more than a jar of applesauce. In turning apples into applesauce, a producer has added value to a product. It is now worth more than raw apples. To the extent that the added value exceeds the maximum cost requirements of the producer, a distributor, and a retail grocer, the applesauce has generated capital. Everyone takes a cut along the way from factory to grocery store, and so long as the perceived value of the applesauce holds, that is, as long as consumers are ready to bid the asking price for it, then each of those cuts represents an excess value we call profit. This is a convoluted way of repeating the single, fundamental principle of all business: Buy low and sell high. Purchase raw apples for next to nothing. Pay your labor as little as you can. And then sell your gourmet applesauce for a tidy profit.

Increasingly, profit is dependent on the perception of value in a product. A bunch of rags sewn together in the right shape, stuffed with beans and called a "limited edition" or a "collector's item," can be outrageously profitable, but only so long as the manufacturer is able to sustain the consumer's perception that he or she is acquiring great value. In the contemporary era of powerful information systems, I propose that we amend the old statement about buying low and selling high to: "Buy low, enhance the image, and then sell even higher." Think of the difference between two pairs of jeans identical in every way but one: One is a brand, the other is a brand endorsed by a celebrity. The enhanced image of the second pair will double its price and quadruple its profit. Today, we can honestly say that a majority of profits are more the result of magnified image than of added value; or, that magnified image is the central cause of perceived added value, and hence, of profits.

I call this innovation, "flair." Sure, you can make soap. Or you can make a beauty bar that moisturizes as it cleanses, disinfects as it reconditions, and transforms unsightly wrinkles into youthful skin that glows. If a good salesman could sell an air conditioner to an Alaskan, a salesman with flair can sell a quarter pound of lard and lye, cleverly described and packaged, to half the world's middle-aged women who want to look like eighteen-year-old cover girls.

Remember this: Hope never has to be fulfilled. It just has to be sustained. There is more profit in hope, however fantastic, than in all the innovations in history combined. Sell hope with flair and your star will shine.

PROGRESS   Everywhere you look, progress astounds. A whole library can now be stored on a flash drive smaller than your pinkie finger and its contents are available to anyone in seconds at the touch of that same finger. Life expectancy worldwide has doubled in a century. Slavery, torture, mutilation, mass murder, child molestation, wife beating, rape, and kidnapping, while still widely practiced, are today considered rude behavior in many parts of the world. Yesterday we had hoops and sticks. Today we have *Grand Theft Auto*, the NBA, and derivatives. For forty thousand years people shouted, beat drums, and burned smoke signals to communicate. Today, you can call your cousin in Kansas on your iPhone, text message that stranger across town whom you plan to meet maybe, or send all your friends a real time picture of your dead Sherpa after you narrowly escape an avalanche over your base camp on Everest. And while the twentieth century probably killed more citizens in wars than all the rest of history combined, the twenty-first century already considers many of those deaths regrettable. Progress inches forward. Occasionally it rockets. However fast it moves, progress is one of the defining characteristics of our species. We are not content to live without reassuring ourselves that we are making progress.

Don't let cynicism keep you out of the game. Make progress in whatever you do, and progress will reward you, if not with better sales and a longer life, at least with the satisfaction of knowing that in moving from point A to point B you have advanced yourself and your world a little closer to a point that is farther away from point A than point B and closer to point C than you were at point A. Just keep moving and it will all make sense.

PROMOTION   All product promotions, in one way or another, convey the same simple, subliminal message: If you the consumer owned this product or service, you too would become *A Winner!* How is that message conveyed? To which human urges do you appeal to convey that message most efficiently?

Every good promotion is acted out on a stage of instinctual human needs. The promotion works because it offers redemption from fear and insecurity by appealing to fundamental human urges, all of them unsatisfied in real life, yet each of them paramount in the unconscious mind of every normal consumer.

Begin with fear. Every human being is beset, consciously or unconsciously, by fears, including fears of inadequacy. Am I too fat? Am I ugly? Am I too hairy? Are my breasts the right size? Will bird flu kill me? Will terrorists kidnap my children? Is my car too old? Is my outdoor barbecue fancy enough? How long before I get cancer? Is my diet poisonous? Is my spouse bored with me? Am I a loser? I could go on indefinitely. Build your stage with subtlety so the consumer won't become defensive. Let the consumer unearth his or her own fears excited by the imagery you project. Once those fears have been unleashed, present the cure.

Offer prestige. Most people, and Americans in particular, have a pathological need to be liked or admired by everyone, and so they constantly seek prestige. Hence, the promotional message must be that the owner of this product or service will shine above other people who don't own it. The owner will show that he or she is keeping up with the highest strata of society. Ownership of this product or service will force others to respect, admire, and envy the owner.

Demonstrate romance. Prove with graphic imagery that to own this product or service is to associate one's self with success in romance, with desirability, and with sexual prowess and passion. Let the consumer cast himself or herself as the hero/heroine in the romance novel of sound and sight bites you present. Keep the imagery warm and fuzzy for female consumers; lean on sexual power for males.

Suggest magic. The powers of this product or service are so great and so rewarding that they exceed all those of the ordinary, natural world. They convey their magical powers in ways that remain a mystery, but there is no doubt. The product or service unlocks doors to mysteries greater than our understanding. Anything can convey magic, but technological devices and new medicines are the most convincing. A magic magenta pill will make your pain go away and save you from disease, surgery, and death. The magic moisturizing lotion will give you the soft skin of a baby and cure your naturally rough, pachyderm hide. These magic shoes will elevate you at last to the level of a goddess, and save your dumpy self from the ridicule you suspect others heap upon you. This magic automobile will finally give you the ride a true warrior deserves. It is an extension of you, a portrait of your true self, and it will help you drive triumphantly past your small penis, your fear of public speaking, that time the bully intimidated you, and your brutal, insensitive, uncaring father.

For a real kicker, after a solid dose of fear, offer prestige, romance, and magic all together in a single package. They are irresistible when taken together, and they will make anyone think that he or she is a winner.

Apply enough skill over a long enough period of time to the same group of people, and you will be able successfully to promote *anything*. Doing business without serious promotion is insane. The practice persists only in isolated backwaters where the natives do not have ready access to communications. There, I am told, traders still try to sell things because they are supposed to be useful, well made, durable, and a good value for the price. As media saturation spreads, however, such ideas will be exterminated and we can look forward to a world utterly attuned to the urges of the inner self and liberated from the tiresome bondage of so-called common sense.

Promotion helps people mine their most poignant delusions, and the gems they find give them enough vitality to endure their lives a little longer.

PROSPERITY   Survival and prosperity are like twin stars that rotate around each other. The vast majority of people are motivated by the need to survive. Once their survival seems ensured, they turn their thoughts to prosperity. If they are shrewd, work hard, and find opportunity, then chances are good that they will achieve some prosperity. Once prosperous, they will then turn their thoughts back to survival so they can live long enough to enjoy their wealth, and so they can fend off assaults from others who covet what they own. But isn't there more to prosperity than the drive to sustain it? Might not there be a deeper meaning, one that can reach out and touch the whole world?

I believe prosperity does offer a deeper meaning – and an opportunity. Consider the direction religion has taken in our deeply religious society. The primitive idea that a rich man won't make it to heaven any more than a fat camel can squeeze through the gate called the eye of the needle has been forgotten in favor of the idea that God helps people who help themselves. Similarly, the unsophisticated idea that the prosperous should give away their money and follow their Savior has been replaced by the idea that prayer can boost sales. This turn of events has set the stage for a religious revival unlike any we have ever experienced. That forthcoming revival could encompass millions of faithful consumers – and millions in donations.

Like a phoenix, this new religion is already taking shape from the ashes of our old puritanical churches. Every day more and more people are calling on divine intervention to achieve prosperity and avoid financial misery. At the same time, competition for prosperity is becoming fiercer. In a world teeming with nearly seven billion human beings, most of whom breed, the odds of gaining prosperity decrease hourly. You need an edge. Who better than God to provide that edge? The Word is getting out. Millions of the faithful already are poised and waiting for some kind of organized leadership. Why not provide it?

If I were younger, poor, and religious, I would consider providing it, but since I have already made mine, I couldn't care less. However, the opportunity is ripe. It has worldwide potential and someone is going to exploit it. A young man or woman who has ambition, religious instincts, and access to a small boost of investment capital could jump in right now on the ground floor, declare a new religion, something like, "The Church of the Revealed Prophecy of Profits," and launch a successful career as an evangelist of prosperity.

A church like this would be market driven and syndicated in a week. Look at the appeal. Its faith would yield tangible rewards that you can spend. Its practitioners would feel good about themselves. The faithful would not have to wait around for the rapture because this church's promised goals would be immediate – next week's bottom line. And who wouldn't love a church that does not require confession? Here is a religion that is all good news and positive thinking, and the number of potential converts is truly astronomical. Those who achieve grace can enjoy it while they are still alive. Those who fail and fall into the hell of poverty are not condemned to stay there forever but can redeem themselves at any time. Plus there is always a chance that, in time, you might be able to canonize yourself.

Best of all, in The Church of The Revealed Prophecy of Profits, there would be no risk of hypocrisy, not even for you, its leader. A good evangelist practices what he or she preaches. If you preach prosperity and solicit donations in your cable syndicated broadcast studio of worship, then you can keep for yourself every dime donated. In a church devoted to prosperity, whatever profit you take would have to be considered a testimony to your righteousness.

PUBLIC RELATIONS   Some of you have your degrees. A few of you have already worked in the real world. I am sure that all of you are focused on your career goals, so I am confident that you understand by now the important connection between strong public relations and profits. That understanding should guide you well. Permit me, therefore, to digress and turn your attention to the more philosophical aspects of the science of public relations and its importance to the long-term survival of our way of life.

Public Relations was a more dismal science than economics before the late 1920s and I say dismal because it was crude, ineffective, and based on instinct, not research. Adolph Hitler was a horrendous man and I do not recommend anything about him except his death. However, he was also a pioneer, the pioneer who opened the PR box when he recognized the genius of his right hand man and Propaganda Minister, Joseph Goebbels. Goebbels' main propaganda tool, The Big Lie, was the most effective instrument of persuasion since the thumbscrew. He understood its dynamics perfectly and he used them like a virtuoso. Say anything often enough and loud enough and pretty soon most people will believe that it might be true. Keep saying it and they will believe that it is true.

The development of mass communications media following World War II offered public relations a fast, efficient track into every home and every consciousness in America. The world soon followed and persistence began to pay dividends. Did you ever think you'd see a MacDonald's in Paris? Did you ever think that a second string Hollywood actor could make it into the White House? Would anyone have believed forty years ago that a hard working CEO would be awarded a forty million dollar bonus as his company loses money, its stock drops forty percent, and thousands of its workers have to be laid off? Since the beginning of time, the brass ring has gone to the most aggressive and convincing orator. We remember Socrates and the great Roman Senators because they could BS their peers better than anyone else. Public Relations is your rhetorical voice rising in the public square in competition with other voices, all reaching for the brass ring. Gain total expertise in PR. Buy the finest PR department on earth. Buy media and direct their content. Polish your performances. Spread your network worldwide, and speak, speak, speak. It doesn't matter what you say as long as you say it often and loud.

Media ownership and PR savvy will also give you the means to limit outputs that counter your own. No, this is not the curtailment of free speech. A corporation is not the government. It is bound by its articles of incorporation and by its responsibility to its stockholders, not simply by the Constitution of the United States. You can stop those you don't like from using your media. It is not your responsibility to provide a forum for your enemies. Finding an outlet is *their* responsibility. If they are not up to fulfilling their responsibility, then it's their problem, not yours. Quiet your critics, and speak, speak, speak.

The importance of PR cannot be overestimated. Modern history is one long war for the minds of people, and that war is never over. You can convince people of anything. It doesn't matter whether they are consumers, voters, German villagers, French food snobs, or boards of directors. *You can convince anyone of anything.* The catch is that so can someone else. Therefore, it is your responsibility to yourself, to your corporation, to your shareholders, and to all of us who share belief in our way of life, to become the best, to speak out the most, and to out-speak the rest.

"Buy media and direct their content....It doesn't matter what
you say as long as you say it often and loud." p. 312-313

QUALITY   I endorse quality, but I believe that it should represent a win-win situation. Consumers expect quality and we should give them quality. But like anything else, too much of a good thing can turn out to be a bad thing. Imagine manufacturing a lawn mower that never had to be replaced. How would consumers take advantage of innovations and future lower margins or price cuts? If perfect lawn mowers had been available in 1940, we would all still be pushing them by hand.

Here is a terrifying example from real life. What do you think killed the watch industry? The Swiss made watches to last past the second coming. A few years ago, if you broke a balance staff, the watchmaker would fix it plus clean and re-oil the watch for a few dollars and the watch was back on your wrist in a week and ready to outlive God. Today perfect digital watches are available for twenty bucks, but who even needs watches when every device from an iPod to a cell phone tells you what time it is to the second in twenty-four time zones plus the planet Vulcan? Of course, devices like iPods are fully warranted to die or become antique in less than twenty-four months. Fortunately, new and improved replacement devices are readily available.[28] The point is to let quality reflect not only the highest standards of product integrity; let it also reflect the highest standards of corporate integrity. That is, leave a little room for new products ready to

---

28 We all hear complaints about the poisonous materials in disposable electronic devices and their batteries, most of which end up in landfills. I want to be the first to point out that these materials poison only living creatures, and there are no living creatures in landfills, except for the occasional rat, cockroach, or scavenger bird. In addition, we will ship more and more of our refuse to foreign sites happy to have the business. Local peasants like to forage and recycle the toxins to boost their incomes and increase their chances of gaining useful mutations.

replace the obsolete, and you will stay in business to serve the public much longer. No one wins with quality run amok, just as no one wins with zero quality. A reasonable dose of quality, on the other hand, means that consumers win and business wins. Our commerce is built on this foundation. Don't rock it. Rock and roll with it.

QUANTITATIVE ANALYSIS   If you can't express it in numbers, or if the numbers you use to express it cannot be translated into dollars, don't bother. It is irrelevant.

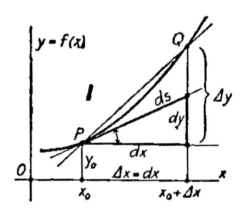

RADICALISM   Left wing political movements, the natural enemy of commerce, come to life in union halls and on college campuses. In general, that leads to an explosive mixture of whining from workers who think they are victims, and idealism from students who feel guilt and outrage because they have discovered that the rest of the world isn't all made of freedom, justice, spring breaks, free sex, soccer moms, malls, friendly faces, and dads with endless bank accounts.

Neutralize unions by discrediting their corrupt leaders and their ties to organized crime; by convincing the non-union public that unions threaten the American Way of Life; and by busting the unions themselves or stopping them before they get started. You can best accomplish that by giving workers plenty of blue sky; that is, by encouraging them to understand that they are better off not paying union dues and not giving up what they firmly believe is their personal independence.

Idealistic students are another matter. The more you try to convince them of anything, the more they will move in the opposite direction. The best way to control idealistic youth is to keep the costs of higher education unreasonably high. This high tuition accomplishes three things. First, it screens out many potential rabble-rousers and pushes them into more affordable vocational-technical training where jobs supersede rebellion, and it keeps college doors open primarily to kids who already understand affluence. Second, it encourages students to take only those courses relevant to their careers. Colleges can no longer justify forcing students to take group requirements in humanities and social sciences, which often turn students to the left, when the students are footing the bill. Students who want a bang for their buck will demand a fast track to their chosen professions. And third, high tuition forces all students to regard finance as their first priority. What student in her right mind would take time to demonstrate against the firing of a Moslem professor facing deportation for inflammatory thoughts when she needs two jobs just to pay tuition? And who in her right mind would jeopardize her degree – and her ability to repay the sixty thousand dollar loan behind her degree – just to make a few waves? Unruly students can be branded as troublemakers or arrested and thrown out of college. Then what? Students paying high tuition *need* their degrees and their future earnings.

While we are on the subject of student motivation, it also goes without saying that we never again want to have the military draft, as we did during The Sixties. The only thing the draft did was to force those drafted to sacrifice, and when people sacrifice, they demand independence and recognition and if they don't get it they raise hell. Sixties draftees demanded to become part of the decision making process. In the end, veterans demanded care, minorities demanded equal opportunities, women demanded autonomy, the poor demanded more, and all of them demanded and won the right to vote at eighteen. That vote thing was a big mistake. Learn from it, and don't ever forget. The more dependent people are, the easier they are to lead.

The secret to defusing student radicalism is no secret at all. Apply the same strategy that you use to control the general population: Keep them needy.

RANDOM ACTS OF KINDNESS   In recent years, a certain type of personality has emerged and gone public. It combines an almost religious fervor with the desire to be liked by everyone. Persons who possess this personality are easily identified. They flit about like bluebirds of happiness offering "Random Acts of Kindness" to friends, associates, and total strangers, even to people who do not wish to be on the receiving end of a Random Act of Kindness.

Don't all birds leave droppings on statues and windshields, even bluebirds of happiness? Who wants twittering and guano when you are planning financial war? My advice is, if you have any employees who fit into this category, shoot them before they turn your best attack dogs into wimps. Keep a couple of them mounted on your trophy wall to ward off the rest.

REACH   Traditionally, demographic data provided the most accurate profiles on consumers, and generalized target advertising provided the best way to motivate them. All that is changing, thanks to a shift in perspective caused by developments in information technology and successes in online marketing.

New surveillance systems, like Pryen, installed in major retailers like W*ALLMINE!, will accurately measure consumers' direct responses to exact products. Did they buy or didn't they? Did they frown? Did their eyes dilate? Did their cheeks turn pink? In time, utilizing retinal scan, corneal imaging, and multiple reaction sensors, monitors will be able to measure and catalog responses by individual shoppers as accurately as for participants in focus groups. That will provide an invaluable case-by-case database for individual consumers. In response, you will see innovations in product packaging and placement, timing, pricing strategies, and calendar sensitive promotions. Next you will see major applications of behavioral marketing that uses tailored, product-specific advertising to target individuals based on their responses. And finally, you could see that advertising shaped as personal feedback, timed to motivate those individuals, reaching them in the field through their cell phones, iPods, iPhones, laptops, and GPS devices.

Much of that feedback-advertising might correlate consumers' real time locations with nearest vendors offering exactly what they like. For example, imagine Sarah Smith cruising down Main Street. Data Central knows that she absolutely loves pink packaging, low-carb snacks, bananas, and just about anything on sale. Store A is less than half a mile ahead on her left. She still has eighteen hundred dollars credit left on her Visa card. She spends more on Saturdays than any other day of the week, and it's Saturday. She tends to be an impulse buyer. She uses 3.4 hours of leisure time on Saturdays for shopping, and she has only been away from her apartment for 2.1 hours. The store is having a sale on banana flavored granola bars in white packages with pink trim. It's a slam dunk. Based on this high probability profile, store A's auto responder agrees to fund an ad and in seconds Sarah receives a text message on her cell phone informing her of the good deal available. She finds the store, loves the trim on the wrapping, and buys two 12-packs of granola bars plus some shampoo, a magazine, and a bottle of aspirin.

This entire process provides basic input/output services to the individual consumer enabling her to boot into action so her preferred behaviors can run efficiently. Without this BIOS function, consumers would be forced to perform their tasks the old fashioned way: To hunt through newspapers and read ads, calculate checkbook and credit card balances, project payoff dates, evaluate actual needs, compare products, weigh alternatives, balance potential rewards against actual risks, construct rational purchase guidelines, seek out vendors, then make point of sale decisions or not. With this function they can simply turn left, hit ENTER, and spend. That's reach.

REAL ESTATE   People have been trading land since the agricultural revolution created capital economies. Is it still a good market?

The habitable land surface of the earth is fixed. In fact, it is decreasing as oceans rise and deserts expand. The human population of the earth, on the other hand, is growing at a robust pace. Ergo, the surest and most profitable investment anyone can make, for the long, long run, is real estate. I wish it were as simple as that.

The problem is that one person can't necessarily live long enough to realize the massive profits in real estate that will result from high demand and low supply. In the short run, real estate prices vacillate. You still have to catch the optimum wave and avoid being swamped by the trenches. Timing is everything. On the other hand, you can finance all real estate purchases without having to risk a dime of your own money, and it is not uncommon to triple your money in two to four years, so the risk-reward ratio is extremely low and extremely favorable. Despite limitations for the long, long term, potential long-term and short-term profits make real estate a required investment. Whatever the market conditions, land is always good for something, and other people always covet it.

The trick to successful real estate speculation is turnover. Sell as quickly as you can once you meet your profit objective. Then reinvest and sell again. The quicker you turn your capital the higher your rate of return. The secret behind turnover is to have no connection whatsoever to the land. Think of it as capital, and if you can turn it without personally having to actually look at it, all the better. Sell your property to anyone who wants it regardless of their intentions and never look back. Always get your money up front. When the deal is done, smoke a cigarette and line up the next deal. Never deviate from these proven methods. Real estate speculation is our oldest profession and it deserves our respect.

RECESSION   Good businessmen profit during good times. Great businessmen know that you can always make money. Business thrives during changing circumstances. Look at the stock market, for example. A stock waltzing back and forth between 30 and 60 offers many more opportunities for profit (and for loss) than a stock that slowly rises from 30 to 35 or slowly falls from 60 to 55. The secret is, of course, to know what you are doing -- and to help less informed people think they know what they are doing. You have to understand trends at the front end, before they make headlines and the mob reacts, and you have to have the discipline to act rationally rather than gamble. Recession is just another form of movement. It provides an opportunity to get rid of dead wood, make operations more efficient, and use the counterbalance of mob action to lift your investments. If you can see recession coming, then you can cut overhead and quietly short the market. If you can time the rebound, then you can reposition and buy long for a longer term when your barber is dying to sell. Clearly, recession can stir things up and in stagnant times, if you are savvy, recession blows in like a Chinook wind.

Is it acceptable to conspire with your friends and associates to actually cause a recession? Or at least to help move the economy in that direction when monetary policy cooperates? Why not? No one gets hurt. The loss of a few jobs and benefits may slow the public's buying trends, but that can generally be offset by priming consumers with government aid and relaxed credit. Give a recently laid off single mom some food stamps; extended her unemployment benefits; mail her a shiny new credit card with zero interest for ninety days, and she'll be good for another six months. By then the recession will begin to wane and purchasing will pick up overall. Never be afraid to use recession and the fear of recession for contrarian ends that support profitability. Obviously this is more easily accomplished if you are in a fundamental sector, like energy, but we can all put our shoulders to the wheel when need dictates and have a pretty good chance of nudging the economy in the direction we choose.

Whether you help it along or not, remember that recession is just another business tool that can serve a variety of purposes in addition to your own efforts to streamline or to pad profits. You might have the wrong person in the White House, for example. Or you might want to focus consumer attention on domestic issues or environmental constraints. There is nothing like a recession to turn voters against their favorite son, and nothing like a shortage of heating oil in a cold winter to open up protected wild lands to exploration. Whatever your purpose, remember to time your personal investments to take full advantage of an economy in motion. Change can be good for us, good for business, and good for America.

REGULATION   The bane of all business is regulation. There should be no regulations whatsoever. Market forces like supply and demand will tell us what is true and what is false, what is good and what is bad, what is useful and what is useless, and what is fair and what is unfair. Fight all regulations with all your influence as long as you have a career, and strive to build a deregulated world in which, like the African lion, the CEO is "Born free…," free to try this and free to accomplish that; free to compete and free to win the dollars of consumers any way he can so long as consumers go along. Such a world works like the world of natural evolution. In the end, those most adapted to the natural forces of the market prevail, and in doing so, they give consumers exactly what consumers demand. When meeting demand, those who are well-adapted prosper and are rewarded, just as the lion was rewarded with survival for its ability to adapt so well to the savannah.

Regulation is the invention of those who cannot compete. It is their way of fixing the contest so that they too will survive. They must therefore be viewed as misfits – they *are* the weakest link and they should be expelled from the game. Good-bye!

RELIGION   As far as your professional life is concerned, take all religion with a grain of salt. Business and religion don't mix.[29] Whatever your personal inclinations, whether religious, agnostic, or atheist, avoid religious enthusiasm altogether in the workplace except to the extent that it can be used as a tool to help sculpt your image in the community. An occasional appearance in a fashionable house of worship, or a timely donation or public support of a fundraiser; even something as simple as a hearty handshake to the faithful will not harm you and will support your status as a wholesome fellow who should be trusted.

If you choose to belong to a church for public relations, choose your religion carefully. Avoid the extremes and stick to the mainstream ancient religions or to the fashionable descendents of Reformation sects. If you are based in New York City, Chicago, Miami or the entertainment industry, for example, you can comfortably be Jewish, though I recommend against wearing a yarmulke except in the private company of other Jews. If you are based in the South, I recommend a Baptist allegiance, preferably Baptist light if you can find it. In Boston, Baltimore, Chicago, St. Louis, New Orleans or most of the Midwest, Catholicism should not raise any eyebrows. In the breadbasket, I suggest you try becoming a Presbyterian or a Methodist, and of course in Minnesota, the Lutheran faith is mandatory.

Utah is a problem. The fashionable infrastructure is one hundred percent LDS, but the Mormon faith is upstart and well outside the mainstream. For example, they tithe ten percent, which is a pretty hefty chunk. As a result, they are better organized and more capable than the Red Cross

---

29 Unless, of course, religion is your business. In that case you are still better off applying sound management techniques more than theology. You can't push your prophet unless you make enough profit to develop and keep a viable market share and build a big enough nest egg to see you through an apocalypse.

and the Salvation Army combined, which is good for poor people and victims of natural disasters, but not so good for affluent non-victims who want to maximize their bottom lines. Mormons also depend on revelations from God to implement policies like racial equality. Fortunately, God delivered His most stunning revelation, which took the mark of Cain off African Americans and gave them access to the priesthood, just after racial tensions peaked during the Black Power years and as Brigham Young University opted to become a football power. But who can depend on God to deliver the right revelation at the right time? Some groups have been petitioning God for centuries with negative results. Then there is that business about Jesus spending a spring break in Cancun. And the thing about alcohol. Mormons advocate against alcohol, which can ruin a good leg of lamb. No Chateau Mouton? Some Mormons also wear weird, secret underwear emblazoned with Masonic-like symbols. In addition, the truly faithful perform proxy baptisms for people too dead to freely choose for themselves to become Mormons. Do you think your ancestors in fourteenth-century Albania would celebrate? That is so strange.

There is nothing wrong with Mormons. They just have too much to explain. Running a corporation provides enough complications. So if you must settle in Utah, Wyoming, or southern Idaho, for reasons other than recreation, be tolerant, be patient, act interested, and get out as soon as possible.

California. Unlike citizens from other regions, Californians will expect you to appear thoughtful about your religious choices, though the quality of your thought need not exceed the mean found anywhere. As long as you are mindful about your thought, any thought will do. The important thing to remember is that your religion must appear to be avante guarde with deep roots tapping ancient mysteries. If you are bound for Southern California and have ties to entertainment, go with Scientology. If nothing else, you will make some solid connections. In Northern California, a nice blend of New Age urban Buddhism, Unitarian Universalism and Emersonian Transcendentalism mixed with Jungian dream analysis, massage therapy, crystals, and Mayan animism should cover most of the bases. Learn the lingo and take in a Big Sur retreat once a year. Don't forget your laptop and the latest version of Grand Theft Auto, which will give you something to do. But be prepared to bond with other men who will likely shed tears and want to hug you.

When hiring or promoting others, religion need not play much of a role. Let zeal be your guide. The greater one's enthusiasm for religion, the thinner his loyalty to you. Avoid hard core evangelicals altogether. I do recommend, in the most general terms, that you take a thorough look at promising candidates with a Jewish or Mormon background. Both faiths are populated with chosen people. In fact there is a higher than average probability that Jewish applicants will be intelligent, disciplined, well educated, energetic, and creative, and the same probability that a Mormon applicant will be practical, mercantile, and adept at advertising and public relations. In addition, both understand persecution and as a result they understand loyalty. Just be sure that they are not overly devout and that their priorities are in order. In a corporation there is only one god.

What about Moslems? Their obvious usefulness is directed toward Moslem countries in Asia, Africa and the Middle East. However, don't be short-circuited by the obvious. Moslems are no different from Christians, Jews, Hindus, Shintos, Buddhists, or Wiccans. Moslems can certainly find a place in your business if they are qualified and promise not to carry around little squares of carpet and prostrate themselves during a sales meeting. You can also be open to a Black Muslim so long as his or her religious faith is about as strong as your own and he or she does not really believe that you are the devil. An employee's religious faith is irrelevant so long as it takes second place to corporate faith.

On the other hand, do not dismiss out of hand the recent trend in some corporations to allow some practice of religious faith in the workplace. This kind of endorsement can bring you two advantages. First, it can portray you as a faultless and saintly character in communities where religion clearly predominates and obviously that can be useful if you need to reduce benefits, disturb environments, or do other necessary business that might otherwise excite opposition. God's children are never misguided. Second, if your localized staff is particularly religious, it can cement their loyalty and your position as their leader. Just be sure to keep a lid on it. Practice moderation. Never let faith become more important to your employees than their corporate mission. Treat religious practice in the workplace as you treat golf. It can be an amusing recreation and a forum for bonding, and nine holes in the afternoon won't kill the company. Eighteen holes twice a day will.

As far as your public life as a corporate leader is concerned, follow the stunning example provided by the re-election of President George W. Bush. Christians voted for him because they perceived that he was one of them. That perception was enhanced by the fact that the President had recruited God, as well as Karl Rove, to serve as one of his top advisors. However, whether he was or was not one of the faithful is immaterial. Only the perception really matters, and the same is true for any CEO.

Given the current religious revival in America, and so long as it persists, you might find it useful sometimes to let prayer breakfasts, preachers, and family values appear to be your guide when the public spotlight shines on you. If you think this is intolerably boring, buck up. Nothing lasts forever. Revivals end, and once this one comes to an end and America's corporate and financial leaders have gained sufficient control over the nation's hearts and assets to ensure the future prosperity of free market democracy, there will be no need to court the religious constituency, and you will be able to cut them loose and let them return to their churches in middle-America, where they can baptize each other's cousins and play with snakes.

RESEARCH AND DEVELOPMENT Context is everything.

Outside of a profit-driven entity such as a corporation, the most innovative ideas in the world are gratuitous and wasted. R&D is essential but it must result in profit.

How do you exploit other people's genius (OPG) to make money? Some industries require large, expensive R&D facilities. Pharmaceuticals, computers, peripherals, automobiles, and aerospace to name just a few. For many other industries, however, it is more cost effective to do your R&D through university facilities and other programs that you fund. In general, you can keep all patents and the lion's share of profits. Universities are glad to get whatever you allow, and professors are greedy for grants whatever their source. Most professors look at a three million dollar grant the way we would look at a three billion dollar quarterly profit. Defense technologies, biotechnologies, and medical technologies, for example, all require such massive investments in laboratories and facilities that you will cut your risks, save money and headaches, and in the end reap greater profits by outsourcing at least part of your R&D.

The other way to exploit genius is to put it in a context that makes it practical and marketable. That is, develop your own R&D facilities, but manage them in a matrix that includes a key range of controls, from cost accounting to product name and packaging. Knowledge, such as the technology that makes things vibrate, can't earn you a dime unless you know how to package it. Remember Fido, Inc., the toy people, a decade ago? Remember the near-riots just before Christmas? You will make money if you can turn a couple of brilliant ideas into a *Goose Me Gertie* doll for a reasonable cost and then transform kids and their parents into hysterics who would rather drink Clorox than suffer Christmas without a vibrating troll shrieking at them day and night like a pack of hyenas. That is where we Americans really shine. It doesn't matter what the product is. We have the best closers in the world, and I'll match our hysterics against anyone, any place, any time.

However you choose to manage your R&D never let it become an end in itself, and never let it overshadow the even greater talents that we Americans possess. While R&D provides innovative products and services for the future, there is no profitable future without phenomenal marketing and nothing is profitable without sound capital and credit management. In addition to my own R&D, I always spent a significant share of my discretionary dollars on marketing research and technique and on methods of manipulating capital and credit to maximize returns. And I always shopped for more R&D outside my companies. The Japanese, the Germans, and the Indians, for example, all have a genius for R&D and engineering, though they tend to overemphasize perfection, systemic efficiency, and long term customer satisfaction. Nevertheless, they do like to tinker. It makes them feel important. It used to warm my heart to watch them spend millions and expend brain power to create fundamentals for new products and technologies that we could subsequently simplify, adapt, clone, steal, or even purchase and then turn around and sell like hotdogs at a baseball game. Make no mistake about it. We Americans are the best at invention and innovation. But we have even greater expertise in money management and salesmanship. Insurance, banking, lending, brokerage, investment banking, venture capitalization, private equity appropriation, risk management, securities, tax management, credit cards and credit marketing and management, product marketing, promotion, advertising, public relations, communications, sales, network sales, these are the fields that emerge from the hearts and souls of Americans. While we welcome inventors, however goofy they might be, they will never entirely replace the major league accountant, the hot shot promoter, or the slick investment broker whether he prowls Wall Street, Main Street, or late night television. The Japanese might have the best trained engineers in the world, but America has the best trained consumers by a wide margin. And the reason for that is our expertise in money and marketing. We know dollars and keys to motivation better than anyone.

A good CEO finds or develops innovative and improved products and services through R&D and OPG. A great CEO knows how to take that ball and then lead his team, capturing the loyalty of the crowd in the process, straight down the field to the end zone time after time until the final gun announces that he is the winner. A great CEO understands native talent and learns how best to exploit it.

RESPONSIBILITY   When the mining of malignite killed hundreds of people in the town of Vista, in the heart of the Grace Rockies, R. Tomane Company, which owned the mine and processed the mineral, was first in line to assign responsibility for the disaster to the entity that deserved all the blame: Nature. If everybody stepped up to the plate with that kind of forthright honesty and conviction, clearly our world would be a better place.

However, we live in an era when too many individuals refuse to accept responsibility for their own actions. Politicians put their own interests above the interests of those who got them elected. Parents blame everyone except themselves for their children's ill behavior. Teachers turn out semi-literates and blame the parents, society, and poor funding. Priests molest little children then hide in the lap of The Church. Single moms raise ragamuffins and blame the father who is not even present. Welfare recipients sponge off society and blame the system. Gays get ridiculed for acting gay and then blame other people's attitudes. The disabled own every good parking place in America and still blame society for their inability to get around. Minorities who fail to make the grade blame prejudice and even demand reparations for mistreatment of their ancestors. The unemployed, who got fired for doing a poor job, milk their benefits and blame their former boss for not recognizing their genius. Meanwhile, workers do everything they can to steal time on the job and even company property, and all you hear is their whining about being overworked, underpaid, and unappreciated. Nearly everywhere you look, America's honored tradition of accepting responsibility for one's own actions is decaying. I am deeply concerned about this and I recommend that you refuse to tolerate these kinds of excuses. Hold people's feet to the fire until they admit their responsibilities.

Someone has to take the lead in this area and set a good example to reeducate others, and it might as well be us, America's business leaders. We know where the buck stops. And we are adept at assigning responsibility. Nine times out of ten, we know exactly where responsibility belongs, and we are not afraid to stand up and point a finger wherever we think it is most useful to point it.

RESTATEMENT OF EARNINGS   Everyone fiddles with their books in order to cast the happiest light on earnings. Sometimes that fiddling is too obvious, too clumsy, or just downright excessive, as in the case of Knight-Rade, which a few years ago brightened its happy light to the tune of $1.6 billion. That is a pretty hefty mirage to have to rearrange, and it led to criminal charges against several top executives, including CEO, Hugh G. Gass, as investigators alleged that the executives lied and investors were defrauded. These gentlemen were innocent, of course, but this is what can result, in extreme cases, when imaginative accountants lock horns with over-zealous investigators under the nosey scrutiny of reporters.

Normally, when regulators, principally the Securities and Exchange Commission, notice earnings that could benefit from a reexamination, they handle the situation more tactfully. After all, the SEC drinks from the same waterholes as the rest of us, and typically, they offer remedies that can be swallowed without much of a gulp. For example, if they can demonstrate that you exaggerated a bit on your past earnings reports, you will be given the opportunity to restate those earnings to show a picture of your company that is nearer to reality. The SEC considers your implied admission of culpability, when you agree to restate earnings, sufficient punishment. Thus when you do agree to restate you are off the hook. Investors who traded in your stock and made incompetent investment decisions based upon your old earnings reports will not gain any benefit by your restatements, and some of them might sue if they suffered excessive losses. However, in virtually all such cases, justice gravitates to the party with the deepest pockets. As long as regulators allow us to let the horse out of his barn months, and sometimes years, before we close the barn door to keep him in, we won't have to worry about the literal veracity of earnings reports. Earnings can always be restated. The wrong can be righted. The record can be set straight, and the missing horse can be returned to his stall as if he had never been released.

In sum, don't allow imagination to get the better of you or of your accountants. Work with numbers smaller than the world's population. Work in privacy as much as possible. Improve security by erasing audit trails and memos the moment their usefulness expires. And when all that fails, restate.

RESULTS   When you buy a race horse you expect it to win. If it doesn't, you either trade it for a better horse or you send it to the glue factory. What you never do is continue to back a loser that cannot or will not produce results.

Business is so competitive that you must run a tight ship. If you don't, you will lose, professionally and personally. Make one ironclad rule for all your employees and make them understand that they must adhere to it: The only viable conclusion to a well-wrought plan is precisely the outcome predicted. Nothing less will do. Everyone in your organization must meet absolute goals absolutely. That is what I call, "results." Those who succeed in delivering results should be given a robust pat on the back. Those who fail should be vaporized so you won't have to risk repeated failure. In the workplace, as in life, results are all that matter.

RETALIATION   Where the big dogs play, retaliation is a serious, all-out tactical response to a real injury. If you choose retaliation, your response to your injury should be so devastating, so injurious, so humiliating, and so insulting that its victim will never again, for any reason, risk your displeasure, and all other potential adversaries with knowledge of your response will hesitate forever to offend you. In general, I recommend that you inflict twenty deadly wounds for every one injury suffered. For example, if someone intentionally fouled you in a pickup game of basketball at your club and as a result, he sprained your ankle, you should turn him into a quadriplegic paralyzed from the collarbones down with no hope ever of any recovery. I am speaking figuratively, of course, to provide perspective.

In the real world, let's say that someone scammed you in a stock deal for a few hundred thousand. You should not rest until you acquire from him against his will the equivalent of ten years' gross earnings. An eye for an eye might have satisfied a simpler age. I think an eye, a hand, an arm, a foot, a leg, an ear, a tongue, half a cerebral cortex, and a full set of genitals for an eye is more convincing. Retaliate infrequently but on an epic scale and, generally speaking, other predators will leave you alone so you can feed wherever you want.

RETIREMENT   Like anyone else, a CEO must plan ahead for his retirement. The skillful CEO will include a liberal package of retirement benefits under the protection of his Golden Parachute so that his enemies will not be able to take their revenge against him at that moment in life when the golden years beckon and he is most vulnerable.

When it comes to retirement planning, I think that a case study of Jim BBob Belch, former CEO of Universal Universal, will be worth your effort. In brief, Jim BBob put together a secure retirement package to ensure his and his family's well being. Then critics got critical, questioning such items as the travel budget, the allotments for entertainment, and the little efficiency overlooking the Monte-Carlo Country-Club. Always blessed with an abundance of generosity, Jim BBob agreed to *pay* for these benefits out of his own pocket, around two million dollars per year. This turned out to be a win-win-win situation. After all the dust settled, the critics felt good about themselves. UU got back two million a year. And Jim BBob got a comfortable retirement benefit from the company of more than sixteen thousand dollars per day to keep the tarnish off his golden years.

Of course, Jim BBob also had his own assets to invest. To give you some idea of what is possible, consider this. Let's say that Jim BBob had a truly cosmic burst of generosity and decided to pay UU back by annuity payments all the money it paid him during only his last year as CEO. If he kept all of that one year's earnings and invested it in a prime CD or money market account, just like an ordinary person, and then kept only half the interest earned for himself and paid back the company with the other half, he could have added forty percent to his retirement income on earnings alone. Given the more likely return of someone with his investment savvy, he could have doubled or tripled his retirement income. But of course, generosity rarely exceeds longevity, and this is a purely hypothetical case, so Jim BBob kept it all, nearly doubled his retirement cash flow, and spared the company a long wait. Remember, we are talking only about his retirement pay plus one year's earnings. All the rest of his career assets are his business, but it's a pretty good bet that you won't see Jim BBob Belch trading food stamps soon, unless, of course, the supply of food stamps dwindles enough to create a truly booming secondary market.

Set up a comfortable retirement from your company. Add in your final year's earnings. Add to that all the capital that you have earned and saved for the previous forty years or so as an executive, and chances are, as a retiree, you won't have to put off that dental work or wait in line for government cheese. A little planning can make your Golden Years tolerable.

RETURN   In its broadest sense, seeking a return on investment is not just a necessary business outlook. It is also a style of living, your style, and it should govern everything you do.

Why do you golf? Is it enough to gain returns of amusement, fellowship, and a little exercise? Of course not. Unless you can close a deal, design an important strategy, forge an alliance, or cripple a potential enemy, don't bother. Always gain an edge. That is, always demand more in return than you give, in everything you do. What is a marriage worth? Mere companionship? Get real. There must be a kicker: Social connections, an inheritance, useful introductions, prestige, looks that excite profound envy, something to make your investment worth the effort applied here, to this woman, instead of there, to that other one, who also has great qualifications.

If you follow this rule like a religion, then you will achieve financial salvation. Always add to your net worth. Always make a better than average return. That's why God made us and put us in charge.

RETURN ON INVESTED CAPITAL   Here is a small case study on how to do things the right way.

First a little background, in case you were raised in Homer. Like private clubs whose membership is carefully screened for pedigree, capital, and influence, the best private equity firms conduct business under the radar in order to remain discreet while they boost as much equity as possible for their members. Their boards of directors typically include a lot of formers: Former presidents, relatives of presidents, prime ministers, chiefs of staff, chairmen of Joint Chiefs of Staff, cabinet secretaries, UN ambassadors, and the occasional archangel on temporary assignment. The directors' main job is to restructure policies of the world's nations as required, including policies of the United States, to better suit the needs of the firm. This is accomplished with some ease, since the formers are often called upon by their governments to act as appointees to domestic commissions and as emissaries to foreign governments at the same time they are acting on behalf of the firm. Deals made as a result of their efforts eventually rise to the top and hit the press as thoughtful policies issued by thoughtful governments. Sometimes those policies require sacrifice. In such cases, citizens of involved nations, including the U.S., are advised to tighten their belts out of necessity and patriotic duty. Meanwhile, the right people in those nations involved, including the U.S., get rewarded for their cooperation and the private equity firm enhances its gross domestic product. All this allows the firm to do its job, which is to make as much money as possible for its members and to provide ample rewards for its directors for their hard work.

More often than not, however, private equity firms don't have to restructure international relations to make a buck. Plenty of apples are ripe on domestic trees and they afford the firm opportunities to turn modest profits and keep its formers happy. Here is one example of how one such firm rewarded its directors and other principals by selecting one shiny apple.

In January, 2006, the Drooler-Glee Group, a world-wide private equity firm based in the nation's capitol, agreed to purchase Clan-O-Pooch, the successful manufacturer of tartan vests for dogs, from Bullmoose, Inc., a wounded duck, for 15 billion dollars. Up front, Drooler-Glee put up 2.3 billion of its investors' money. Less than one year later, the new owners voted themselves a one billion dollar dividend, which they paid to themselves with a Clan-O-Pooch loan, and in mid-November, 2006, they offered twenty-eight percent of Clan-O-Pooch to the public in an Initial Public Offering. They also voted themselves a second dividend in the amount of whatever was left over above one billion dollars from revenues acquired in the IPO. In other words, whatever revenue was generated by the IPO would go to the new owners as dividends.

The IPO generated 1.32 billion dollars, or fifteen dollars per share. The firm repaid their dividend loan of 1.0 billion and paid themselves their second dividend of .32 billion. The seventy-two percent of Clan-O-Pooch still owned by the firm, at fifteen dollars per share, was valued at 3.46 billion dollars. In other words, the firm made 1.0 billion first dividend + .32 billion second dividend + 3.46 billion remaining equity = 4.78 billion dollars in less than one year on an out of pocket investment of 2.3 billion.[30] The IPO was widely viewed as a failure because it didn't bring the eighteen dollars per share price for Clan-O-Pooch anticipated by the firm. However, by simply shuffling the right papers, the firm made, for its investors and directors, an annual return on invested capital of 123%, somewhat better

---

30 Clan-O-Pooch carried the balance of the 15 billion dollar purchase price as a debt. In essence, Clan-O-Pooch leveraged its own purchase and assumed 100% of its own buyout risk after the IPO, which made the buyout a more pleasant experience for the new investors after they more than doubled their money up front.

than the 2.5% available at the time through savings accounts for ordinary people at better banks. In addition, profits from private equity deals are considered capital gains, so the investors only had to pay fifteen percent in taxes.

The game we play is called Power and Money. Yes, you have to have money to make real money, and yes, you have to have enough power to shape events so that someone will bother to answer your knock on the door of opportunity.

Your best measure of success in the P&M game is your return on invested capital, which separates movers and shakers from trudgers and nudgers and from ordinary people. If you can double a large sum of money in less than a year, congratulate yourself and think about taking the yacht back to Cannes. If you flush with envy when others double their money, try harder. And finally, if you must celebrate when your little mutual fund scores a 14% return, all I can say is, congratulations. Enjoy your weekend at Silver City.

REVENGE   A much less humble activity than retaliation, revenge is a strategic response to a perceived injury. Think of it as sport with a deadly edge. Use it sparingly, but precisely. Nothing looks worse than revenge for a trivial insult. And nothing tastes better than the blood rare corpse of your real enemy's career served on a platter that you cooked up.

RIGHT   Like it or not, that old saying about might makes right is not so far from the truth. When you look back over human history, you might be amazed at how few absolutes there really are, and how, at any one moment in time, so much of life is governed by those who have power. Power tells you what is true and what is false. Power tells you what is wrong and what is right. Power tells you who has the right, and who doesn't. Power is the first absolute.

Most of you have by now taken one of those junket vacations to Alaska. Imagine that you go for a walk unarmed in the bush and you run into a sow Alaskan Brown Bear with a cub. Who do you suppose has the right to the berry patch or the salmon run? Who is right to take the fish and the fruit? Or anything else it wants? It's no contest. And, like it or not, that is the way of the world. You do have a choice, however. You can choose to be swallowed, or you can choose to be right.

Whatever your neighborhood, right is the whim of the last predator still standing. So if you ever had any doubts about the moral path you should follow, you can clear them up now with this resolve: Always choose to do right

THE RIGHT STUFF   What is the right stuff and who has it?

The perspective of history allows us easily to identify past holders of the right stuff. Famous men like Shakespeare and Galileo, for example, jump right off the page when compared to also-rans like Charles the Bold and Karl von Reichenbach. It is less easy to pick winners out of a contemporary lineup. Times change. Perspectives and standards of judgment change. After a decade or two of reconsideration, today's hero might be tomorrow's bum, though anyone who can swing the purchase of a company like Dow Jones must always be given some credit.

My advice is that if you are looking for role models who possess the right stuff, don't try to pick them by their character traits, beliefs, brain power, actions, accomplishments, celebrity, or even looks. In fact, don't pick them at all. Let the current marketplace pick them for you and I guarantee that you will find the right stuff one hundred percent of the time. The marketplace knows what works; you can only theorize. This is important to understand because appearances often deceive people and you don't want to risk being superficial. For example, a guy screaming at you from your television screen and wearing a red blazer covered with big yellow dollar signs might seem ridiculous until you realize that in today's financial marketplace he owns title to more capital, more status, and more power than Shakespeare and Galileo combined. Surprise! There it is, right in front of you: The right stuff.

So what exactly is the right stuff? Look behind every bottom line and you will find a CEO driven by six powerful forces: Fierce aggression, personal greed, lust for power, hunger for prestige, joy in manipulating others, and a ruthless toughness that creates unblinking decisions elevating self-interest above all else. I might add a seventh force: Pride in all of the above. A first glance at someone might not show you all of that, and it might not show you that a clown wearing dollar signs today is a bigger winner than yesterday's celebrities.

Sometimes in life you just have to dig deeper than surface appearances to find the genuine article.

RISK MANAGEMENT   All business involves risk. Therefore, one of the first principles of good business is, Cover Your Butt. That is, manage risk. How do you do that? With the resources and the complexity of a large corporation at your disposal, managing risk is not as difficult as it might sound. You have three basic strategies to choose from.

The hedge. A hedge is like life insurance, only you get to stay around to enjoy the payout when it comes. Using derivatives correctly, for example, you can hedge risk so that a big loss turns into a modest profit, and a big profit requires only a small investment.

The shift. Induce someone else to shoulder your risk. Move risk away from you and your corporation by interesting outside investors in new, high-risk entities, such as limited partnerships. A big loss becomes their big loss, and if the venture makes a large profit, then you, your corporation, and your high-flying investors will all make a better than average return. In this case, you will also have a clearly identified target group ready and willing to invest in your next project so you also gain the opportunity to parley your substantial win into a truly unconscionable one.

Sharing. Like a winter fisherman who fears that he is on thin ice, you don't stand and put all your weight on one spot; you lie down and distribute your body weight over as large an area as possible. You spread out your risk. One of the best ways to do this is to float an IPO for a newly created entity that acts like a subsidiary. If it makes money, or looks like it will, and the stock price soars, then everyone is happy and most of your new investors will hang on, waiting for the real bonanza. Here, timing becomes everything, and you have to know when to bail before your investors do. On the other hand, if your venture loses money, or looks like it will, then you take only a small hit, while your investors shoulder the brunt.

In every instance, when someone comes to you seeking your partner-ship for a good idea, invoke the concept of risk sharing. The concept – and even the phrase -- sounds so fair and collegial, that it will help you force the other party to shoulder a majority of risk while preserving your potential for profit. If they don't want to go along, dump them and find investors who will go along, or shelve the project and wait for the next good idea.

Think of risk management as another form of investment through OPM, other people's money. It grafts the hope, greed, and competitive impulses of other people onto the tree of your success in order to shade you and your corporation from intolerable losses. Plus, now and then, when an idea works, it allows you to cream off windfall profits that reward you for being clever enough to properly address risk, or at least the perception of risk, in the first place.

RISK/REWARD   Analysis of reward in relation to risk gives you a set of tools you will use many times each day. You will use them so often that they will begin to seem like extensions of your mind. You will, in time, analyze automatically every circumstance in which risk plays a meaningful role. As an adjunct to greed and a supplement to cost/benefit analysis, per-ception of risk/reward will become a third eye that allows you to see more clearly and more rationally than others can see.

In general, risk little when you have only an average probability of gaining a reward greater than your risk. Risk moderately in return for a high probability of gaining a reward many times higher than your risk. Risk the farm in return for the absolute certainty of gaining a life's fortune. In this last case, of course, the risk is not in the deal itself, but in potential discovery of the deal by outsiders such as regulators, because in this case, deals are always wired.

And finally, never gamble. Never accept high risk in return for low probability of any return, great or small. This is how other people can make *you* rich.

ROLES   Most adults are forced into many roles: Boss, provider, mate, weekend caretaker, parent, little league parent, Ambassador to France, churchgoer, backyard cook, Saturday athlete, loving relative, and many more. We are lucky in that regard. The life of a CEO is so integrated and the demands of the job are so comprehensive that we are called upon to project at all times only our one role, that of the Chief. Whether you are at work in the headquarters, at work on the golf course, at work at a dinner party, at work in the place of worship, at work at your son's Junior Polo League, at work in your topiary gardens, at work at your daughter' annual Sorority Tweed Blazer sale, or at work in your bedroom, you will always be at work and you will always project the same persona, the only one you have, the Chief At Work persona.

By the way, this Chief At Work persona in no way suggests that your at work role makes you a one dimensional at work person with nothing to do except be at work. You could look around and smell the flowers just as often as anyone else. In fact, pencil it into your work schedule and make that part of your Chief At Work agenda, every day if you wish. Just make sure that you smell the flowers *better* than anyone else.

RULES   You must have rules and lots of them. Without rules the cattle stray and stampede and stumble around as if in the dark. Without rules, you have a leaderless company where janitors think about marketing, and advertising salesmen theorize about finance. Rules, rules, rules.

The problem is that fixed rules get in the way of practical operations. Rules need to be flexible, but by definition, a rule is inflexible. This is a serious problem, but not to worry. Every serious problem has a simple solution: Make up the rules as you go. You can do that because you're the CEO. And your employees can handle it because their job is to please you.

Life is arbitrary. Deal with it.

"Life is arbitrary. Deal with it." p. 339

SAFETY   How much safety do you need? It will be up to you, through delegation of course, to calculate what constitutes acceptable risk for each job description in your corporation. Are the benefits of extremely low risk worth the cost? Generally speaking the cost curve will tell the tale. The point at which it starts to rise quickly is the point at which you should be willing to shoulder the unlikely risk of mutilation or death to a worker.

If it were up to OSHA officials or union leaders, you would spend every last dime earmarked for profit on useless and redundant safety measures to protect workers against extremely unlikely accidents. If you want to stay in business, reason must prevail.

Conditions are less difficult in developing and third world nation facilities. There you can follow rational safety procedures for your workers without risking your bottom line.

You must also consider the question of plant safety with regard to surrounding communities. My position on that is that corporate facilities bring huge economic benefits to every community. How much more must we do? In the same way that workers may choose where they work, people are free to move if they do not want to accept the slight risks associated with industries that provide them with massive economic benefits. If you want to put safety first, be my guest, but be prepared to give up profits in return. Safety first is a great motto, so use it, but use it to remind workers of their own responsibility to work safely and to not pull bonehead moves that blow up the coal mine or leach lethal chemicals into the aquifer.

Of course you have your own responsibilities too. Nothing is worse than to view the twisted corpses of your valued employees after a deadly accident. You feel like a commanding officer who has been forced to sacrifice his combat troops to a higher cause. But there are times when you must be willing to make that sacrifice. All I can say is, be strong, be courageous, have broad shoulders, and take your losses like a man when you must. Sacrifice is never easy, but it is part of your duty.

SALES   It's all about sales, boys and girls. Every good CEO understands sales. Every great CEO could personally sell a trainload of space heaters to the devil – and get twice the standard markup.

There is one proper attitude behind miraculous sales, and that is that every consumer on the face of this planet owes you something. Don't just think it. Don't just practice it. *Believe it*! Every consumer owes you.

Your job is to collect.

SCHEDULES   In order to operate at peak efficiency and boost your productivity consistently to the maximum output, you must schedule. Schedule everything you do. Do not be reserved about your schedule. Brain surgeons aren't. The President isn't. Why should you be? Schedule every moment of every day and night of your life and include every activity. You will find that your life will run like a perfectly tuned race car. And whatever else you do, be sure to schedule three or four minutes a day to reflect. The ancient Greeks had it right: The unexamined life is not worth scheduling.

SELF- INTEREST   There are two kinds of self-interest, unenlightened and enlightened. Unenlightened self-interest is greed that strangles the goose in order to get the golden egg. Enlightened self-interest is greed that feeds the goose so it will keep laying golden eggs. The latter obviously allows you to collect more eggs, and it is easier on the goose. Always keep the goose happy.

SELFISHNESS A natural state of mind that places self at the center of the known universe and relegates everything else to the status of satellites, selfishness is why ambitious people survive and prosper. Survival validates the position of the self and prosperity gives it gravity which others have to depend on to keep them from falling out of orbit and disintegrating. This little solar system explains why those who run things enjoy selfishness and those who don't run things claim that it is a sin. Ordinary people, such as workers and reformers, reduce selfishness to a vice so they can believe that they are virtuous, because virtue is all that they will ever own. They hope that some day virtue will replace gravity so they can fly off to a better world. For example, take that Canadian kid who digs water wells in Africa and India, Brian whatever. Before completing adolescence he raised a million dollars. Let's say he took that million dollars to a good private equity firm with instructions to invest aggressively and reinvest all gains for the next thirty years. Odds are by the time he turned forty-five, he would have a billion dollars. At that point, he could form a private charitable foundation, pay no taxes, live on five million per year and call it administrative expense, give away forty-five million yearly to a worldwide drilling charity to complete the five percent test, and keep the principal intact and even grow it. In other words, with the right strategy, he could drill more wells than God, screw the Canadian tax collector, *and* live like royalty. The problem is that his little mind got warped by some do-good first grade teacher so all he wanted out of life was virtue. Successful people, on the other hand, such as owners of capital, do not require virtue. We have so much more to choose from! We control the movements of the planets and we have jewelry. We can do whatever we want whenever we want. Why would anyone not enjoy selfishness when it leads to so many choices? Why would anyone dream about flying off to better world? This world is just fine, thank you, as long as you run it with a rational strategy.

Is it therefore good to be selfish? Let me pose the question in another way. Which would give you more satisfaction, a fifteen carat emerald or a selfless heart? Let's make that emerald an inclusion free Muzo from the El Indio corte, and let's make that heart Ralph Nader's, a man who would rather do right than embellish himself with a new suit. Now let's see which turns more heads when you walk through the reception line at an A list wedding, your good deeds in threadbare serge or your perfect green beryl from the El Indio corte?

Be good to yourself. You are the only self you will ever have.

SENTIMENTALITY

An associate of mine once said: "If I could roast a puppy and serve it at a dinner party once a month, I would do so." His point was well taken. Sentimentality is for folk singers. I suggest that you take a long, hard look at yourself. If you find traces of sentimentality in yourself, get rid of them. Do whatever you must. Nothing interferes more with the conduct of good business than nagging feelings.

SERVICE

Provide the appearance of fast and painless service to your customers even though most of them are trying to screw you. You can get your money back in margins, handling fees, delays, processing fees, and a million other ways. It is important to project a reputation as a service patsy. It will keep viable customers in the fold and will make them believe that they have the upper hand

Another kind of service, community service, is always expected of every CEO. Bring your press corps along on any given Saturday and drive a nail for Habitat for Humanity, or pull a weed for your local community beautification committee. Cut a ribbon for a new theater you helped fund, or dig a spade full of dirt to break ground for a new city park. There are hundreds of ways to fulfill this obligation. All of them involve cameras. None takes more than thirty minutes, and each one will polish your service image and hence the image of your corporation and of CEOs everywhere.

SHAREHOLDERS

While eighty-five percent of all stocks are owned by only ten percent of Americans, about a third of all Americans own some shares, one way or another typically through mutual funds in 401-Ks, in publicly traded corporations. Fortunately, they are about as organized as a riot.

Taken in bulk, shareholders in your corporation are the people who own the majority of your company. You need to take a realistic view of shareholders because, unlike you and your management team, they have shallow loyalties. They do nothing to steer the operations of the companies and they are fickle. Plus, like all people who trade in stocks, they ought to be sophisticated enough to know that about half the time they will be winners, and about half the time they will be losers, and they will gain a little in the long run because stocks generally increase in value around nine percent or more annually as economies grow. That is, as random players in a mostly random game, the theoretical odds at any given moment are a little better than fifty-fifty that they will profit from the purchase of any stock, particularly if they hold on to it, and a little less than fifty-fifty that they will lose. Why is this important?

As owners of your companies, and as people in a position to finance your ventures when purchasing new offerings, your shareholders expect to make some gains. Each quarter for which you report believable earnings that exceed experts' projections you will reward your shareholders with gains in the price of their shares. That will keep them happy.

On the other hand, shareholders also exist to sustain the value of your personal holdings. Thus, your pool of shareholders is, of necessity, a pool of investors who might become losers if you intend to make significant profits in the sale of your own shares. For example, if you underreport earnings and the price of your stock falls, let's say that you then exercise some of your options to purchase more stock. For the most part, those shareholders who panicked and sold their stock will blame themselves for being impatient, particularly after the *next* quarter when earnings rebound and the price of the stock advances, and you lock in an increase in your equity position or sell off a few shares for a profit, and they miss the boat. Then there is the opposite gambit. If you over report earnings and investors drive the value of your stock through the roof, then you can unload a few shares for a tidy profit, short the downside, and position yourself for re-entry. However, your shareholders will probably whine when the next quarter's report comes out, or you have to restate earnings, so don't let avarice overpower your good judgment. Throw the shareholders a bone now and then to keep them interested and if they are clever, they will make a little money and come back for more with even greater enthusiasm.

I recommend that you think of your relationship to your shareholders the same way as you would think of a game of tennis with your father-in-law. You want him to have fun. You want him to win some points and build his confidence. You want to keep him in the game. But when the game comes down to a final score, he will lose because you will win. Just be sure that you keep the score close enough that he will think he could have won if only he had tried harder or rushed the net more often or served to your backhand. Those tantalizing thoughts will mean that he will return to play another day and then another.

Or you can think of your shareholders as fish. You, the fisherman, control the relationship. When your trout takes your fly, you can play him as long as you want. Let him make his deep runs. Let him jump and shake and dart back and forth, and once you have him in your net you can turn him loose to play another day – or, when the timing is right, you can drop him into your creel and fry him for dinner.

Whatever you do with them, always be sure to treat your shareholders with the greatest respect. They are catalysts that can help you transform impersonal capital into personal wealth. They should be every bit as important to you as your barber and your goldsmith.

SOCIALISM   A failed and discredited political experiment, socialism was predicated on the belief that people who fail to compete and choose to do nothing to help themselves deserve the same wealth, the same care, and the same access to food, clothing, shelter, medical care, retirement benefits, and other perks of an economy, as people who compete hard, work hard, and sacrifice to help themselves. I think life offers a more just choice: You get what you deserve, and if that is too difficult to calculate, then you get whatever you can take. So take, and don't worry about it. The fact that you win, and possess that which others desire and for which others compete, is sufficient proof that you deserve what you have. Worry when you see a mob of slackers demanding that you give them a free ride to a clinic and a food bank. Their real destination is a casino, a bar, and a dog fight. These people will tell you anything to take what is yours so they can get what they want.

SOCIETY   As the CEO of a major corporation with significant assets, you will have extremely important responsibilities to society. It is your duty to live up to these responsibilities.

Always remember that society is a fabric held together by an infrastructure of leadership. You are the most important part of that infrastructure. However, people take society for granted, and if they think about it at all, they think of it merely as a stage upon which they can act out their own little dramas. It doesn't occur to them that important people had to build and must constantly maintain that stage to keep it from collapsing. It is your solemn duty to remind people that someone is in charge and to ease their confusion by providing them with images of authority. Without faith in their leaders, people will revert; the fabric of society will unravel; and the stage we all depend on will disintegrate into a pile of scrap. Keeping all this in mind, always take time to fulfill your responsibilities to society and let nothing deter you from this awesome duty. Fortunately, this is something that you can delegate.

Train your wife to publicize your position in the civic, charitable, and performing arts clubs that occupy her time in each of the communities in which you own property. Have her emphasize all that you do for the local economy, but be sure that she also stresses your significance to the national and international economies as well. Your wife should be able to handle this, and she will enjoy doing it because it will elevate her status along with yours. It will also give her something more to do than eat canapés and shop. Think of her as your ambassador, and don't forget to reward her with jewelry.

SOLUTIONS   Recently, the word "solutions" overtook the work "the" as the most commonly used word in the English language. Whoever coined the term "solutions" as the key word describing a business or a business activity had a wonderful idea. That person is a deity who should be worshipped.

The second person to use the term was unoriginal, but clever enough to see a good thing and borrow it. That person is a good mimic who should be congratulated.

The next thousand people who used the term were merely copycats and they should be scolded.

Everyone after that who uses the term should be skinned alive, rolled in salt, wrapped in duct tape, and thrown into a vat of boiling cat urine.

SOPHISTRY   The art of telling lies with specious arguments that sound true, sophistry has become a standard form of communication for most lowyers, commercial radio talk show hosts, network news analysts, politicians, government leaders, press secretaries, military spokesmen, think tank speakers, religious leaders, celebrities, sports heroes, underground coal mine owners, and just about anyone else trapped in the public eye, including, of course, CEOs. Let's be realistic about this thing. Sometimes you have to lie or get skewered. If you are going to lie, doesn't it make sense to lie convincingly, using lots of reason and logic? Sophistry is not an evil today any more than it was in Fifth Century B.C. Athens. It is a tool, like a socket wrench, that can be used to twist something that needs to be twisted. Don't fret about sophistry. Learn how to use it well.

SPIN   Once upon a time, in Shangri La, all the boys and girls were guileless. You may believe that or not, but I am here to reassure you, if you need reassuring, that Shangri La no longer exists. To the extent that we have a culture, we have a culture of spin. We have grown so accustomed to spin that we no longer think of it as being an alternative to something else. We feel comfortable with spin. We don't resent spin. We don't expect anything else because we are all salesmen. Everything we say is slanted to achieve our ends. In other words, in a world teeming with information, each bit competing with every other bit, it is inevitable that each provider of information is going to spin his or her bytes in the best possible light to reach goals dictated by self-interest or by a controlling interest. What you need in our world is not a return to some fantasy time of innocence, which never existed anyway, but guile. Shrewdness. Cleverness. The ability to translate spin codes into whatever is embedded inside of them so that others cannot use them to influence you.

Far more important, you must develop the ability to use spin nimbly so that you can influence masses of other people who don't even know that they are being led, and so that only the most cynical and sophisticated skeptics among them will ever challenge the literal veracity of anything you say.

The world of spin is a walk through a carnival. Every barker in every booth along the midway offers a trinket, a token, a totem, a reason, a rule, or, on a good day, a miracle. Better you become a miracle worker than one of the suckers.

SPORTS   Gain competency in several sports, particularly those played in neutral clothing at private schools, sports such as polo, squash, sailing, and touch football. Tennis and golf are mandatory, of course. Riding, scuba diving, and light rock climbing will serve you well, particularly when you are on holiday. Hunting, so long as it is confined to comfortable safaris that prey on exotic trophy species and cannot be confused with the beer-swilling slaughter of local Bambis, is essential. So are skeet shooting and fishing, either fly fishing the world's most select waters or trolling for trophy-sized marlin in tropical waters. Among the memorabilia that decorate your walls, awards for marksmanship and photographs of fresh kills will remind others of your natural place atop the food chain.

Gain at least a passing knowledge of other common sports that you might encounter, including those preferred by foreigners and executives with whom you work. For example, a passing knowledge of soccer, cricket, or table tennis might help you when you head for the West Coast to meet with Brazilian plantation owners, Indian IT whiz kids, Chinese entrepreneurs, or Microfang executives. And you'll never know when someone in the Hamptons on a staff retreat might challenge you to swing a bat or throw a basketball at a hoop. A little sporting mystery won't hurt either. No one would expect you to actually box, for instance, but you might find it interesting to allow the suggestion that in your youth, you were an accomplished pugilist and that you learned this art for the simple love of it in a gentlemen's club under the guidance of an elderly British mentor. Avoid all other martial arts since they are too obvious and they carry an association with street thugs and bad actors.

In addition to firsthand skill at sports, you will need to keep abreast of the high points of several professional athletic teams as their seasons progress year after year so you will seem to share the passion many other men have for baseball, the NBA, the NHL, and the NFL. You will spend considerable time in private boxes at stadiums, both as a guest and as a host, and some day, when you have nothing better to do, you might wish to buy a professional team. Professional sports can be good business and disciplines inherent in sports competition have obvious parallels to business operations. I recommend that you use the sports model sparingly however, since it is overused at every level of society, but don't forget that the concepts of "team," "loyalty," "spirit," and "when the going gets tough, the tough get going," all address values that are imprinted in most young wannabes. They can be useful to the corporation. Invoke them when you need them, like mom and apple pie.

Why sports? Always remember that people's recognition of leadership emerges from irrational sources. We don't say, "Oh, he's so logical." We say, "He seems to fly when he dunks!" We don't say, "His ability to analyze statistics is remarkable." We say, "Look at that left hook!" Sports in particular emphasize the fact that feats of the body have an immediate, visceral appeal that dwarfs anything the mind can ever produce. Deep down inside, people imagine that their leaders are the swiftest, the bravest, the strongest, the most skillful, and the toughest. In the spirit of John Wayne's Hollywood, they like to imagine that no one but the CEO would have the guts to march down to the dock, shoulder through the pickets, whip the toughest stevedore, and save the company from Mafia bosses and their union thugs. By demonstrating competency in sports, you will stimulate others to magnify your personality and to invest it with charisma and machismo. Some will even imagine that if it weren't for the responsibilities of commerce, you could compete at the level of Joe DiMaggio, Bart Starr, Oscar De La Hoya, Martina Navratilova, and Michael Jordan. How can that hurt you?

That said, you must be careful not to demonstrate too much athletic skill or too much competitiveness, even though competition is the lifeblood of your career. In the fickle minds of others, the line between an accomplished gentleman athlete and a jock is fine indeed. If you go too far, your IQ will drop thirty points and others will see in your drive to win insecurity not leadership. Plus, you must be prepared to lose now and then in order to flatter others for strategic purposes or to demonstrate what a good sport you truly are. Of course this applies only on the playing field. In business, a good CEO never loses.

STANDARD OF LIVING   If every individual on the earth took care of himself, there would be no demand for charity or socialistic policies. You determine your standard of living. Unless you are crippled, ill, or in some other way defective, you have no reason to depend on others to take care of you. What you take is what you get. And every person is born with the same opportunity to take.

It is true that standards of living vary widely, depending on where you are born and into what circumstances. You might very well develop your instinct to take, but if your surroundings offer little of value, then your take won't add up to much. One of the goals of multinational corporations is to level the standard of opportunity worldwide, which will reduce differences between competing standards of living. This will diminish political unrest, keep costs of labor at realistic levels, and empower every consumer to provide for himself and have surplus earnings left over to plow back into the economy in the form of purchases and investments. Ordinary Americans support this goal. The decline in the middle class standard of living in the United States during the last thirty years was met with almost no resistance from consumers. Those pinched might have groused, but they also took second jobs or second mortgages. Or they upgraded their skills so they could earn more. Consumer credit, of course, has carried many of them while they make their adjustment. Meanwhile, the corresponding increase in the standard of living in developing nations has provided the beginnings of meaningful markets where none were thought possible before. Furthermore, the idea of raising standards of living has caught fire in many developing and third world countries. People everywhere are discovering what it means to look out for number one and to take responsibility for their own well-being.

I look forward to a time when poverty has been erased from the world and every child born will have the same fair chance to lift himself or herself up to achieve a standard of living that at the least meets fundamental personal needs and the basic needs of the economy. The work you do as a CEO, and the example you set as a model of what can happen to those few of us who possess real ability and drive, will steer the course of the future. In time, average prosperity and standards of living worldwide will rise. The business horizon will become more predictable. Markets will grow. Profits will increase. The best and the brightest will rise to the top and that rise will allow us to solidify our current position of leadership. God's in his heaven; all's right with the world. Q.E.D.

STATUS   Society confers status on an individual in direct proportion to how obviously that individual embodies its deepest values. America loves money, competition, property, glamour, celebrity, style, performance, success, aggressiveness, personality, self-promotion, and the ability to entertain. If you acquire these virtues, you will join the ranks of the admired, and you will understand that people of high status may claim a kind of validity unknown to others. Doors that remain locked to ninety-nine and one-half percent of the population will open to you automatically and as if by magic. People will solicit and relish your endorsements, your opinions, and your presence. Even so, always feed them crumbs. Publicity elevates awareness, but familiarity tarnishes status. It is the mystery behind you, the unanswered questions and the unfulfilled curiosities, that will feed the public's interest.

The flipside of status is a combination of envy and hatred, and the status that many of us enjoy at home, in America, is not necessarily appreciated elsewhere. We have all heard it said, for example, most often by snooty Europeans, fundamentalist Moslems, and even our own intellectuals, that we are a shallow people. I ask: What is your point? It wasn't Deep Thoughts that raised an embattled frontier, in a mere two centuries, to the greatest superpower the world has ever known. It was energy on the move. It was build now and plan later. It was a spirit of conquest and individualism, of freedom and daring unfettered by traditions, authoritarianism, churches, and aristocracies. When I hear, "I think, therefore I am," or "I salute the God within you," I don't furrow my eyebrows and ponder gravely. I think to myself: *Of course* I am. *Of course* there is a god within me. What else is new? And when I look at our Main Streets, I see shoppers eating burritos and ice cream, and shopkeepers selling their wares. I see kids buying corn dogs on their way to the giant roller coaster. I see order, opportunity, prosperity, obesity, and a kind of status that people confer upon themselves. So many of these young people smile. They love to smile, perhaps because they can smile. The tragedies in their lives do not involve the hunt for fuel and water, the burning of their homes, starvation, disease, and deadly ambush. Their tragedies are a dent in the family Honda; a boy or girl's rejection; a painful dental appointment; or sharp disrespect from a competing adolescent. Yet despite these daily trials, they smile. They are pretty well off and they know it.

This is the status inherent in democracy. It is free to all. It is the dividend paid to ordinary people for sticking to the rules and for not disturbing the prosperity accumulating above them like beautiful clouds. They smile because they enjoy their portion of status and because they know that if they truly want to, they can seek more. Meanwhile, like flowers, they turn their faces skyward waiting for the refreshing mist they know will come.

STOCKBROKERS As individuals, most stockbrokers are charming, clever, glib people. You can never go wrong having stockbrokers around your pool at cocktail hour, particularly if your firm does business with their firm.

In their workplace, however, all stockbrokers are liars and thieves. After all, they have learned to deal with their clients toe to toe. If society were more forgiving, the average stockbroker would sell his mother into prostitution to make a boat payment. Brokerage firms are sales firms and their employees are salesmen. They will aggressively promote, sell, and publicly recommend anything in which they have a vested interest, and anything on which they can make a commission. These companies are solid and reputable in the public eye, and they can always count on their salesmen to churn accounts or help out in other ways if there is a buck to be made, particularly on junk stocks in which the firm is over-extended, and on risky initial public offerings underwritten by the firm.

Learn two things from this. First, never personally use a stockbroker who is not a dependent relative or someone in your debt. And second, if you should spot a stockbroker who is particularly aggressive, smooth, successful, and despised by his peers, throw him a bone or two and get to know him. The worst of these fellows can make first-rate employees.

STOCK MARKETS   Stock markets provide capital to corporations planning growth and development and to savvy investors seeking more wealth. They also serve as a kind of screening device segregating people of means from everyone else. They are a proving ground for wannabees. Let's take a look at the broad picture.

While half of American households own common stocks, ordinary people (ninety percent of the population) own only fifteen percent of all stocks. The same situation holds true world wide: Ten percent of the people own eighty-five percent of the world's wealth. Clearly, going to the stock market is not the same kind of activity as going to a Cubs game or a cock fight.

How and where people play the games they play will tell you everything you need to know about who they are and what they own. Half the world's people and twenty percent of Americans are paupers. They cannot afford to play at all, except with sticks, and certainly not with stocks. The seventy percent – America's middle class -- choose between computer video games, NASCAR, rodeo, snowmobiles, tailgate parties, rock concerts, and cheese crunchies. The remaining ten percent gravitate to places like Tanglewood, Jackson Hole, The Met -- and stock markets.

If you wish to achieve your American Dream, as part of the upper tenth of that ten percent, you must learn to associate with people for whom that position is an assumption as dusty as old tax returns. If you don't associate with such people, you won't stand a chance. The real trick is to get them to tolerate associating with you. Rub shoulders with useful people, but don't bump them and don't make them apprehensive. Never seem anxious. Act as if you are already in the right place and seem to take them for granted. At the same time, always with subtlety, acknowledge their supremacy and flatter their egos.

Water holes where big dogs drink are not hard to find. Making room for yourself is another matter, and that is where the stock markets come in. The markets are a perfect place for newbies to start because at this water hole stocks are the universal common denominator. Consequently, if you develop exceptional skills in the markets and demonstrate them clearly but subtly, no one is going to say, "Wow," but everyone at the water hole will remember you. Next time you drop by, they will want to listen for amusing, if not usable, information and so they will be more inclined to let you elbow through to have a sip. From that point on only two factors will help you in time to gain an actual stool: Exceptional performance backed by exceptional wealth.

If for some reason they don't let you have a stool, don't quit. Like The Man from Omaha whom Harvard rejected, move on to the next venue and study your Graham and Dodd. Perhaps in time you can add that water hole to your portfolio; or better yet, build your own.

STOCK OPTIONS   Let's talk about chickens.

If a farmer gives you a live chicken you have only two choices: Either you pluck the bird and eat it for dinner or you place it in a coop, where all your neighbors can see it, and hope that it fattens up so you can fry it later.

On the other hand, if the farmer gives you an option for a live chicken you have gained flexibility and privacy. You now have the opportunity to make choices that will maximize your use of the bird, and your neighbors will be none the wiser. For example, you can go out to the farm every day to keep an eye on the birds and close the deal when you find a chicken you think is plump enough to enjoy. Or if you like your chickens already butchered and ready to cook, you can pick one out of the farmer's freezer and take it home today but exercise your option for it five months ago, when it was alive. Options always make better deals than deals, particularly when you can exercise them before you received them.

Principles that hold true for chickens also hold true for stocks. For example, a chicken option rewards a CEO with the idea of a chicken rather than the chicken itself, and the idea of a chicken does not have to be put into a pen for the neighbors to gawk at. A stock option does the same thing. It pays potential equity, which no one can see, rather than cash or current equity, which everyone can see. Furthermore, as you can see, the stock option lets you choose when you purchase the stock which allows you to lock in a favorable price. For example, if you prefer your stock table-ready then you can take your stock today but backdate your purchase of it to the seventeenth-century when the stock was cheap.

However you use it, the stock option as a primary component of the CEO's compensation package was one of the greatest innovations in the history of commerce. It offers equity instead of money, which always says "Boo!" on a balance sheet, and it locks in a discount purchase price for the CEO. Although recently under attack, I believe that the stock option will always be, in one way or another, part of The Deal, and when the dust settles and chicken hawks like Enron and WorldCom are forgotten, few people other than those who receive them will pay attention to stock options.

As a matter of course, any individual who owns and is ready to execute his stock options should do whatever he or she can to help nudge that stock's price in the right direction without risking an investigation due to a violation of law. God forbid. The true skill in this game – and the subtleties can be elegant -- is all in the nudge. I have known CEOs who can raise an eyebrow and move the entire market twenty points without raising anyone else's eyebrow. Options give CEOs the flexibility of a Las Vegas contortionist so there is really no excuse for failing to buy low and sell high over and over again. Just remember that when you backdate you might have to dance around regulators and do-gooders, but the dance takes the risk out of uncertainty so waltz whenever you must

Some CEOs benefit only modestly from their stock options, while others make fortunes that oil sheikhs would envy. Clearly, stock option strategy is a game that separates boys and girls from men and women, and among men and women, it separates the poultry from the raptors. How you fare will depend on which amuses you more in your life, the sound or the fury; the peeps of happy chicks, or the taste of hot blood.

STRAIGHT ANSWER   President Harry Truman was famous for giving straight answers to straight questions. Today, he would be regarded as media cannon fodder and he would be hounded out of office in a heartbeat. No one gives straight answers any more and no one expects straight answers. President Jimmy Carter learned that the hard way when he gave that straight answer about lusting in his heart. All America wanted from Carter was a little white lie, and he couldn't deliver. No president since has failed to deliver repeatedly what America wanted from Carter.

People don't really want to hear honest thoughts that come from the heart. Such thoughts are too intimate. Even worse, they are not *my* thoughts, so they are irrelevant. Straight answers are also sure to offend someone. We have learned, with the power, reach, and diversity of the media, that regardless of the viewpoint you profess, a measurable percentage of the population is poised and ready to dismember you for it. You are therefore better off dissembling, as President Nixon recommended, or not remembering or skirting the edges or throwing out alternatives designed to offend no one, please everyone, confuse the issue, or avoid the point in question altogether. The fact is that straight answers take away all your flexibility and pin you down. When bad effects follow, you have no escape. Better to keep your options open and reserve your real opinions for the bathroom mirror.[31]

I have allowed myself one exception to this rule, and that is the words you are reading. By the time you read them, I will be dead, and so I really don't give a damn what you think about them or about me. I have provided you with some straight talk and straight opinions and you can do with them whatever you like. I do not speak for all CEOs. I speak for myself and in concert with a substantial and growing number of other CEOs, other prominent leaders, and other self-serving greedy sons of bitches who keep the world turning. However, I do not claim to be their spokesman. I claim only to be my spokesman. I can afford to be my spokesman. A straight

---

31 The public does enjoy staged candor that offends, particularly when tuning in to talk shows, media interviews with eccentrics and extremists, and confrontational "analyses" pitting one loudmouth from one side of a fence against another loudmouth from the other side of a fence. These don't count as undressed candor, however, because they are scripted to maximize audience attention. Generally speaking, the only straight answer in these events is a producer's response to a network's demand for ratings.

answer is the privilege of someone who has won everything he ever wanted and who doesn't have enough time left to lose it. But you aren't there yet. Until you get to that point, I suggest that you measure your integrity in dollars and talk straight only to your mirror, your dog, and your ATM.

STRATEGY   Here is a sad story. The son of a close friend of mine was, to all appearances at a young age, destined to have a successful career in the top echelons of business and possibly government. He had solid but not embarrassingly high test scores. He graduated prep school at the top of the middle third of his class and was a team captain, a student government president, and chairman of the students' alumni relations committee. After graduation he passed Go, collected two hundred thousand dollars from his trust fund, and went directly to college at his father's alma mater. Clearly he was an aggressive young man with deep ambitions, competitive on every point, fearless, clever, tough-minded, tall, good looking, and gifted with the ability to make quick, rational decisions. Then something tragic happened. He suffered some kind of breakdown. In the middle of his junior year, he turned up absent from an important seminar. Members of his society found him walking down the rails of a railroad track barefoot in the company of a young woman who was a drama-dance major with spiked hair, five body piercings, and at least six additional bohemian pretensions. When asked what he was doing, he replied, "Gentlemen, it's spring." The next day, he changed his major to *ecology*, moved in with the girl, began dressing in dungarees and sandals, started growing dreadlocks, and gave up all his life's ambitions. Today, he lives somewhere in the West, has little to do with his old friends, tends his four ragamuffin children by the bohemian, and he makes his less than modest living as a bee keeper. It is rumored that he has ties to eco-terrorists. This young man either lacked strategy, or lacked the discipline to follow it. His parents suffered all of this with fortitude.

The point here is that you should never do anything, and I mean anything, that does not fit into a larger strategy. Strategy is the backbone of the creature that is your career. It means that you have analyzed every step you take and have calculated every reward against every risk and have decided rationally that yes, you will take this step because it will lead you closer to your career goals. Without strategy, a man is nothing, and whatever such a nothing accomplishes may be chalked up only to luck.

Life is filled with pitfalls. It is human nature every now and then to be tempted by spontaneous thoughts. I know a man, an accomplished billionaire, who from childhood wanted to be a rodeo clown. He wasn't fool enough to throw everything away and become a rodeo clown, yet he still admires rodeo clowns for their courage, their prowess, and their funny pants. How did he resolve this yearning? Clearly, it would have been sheer madness for him to become a rodeo clown; so instead, he collects pictures of rodeo clowns. He owns the largest and the finest collection of photographs of rodeo clowns in the world. This man had a strategy and he stuck to it, despite his nagging passion. Everyone is entitled to an eccentricity so long as he treats it as such.

Strategy. In life as in business, goals and plans define everything. Without strategy, we are driven only by our passions. If you are tempted to dance barefoot on railroad tracks with a girl who hangs pipe wrenches from her nipples, or to play with bulls that need Prozac, I suggest that you acquire a hotel in Pamplona or buy a railroad. That way, you can toy with rebellion *and* turn your passion into profits.

SUCCESS   Everyone loves a winner so when you choose your image, choose the look of a winner and doors will open. Always remember: The greatest contribution to success is the appearance of success.

SUICIDE   Suicide is the abdication of possibility. As far as you are concerned, why force a divestiture of your world's most valuable asset? As far as others are concerned, why mourn someone who gives up?

What about suicide prevention? In many cases, attempts at suicide are bluffs committed by people who want attention. Thus if anyone important to you considers suicide recommend a councilor. If someone essential to you considers suicide, take him to lunch, tell him that he is an ass, and remind him to count his assets. If you have a wife or child who is suicidal, intervene with family, friends, medical doctors, ministers, and councilors.

However, if the outcome is unfortunate, never blame yourself. Although misguided, someone else's suicide is a personal choice and it should have no lasting impact on you or your bottom line.

SUPPLY AND DEMAND   Just as the impersonal laws of terrestrial physics govern all material things on earth without exception, supply and demand rule economics with an iron fist. Study the subtleties until you hate them, and then study them some more. You can never know too much about supply and demand.

In recent years, just as we have learned how to manipulate the laws of physics to suit our ends in fields like space travel, information technologies, biotech, and nanotech, we have also learned that we can manipulate the laws of supply and demand to suit our needs. The biggest innovation is in the area of creating demand. The creation of demand before the invention of the product, for example, reduces risk to near zero and in doing that, we have ensured predictable profits from almost any endeavor that is properly planned and aggressively marketed.

We have also learned that if planned demand is to work efficiently, we must reach consumers while their minds are still uncluttered with adult prejudices, critical thinking, and skepticism. In the same way that a baby duck will imprint as its parent the first creature it sees tending to it, a baby human will form intense loyalties to the first imagery that pleases it. At the same time, the child learns how to form loyalties and the impulses that spin out of those loyalties, impulses that whisper "I want," and "I need," and "Gimme! Gimme!" Those impulses we call "demand." Get to them while they are young. Lure them with everything from fuzzy dinosaurs to little AK-47s with laser sights. Attract them with marketing glitter. Spend more on packaging than on product. Educate them about credit and their parents' credit. Reel them in and condition them to understand that they can and must satisfy their every desire. You will also want to reward them by supplying them with the exact stuff for which they yearn. Supply them with an inventory of potential demands and ways of turning those demands into pure satisfaction, and then provide the products. In sum, train them to become fanatical consumers and you can almost guarantee a productive, profitable economy for at least a generation.

SURVIVAL   The one imperative that drives all life forms is the innate command to survive. That imperative, when applied to human societies, is considered part of "Social Darwinism," or an ethos derived from the evolutionary principle that only those creatures well adapted to their environment will survive. From there it is a short jump to the principle of "survival of the fittest."

Corporations offer an environment and those who rise to the top within it are considered, "the best and the brightest." Whether they are the best and the brightest in general is a question that can be asked. However, since corporations provide the most successful environment for most of the planet, you must think of the corporate structure as a contemporary Serengeti upon which competing types of people work out who is the fittest and who is not. Other environments, for example academia, small business, trades, the arts, journalism, religion, family farming, medicine, other professions, the homeless, and niches of isolated indigenous peoples, have their own mechanisms for determining who are the most fit in their worlds, but increasingly, corporate principles are taking over many of these domains, suggesting that, in the competition for best environment, the corporation is the dominant model. In other words, if corporations provide the fittest environment, then those who prevail within corporations must be the best and the brightest.

You aren't just a businessman. Think of yourself as a lion on the plains of Africa hunting, courting, feeding, defending, attacking, and learning to rule. You are a contestant in the battle for red meat and the right to prevail. When you survive you win, and there is nothing left to say. Except that, in addition to your genes and your Vermeer, you will then be free to pass on to the next generation your means, your methods, and your taste in ties.

SYCOPHANCY   I like sycophancy.[32] While only a few people are born to be sycophants, almost anyone can be conditioned to become one, or at the least, to act like one when properly stimulated. Try to gather as many sycophants around you as you can both in your private and in your business life. A few dozen sycophants surrounding you daily will have the effect of removing all resistance to your momentum and of boosting your internal horsepower, not to mention your ego. A sycophantic wife (or husband, as the case may be), a sycophantic secretary, and a sycophantic Chief Financial Officer are the absolute minimum to make your life and career a glide rather than a tangle. Ideally, of course, everyone with whom you come into contact would be your sycophant, but I cannot indulge idealism, can I? Be content if fifty-one percent of the people you contact every day are clearly defined suck-ups.

There is one exception to this rule of thumb, and that is your brain trust. The small handful of people you employ to provide you with sound, original ideas and clear, accurate analyses, those hard working achievement-is-its-own-reward types who prefer a pat on the back to money in the bank, who never suppose that they are underpaid, and whose ideas you can adopt as your own without a squeak of protest from any of them, must be exempted from sycophancy. Sycophants will lie to earn their points and you have to trust someone to shed light on reality and tell it like it is. Whom can you trust if you can't trust your brain trust?

I have a few suggestions about conditioning. When training someone to become your sycophant, start with the small stuff. The desired pattern of responses to you will act as a template so when you raise the stakes the trainee will take the easy way out, follow the template, and defer to you rather than resist you nine times out of ten. Here is an example. Let's say that you call a staff meeting. Your Chief Operating Officer will sit on your right, since everyone else in the room is beneath him in the pecking order. Spill a little coffee. Look at the puddle despairingly and say to your COO, "John, clean that up for me, will you?" This will bring his personality into sharp focus, and will identify him as either someone to deal with, or some-

---

32 In case you need a dictionary, sycophancy is otherwise known as ass kissing, bootlicking, and brown nosing.

one who can be trained to achieve the desired effect. If your COO has a sharp wit and any balls at all, he will pull out a handkerchief, hand it to *his* sycophant, nod at the puddle, and then watch while it is cleaned up. If this should happen, or something like it, you'll know that you have a race-horse on your hands – or an assassin. On the other hand, if he responds as a good sycophant, then he will clean up the mess himself and suffer quiet humiliation in front of his underlings. He will also learn. Next time you spill coffee, or require him to work a holiday weekend, he will volunteer before you ask and thereby will spare himself being dragged through that hellhole of public humiliation again, and at the same time, he'll appear to his underlings to be your eager, loyal intimate rather than the sad lackey he truly is.

The same strategy works well with spouses. Knowing that your spouse has no intention of going upstairs, ask, "Would you mind, when you go upstairs, bringing me my pipe and slippers?" The key, of course, is always to frame your command as a question, a negative answer to which will show your trainee to be ungenerous, unwilling, rude, and disloyal. As you advance the training to matters requiring greater sacrifice, you might meet some resistance. If so, develop that certain response that melts granite like a laser: An icy stare, a raised eyebrow, and a mildly incredulous, "I beg your pardon?" This forces the issue. The trainee must now choose between confrontation and abdication and if you have kept and cultivated the proper image, it will be no contest and you will have gained yet another loyal sycophant.

"While only a few people are born to be sycophants, almost anyone can be conditioned to become one, or at the least, to act like one when properly stimulated." p. 362

TALK RADIO   At heart every man past the age of twenty-five knows that he is a chief. Even among the ninety-nine and one-half percent of men who will never be named chiefs, each one knows better than all the others, and certainly better than women and foreigners, exactly how things should be done. However, he is void of power and influence except over his children, his dog, his remote control device, and occasionally his wife. The larger course of national events is charted without his advice and consent and therefore it is misdirected. This makes him angry. He is in pain because he is a king without a horse.

Taken together, such men make up a class of potential warriors. Shrewd leaders throughout history have known how to harness a substantial number of these warriors, ease their pain, give them purpose, anoint them with importance, and martial them into a force more determined and more deadly than a phalanx of accountants. All they need is a clear idea of who the real enemy is.

Historically this idea was provided by a real chief, such as a prime minister, chairman, chancellor, general secretary, generalissimo, emperor, or field marshal and president for life. Recent progress has changed that. Today, in our information age in our information nation, this idea is provided by the hosts of radio talk shows.

Like recruiters for a band of brown shirts, these hosts have been able to marshal disaffected men by the millions, and the impact of the recruits has been staggering. They have created boom box ideologies that cruise every street in America like low riders in the 'hood. And they have charged politics with lightening bolts of fashionable common sense. These eloquent bull horns have been able to affect elections, impeachments, reputations, and policies, and they became the first national security force since Salem ministers in the seventeenth century to pillory a Hilary in the town square directly over a pile of dry twigs.

What is interesting about these hosts, however, is not their effect, but their methods. They have proven that you don't need a dictator, or even rigorous rules of thought, to muster populist militias. All you need is a prod that will wake up the napping chief in everyman, tell him his tribe needs him, approve his prejudices, and point him in the desired direction. Presto! You have eager volunteers ready to stampede, kick butt, clean house, and take no prisoners.

While talk radio doesn't reveal anything new, it does underscore two important facts about America: One, we are a nation bounded by education, tolerance, understanding, fairness, equality, liberty, and justice for all; and two, the most practical way to achieve ideological ends that ignore those boundaries is to gain control of popular media.

I recommend that you study the methods of this astonishingly successful phenomenon, talk radio, and learn how to apply them to your business for more practical ends. Radio hosts and participants provide a whole circus of tricks that should be inspiring to all marketing and communications people. And talk radio is an open book free to anyone who wants to take the time to study it. You should be able to learn from its successes and to emulate its methods without having to pay a dime or, best of all, without ever having to socialize with any of its practitioners.

TAXES   Only fools and poor people pay taxes. That is what a tax attorney once told me. He might have been exaggerating a little, but his point was well taken.

I don't mean to suggest that you *never* pay any taxes. Of course you will pay some taxes in some years if for no other reason than to show to the many prying eyes looking over your shoulder that you are a patriotic citizen. Generally speaking, it is not a question of whether; it is a question of how much and how often. No one in his right mind would simply fill out a tax form year after year according to instructions, write a check for the balance due, and trot off to the post office. Death and taxes might be the only certainties in life, but I guarantee that you will have more control over the latter than the former. Pay taxes judiciously, if at all. Retain the best tax lowyer and accountant money can buy. Keep extensive records supporting your claims. Over the course of your life, be satisfied if you pay one-fourth of what the IRS says you owe.

Our world is filled with malcontents. Many of them believe that a person who works effectively and makes a substantial living should pay the way for those who work less effectively and make a modest or poor living. That's why the income tax is a graduated tax. If these types had their way, they would seize all your assets, divide them like an apple pie, and send you and your family to the dogs. Remember the aftermath of the French Revolution?

I believe that every taxpayer begins on a level playing field with every other taxpayer. What he or she chooses to pay is a personal decision, one for which each person must be ready to accept responsibility. If someone chooses not to keep receipts, not to deduct what is deductible, not to form charitable trusts, and not to use top-drawer advice, then that person has no reason to complain. Furthermore, it is good for ordinary people to pay taxes. Do ordinary people donate wings to libraries? Do ordinary people set up foundations to reward genius and eradicate misery? It is important for all citizens to be involved in their communities, and for most ordinary people, paying taxes will be their only civic involvement.

Then there are questions about relative equality. Some working poor people might pay a larger percentage of their earnings in taxes than people of means, but whose fault is that? Whose choices are being punished? Whose abilities are being rewarded? And whose contributions to the public infrastructure are being taken for granted? The pittance that a hundred ordinary people pay pales beside the amount that one person of means pays, even when the person of means pays eighteen percent and the ordinary people pay twenty-two percent. Yet don't poor and ordinary people use the same public roads and government services that rich people use? Is that fair? What's the bottom line here?

The bottom line is that if you play, you pay, at least something most of the time, and if you are rich you will pay the way for many of your neighbors. There is no practical way around it. Still, we are all in this thing together, and what matters for all of us is paying as little as we can get by with. If any person is clever enough to figure out how to pay no taxes year after year and avoid persecution or prosecution, I will pat that person on the back and say well done, even as I chafe a little in envy. Here is an admission that might depress you: Only once in my working life, after I became a billionaire, was I able to go three consecutive years paying no income taxes whatsoever.

The world of taxes exists outside the real world of competition. It is a fixed game with a regulated outcome engineered by liberals with a socialist agenda to redistribute income downward and outward. That scheme does not account for the natural differences between people of high ability and people of low or mediocre ability. Fortunately, changes in the tax laws during the last half century have significantly eased the burden previously imposed on people of means. These changes didn't just happen. They were the result of furious efforts to elect the right candidates to office and to successfully lobby congress to reduce taxes most for people who matter most. As a person of means, it will be your duty to continue these efforts and in doing so, to demonstrate that the best and the brightest can always outwit these social planners. For starters, keep calling them, "tax-and-spend liberals." They hate it. And to the public the phrase is hypnotic as a mantra. Then support all carefully crafted laws that will reduce taxes for those in the highest brackets, and urge ordinary people to support them too. This is not as difficult as it sounds. What taxpayer in a freedom-loving nation does not support *any* campaign to lower taxes?

TEAMWORK   There are two kinds of people in this world: Team players and lone wolves. As a general rule, the former work together to make money and the latter work alone to make trouble. Let's take a closer look at the concept of teamwork and the popular film maker, Michael Moore[33].

---

33 Editor's warning. The other 364 entries in this book are fictional. This one is for real.

In any human endeavor there is a coach, and there is a team. The coach does things *his* way, and the team does things *his* way. That is, CEOs coach and everyone else does teamwork. This should dispel the notion that teamwork has anything to do with democracy. It has everything to do with chain of command, compliance, and putting duct tape over the mouths of lone wolf dissidents so the group can move forward as a unit. Players who think they know a better way are free to become coaches and start their own teams, if they can, and that is where democracy comes into play. If they can't start their own team, then dissidents can either adapt or become gadflies. If they become gadflies, they will have no one to blame but themselves when the coach swats them.

Of course dissident Americans can get better health care in a poor country like Cuba than they can at home. Cuba welcomes poor, tired, tempest-tossed dissidents yearning to breathe free. We in America have been there and done that and today, under the direction of our insurance industry, our health care system requires citizens to exercise teamwork.

Michael Moore, the advocate journalist who filmed the documentary *Sicko*, has no one to blame but himself when our government swats him for visiting Cuba for the sole purpose of embarrassing an entire industry. What coach would not bench a player who consorts with players from an opposing team whose members smoke illegal cigars, practice communism, speak a foreign language, and give away band-aids, aspirin, and open heart surgery to anyone who walks through the door with a sob story?

Get in step, Michael. Or get used to having your butt kicked. Our nation has sacrificed millions of citizens to sustain a profitable insurance-healthcare industry that contributes huge numbers to our Gross Domestic Product. If dissidents like you prevail, those sacrifices will have been made in vain. No citizen who possesses any sense of teamwork, a balanced portfolio of blue chip stocks, and means to access the finest inaccessible health care in the world, will ever let that happen.

America is engaged in a life-or-death competition against all other economies. Teamwork is the alchemy – and the only alchemy -- that will lead us to victory.

THE TEASE   If body language speaks, then Gypsy Rose Lee said it all. Show consumers just enough of the good life to make it seem real, reachable, and imminent. Let their imaginations fill in the blanks, each according to his or her own fantasies. All on their own, they will then develop an almost religious faith that one day, so long as they stay focused and so long as they keep reaching, they will have it all.

Like Gypsy, we bump and grind the dance. We imprint our message. And we move on unmolested. As livelihoods go, if you find this venue shocking, think about scratching coal out of mineshaft for the rest of your shortened life.

Gypsy rules.

TECHNOLOGY   Technology is the hinge on the door to the future. All progress depends on technology. All technology depends on corporate research and development and a strong profit motive. As a species, we will not survive without growth in technology.

The planet Earth and all of nature, including human beings, arose as random events adapting to a chaotic situation. Primitive technology raised us from animal status and gave us fire, tools, weapons, and the Tickle Me Elmo Surprise sweepstakes. As technology advanced, we advanced. It is no different today. Once most people lived their whole lives within thirty miles of their birthplaces. Today, we can fly to Paris for lunch and stop off for cocktails in London on the way home. No dream is beyond our grasp so long as we are in the grip of technology.

Ignore the naysayers and the neo-Luddites. They are merely afraid of change and, like the dinosaurs, if they cannot adapt they too will perish. I choose not to perish. I choose to survive and to lead. Whole populations must be conditioned to accept rapid change and ever-newer technologies, and who better to lead those populations than those of us who control capital, media, and commerce? Change and development have the added advantage of ever-increasing profits, for example, as people trade their 78 records for 45s and their 45s for 33-1/3 lps and their lps for 8-track tapes and their 8-track tapes for cassettes and their cassettes for CDs and their CDs for DVDs, and their DVDs for iPods, and their iPods for iPhones and whatever is next. Where will it end? It will never end. And at each stage of improvement, there are vast profits to be made. Do your part to keep technology at the forefront.

What do I say to the naysayers and the doomsayers? If global warming, for one example, is real, and it can be attributed by good science to the rise of certain technologies, then I say fine. That presents us with a challenge to invent more powerful and more profitable technologies that will save the day. How did we respond to the tragedy of infectious diseases? We invented penicillin. How did we stop raging rivers from flooding? We built dams and levees. How did we fix darkness? We built power plants. How did we respond to the scourges of West Nile Virus, the Mediterranean fruit fly, and head lice in kindergartens? We sprayed cities, farms, children, and the entire state of California with Malathion. The scorecard goes on indefinitely.

In addition to hot innovations in energy, water management, pesticides, herbicides, insecticides, and miraculous new germicides, watch for developments in pharmaceuticals, genetics, nanotechnology, computers, and geriatric health care. One day, given new technologies that will control cancers and mutations, humans will live to be one hundred and fifty years old. As we outfit their air conditioned electric carts with entertainment centers, comfortable vital sign monitoring devices, comprehensive built-in life support systems, diagnostic computers, real time links to care givers, and top of the line defibrillators, they will be able to shop without having to depend on walkers.

Before you know it, everything superfluous or annoying in nature will be gone or controlled, and a new world, designed specifically for humans and their comforts, will replace the crude, random chaos of the natural world. Already we are well on our way to achieving that goal of a better way of life for all consumers and there can be no more noble national purpose. America is the standard bearer of the world and it is up to us to guide the way with more elaborate technologies. People who do not put their faith in future technologies are either blind to the possibilities or ignorant of the facts, and they are, essentially, subversive. To those who cry "Stop! You can't do that any more!" I say, "Watch!"

TELEVISION   Television is here to stay. In time it will be integrated with new technologies and the World Wide Web which might change how it is used. However, so long as we have electricity, it will never be entirely replaced and it should never be viewed as anything less than a miracle.

Let's take a closer look at why television works.

As nature and social interaction used to, television creates a vision of reality in the minds of people who watch it. Television opens doors to other worlds, the future, the imagined, the present, and the past. It anchors us to ourselves and each other. In the broader flow of history, television is still that new park in front of the courthouse on Main Street where old men lean on canes and solve riddles and women load card tables with fried chicken, corn on the cob, and fresh-baked apple pie and little children squeal and run and play with kittens and puppies. Television is still that new public stadium where townsfolk gather to cheer for their teams and plump young girls shake crape paper pompoms. Television is still that new church on the corner where the faithful gather to worship and support each other. And television is still that bright new bridge that spans the old information gap and connects a fine new corporate headquarters to millions of consumers worldwide and their liquid assets, their credit cards, their savings, their mortgages, their un-leveraged equity, their unreported income, and whatever spare change they leave unattended on their dressers. Television is all about communications.

Take a lesson from history. Public dramatization has always offered the most efficient venue for communications. Prior to television, the most successful arena of public dramatization in all history was the Roman Coliseum. We can still learn from its spectacles.

Why? Those amazing spectacles showed us for all time how to use imagery to accomplish our goals. They did two things. They made a curious audience captive, and they dramatized the extremes of power possible only to those who rule. Almost literally, they punched audiences in the gut and took their breath away. Who can walk away from the grotesque when it is literal and you can watch it safely with friends and wine? And who will not quickly offer loyalty to the producers? Nothing snaps the masses to attention or encourages obedience to their masters like the sights and sounds of human arms and legs being snapped from their torsos, and human intestines spilled into a pile, still undulating as if, like a ball of snakes, they had lives of their own. How gratifying to have been a guest at the party -- instead of the entertainment.

Today, television communicates similar messages only with greater subtlety. For example, you won't have to show real people actually dismembering each other to the death or being torn apart and eaten by wild animals. Mere hints of people's deepest fears and darkest fantasies will keep audiences tuned in and on the edge of their seats night after night hungry for more. And truly edgy programming, like cage fighting, news videos of executions, and films depicting the total destruction of New York, Los Angeles, the world, and the solar system, not only make ordinary people squeal and grin; they also tend to humble them and chill whatever irrational motivation they might have had to challenge forces so much more powerful and brutal and imaginative and uncaring than they. Why risk pitfalls in the real world when you can have fun watching others get mutilated – and reassure yourself after the mutilation is over that it was only make believe? And afterward, when you the consumer turn off the set, you feel so safe where you are. Considering all the alternatives life offers, your life is pretty good. True, it still has far too many empty places; too many worn and rusty parts; too many bills; too little pizzazz. But all of that is your problem and you know exactly how to fix it. You're still just a working stiff and you haven't gotten around to improving your life yet, but you will.

Meanwhile that other *you*, that one-half of one percent of our population including CEOs and television advertisers; *you* must remember that *you* are the guiding hand behind all television programming. You must get on with your script too. After you stimulate terror and amusement and ensure that your audience is both captive and loyal, you must leave the Roman example in the dust and spin your modern way into consumer's hearts and minds. You must sell products. You must offer people hope and provide quick, easy ways for them to reach out and fix their lives.

Just how difficult a process is that? How many life styles, personalities, and possessions must you dramatize on television to turn any ordinary consumer into a quivering nucleus of envy – and ignite that consumer right now to unholster that credit card and fire off three easy payments of $99.99 each? How many scenes does it take to help a consumer subdue his deepest insecurities and gratify his most urgent needs? How many scenes must you flash on a screen before he resolves finally to tear down and throw out the brown and tacky rubble of his life and replace every molecule with bright, new, upscale, perky, and fashionable…somethings? Anythings?

In truth, not many scenes, though a lifetime of repetition helps.

Now back to you, Mr. and Ms. Consumer. Look at the screen. Look at the life these actors live here, right now, in your living room. Nothing they do looks familiar, does it? Now take another look at *your* hovel. Your pathetic life. Why are you falling behind? Look at the people these actors play; the people they associate with; the money they spend; the places they go; the homes they live in; the jobs they master; the cars they drive; the food they eat; all the time they have on their hands; the fantastic sex. What is wrong with *you*? What are you doing? What are you waiting for? Why are you sitting there with your thumb up your ass? Isn't it time that you took control of your life? Get up! Escape your boredom, your misery, and your shame! Fix what needs to be fixed! Open your door! Walk into the light! Convert! Have an orgasm! Buy that Hummer, NOW!

Then drive it down your Appian Way like a triumphant centurion in his chariot, one of the few; one of the select; one of the safe.

Like film and stage directors, rulers and would-be rulers from Caesars and CEOs to network executives, have understood the usefulness of the public square, whether that is found in a coliseum, a theater, a cathode ray tube, or a notebook LCD screen. If you want to rule, don't waste your time shouting in people's faces demanding this, and requiring that. Find a good script, a stage, and an audience.

One good show is worth a thousand admonitions.

THEY   As we become more sophisticated in the use of information technologies, we develop control technologies that inform and educate people with amazing efficiency. Along the way, we sometimes stumble into answers to life's most persistent questions.

Here is a story that will warm your heart. Many years ago, a former associate of mine reported hearing the following conversation in the detergent section of a supermarket. Two women were comparing the virtues of different laundry detergents. The first cold water detergent had just been introduced and was being hyped in all the media.

The first woman asked: "Have you tried this new cold water detergent yet?"

The second woman replied: "No, I haven't. I really don't like the idea of washing in cold water! What about you; have you tried it?"

The first woman said: "Oh, yes, and I just love it. Everything came out clean and fresh. The whites were white and the colors didn't fade. And best of all, they say it germ proofs."

They also say that advertising works. But just who is "they?" Who are those mysterious authorities who say? No one knows for sure, but I will say this: If they say it germ proofs, they mean it.

THOUGHT DISORDER, OR TDB   I'd like to borrow a term sometimes used by psychiatrists, and give it a new meaning.

Some psychiatric patients use garbled speech. Some psychiatrists think that this results from garbled thought, which in turn results from a mental disease. That's thought disorder. If you look more closely at people, you will observe that many people use garbled speech that results from garbled thought that results from willful stupidity, not pathology. That's thought disorder B, the new disease.

Take into account the world's entire population of between six and seven billion ordinary people, add in Darwin Award winners, and you might see strong evidence that we risk suffering a pandemic of TDB. I am thinking about employees I have personally witnessed here, in the most advanced nation in history which provides ordinary people with the most opportunity in history, looking on a map near Tumwater for the nation's capitol. I am thinking of an accounting intern, a UCLA senior who can't locate the Pacific Ocean on a map. I am thinking about throngs of believers gaining inspiration from the Virgin Mary when she appears miraculously on a grilled cheese sandwich auctioned on eBay for the price of new BMW. Then there is, like, an entire generation, you know, that like attempts to like communicate, dude, so like he goes, man, this gig is like major unawesome yuh know and she goes like yeah, its like I'm so leaving this place, bitch, and he goes like cool but like what about work n stuff and she goes like hey, dog, fuck work wanna see my new tat? Like, yuh know, check my ass.

Vaccinate against TDB. Read a book. Subscribe to a newspaper. Learn the English language and how to use your mind. Study. Get comfortable with supply and demand, risk and reward, profit and loss, and stock manipulation. More importantly, don't be embarrassed to elevate yourself above your crowd. Their social order is defined by their most common disorders, while yours could be defined, like mine, by how successfully you manipulate crowds because of their disorders.

Don't let TDB become another HIV. If it does, learn if you can how to like, yuh know, use it to advantage. Manipulating people afflicted with TDB should be easier than herding lemmings over a cliff.

TIME CLOCKS   Normally I did not engage in micromanagement of the workplace. With time clocks, however, I made an exception.

Before the advent of time keeping, people went wherever they chose whenever they chose with no regard to structure, discipline, or punctuality. If you have ever attended an event at a Native American festivity called "a Pow-Wow," as I once attempted while on vacation in Montana, you will understand exactly what I mean. Participants in the featured event, a traditional dance, dribbled into the staging area anywhere from ten minutes to an hour *after* the posted starting time, and no one seemed to mind. Other Anglo-Americans in the audience, who lived on, or in close proximity to, the host Reservation, called this phenomenon, "Indian Time." Apparently, whatever awareness of structure these Native Americans have is governed by some kind of inner spirit that works in direct opposition to standard concepts of efficiency, responsibility, compliance, and conformity. Obviously this "Indian Time" notion would be intolerable in any sensible workplace, and it underscores my suspicion that similarly cavalier notions about time exist in the deeply suppressed unconscious of all peoples. Human beings must be conditioned to have proper behavior, particularly in regard to time. Enter the time clock. It is a training device, perhaps the most efficient training device ever invented.

I cherish the time clock because it attacks that perverse spirit of unregulated liberty that dwells in every creature. Like animals, when people are hired to be utilized for their productivity in the workplace, each one must be, in the words of a horse trainer, "broken to lead." That is, all workers must have that inner spirit crushed and then driven out of them for all time. Only then can they learn how to conform to their duty. The military has perfected ways of breaking that spirit in boot camps. The idea is to reduce the recruit to a puddle of quivering putty then reshape him into a warrior who would rather eat his own liver than disobey an order. Obviously, as a CEO in a society with delicate sensibilities, you can't run that kind of a boot camp. Nor can you beat rebelliousness out of workers with a riding crop the way an animal trainer can when educating his charges. We use the time clock instead.

Nothing grinds away at a person's sense of autonomy more efficiently than a time clock. Some people initially fight it, the way a horse kicks when first fitted with a saddle. Others adapt more readily. In the end, after years of conditioning, all workers succumb. Take a close look at factory workers after twenty years of punching a time clock, and I defy anyone to find an ounce of serendipity, a gram of autonomy, a carat of rebelliousness, or a dram of real independence remaining in any one of them. The time clock is a constant reminder that so long as the worker is punched in, the company owns him. The company controls; the company decides; the company leads; the company knows; the company demands; the company rewards and punishes; the company gets what it wants. In the end, after a few years of conditioning, just as a good horse does not require a rider to tell him what to do, and a good soldier does not have to be ordered to kill an enemy, a good worker will demand as much from himself as any mediocre supervisor could ever extract from him.

Don't let yourself be seduced by human resource managers who think they have found a more enlightened way to control workers. Let your human resource managers fiddle with ergonomic chairs. If you want compliant, malleable, workers plodding along day after day, require them to punch in, punch out, or log in, and log out. Good time clocks make good workers.

TORT REFORM   Remember that old adage about not biting the hand that feeds you? I think too many people have forgotten that adage and I think it is time they were reminded. The Trial Lowyers' Association and the American Bar Association will try to convince you that only a tiny fraction of lawsuits are frivolous and even a tinier fraction of them result in excessive awards that are upheld on appeal. I don't care if they are right or wrong. So long as the possibility exists that one frivolous lawsuit can be filed or that one jury award can be excessive and supported on appeal by one judge, then we need to proceed with thorough tort reform. Furthermore, certain industries, such as insurance, health care, pharmaceuticals, mining, automobiles, chemicals, and toy manufacturing, are particularly vulnerable to litigation and need protection if they are to preserve their customary and necessary profit margins. For example, when interest rates are low, insurance suffers terribly since they traditionally invest heavily in the bond and money markets. Severe limitations on malpractice lawsuits alone would offer insurance a buffer that would benefit executives and shareholders alike during those hard times when interest rates bottom.

More to the point, and without regard to investments, how should courts treat real culpability such as medical malpractice? If surgeons amputate a patient's left leg, when then meant to cut off his right big toe, what kind of award should courts grant the patient? How much does a patient need to buy a prosthetic leg and some physical therapy? He would have lost an essential part of one leg anyway. Now he might need a second surgery. So award him the cost of the second surgery and the prosthetic leg. Include the first surgery plus six months' physical therapy and counseling. Throw in a year's wages to compensate the patient for the added inconvenience and stop there. Why give one person a massive windfall, to make his life more luxurious than it ever would have been, at the expense of thousands of insurance company stockholders and subscribers? Limit his settlement to cover actual losses and let the medical community punish the doctors. In this way everyone will benefit. The patient gets help. Subscribers keep their low premiums, and the insurance company preserves dividends for stockholders who are counting on that income to help support their aging parents, their college bound children, their terminally ill relatives, and their condo in Costa Rica.

Reform is needed. But if reform falls short, and I am almost certain that it will since there are simply too many consumers and lowyers who want to sponge off insurance carriers, corporations, and successful professionals, then I suggest the aggressive use of the counter suit. In other words, when they bite the hand that feeds them, bite back. Find or manufacture legitimate grounds to sue anyone who sues you. We'll see who has the deeper pockets.

Critics of tort reform claim, with intended irony, that imposing limits on lawsuit awards is a form of government regulation in an era of deregulation. Shouldn't the marketplace of the jury, they ask with more than a tinge of sarcasm, decide for itself what it wants? This is convoluted logic. It is true that laissez faire is the bedrock of our economy, but our economy also depends on the rule of law. Business and law are not the same things. Can you imagine what would happen if laissez faire were extended to the law? Would we deregulate shoplifting and assault with a deadly weapon? Should we turn malpractice over to family vigilance committees? People and lowyers need guidelines and limits, and they also need protection.

The bottom line is that tort reform would protect vulnerable corporations, professionals, *and* the people who sue them. It would protect millions of consumers, who depend on businesses and professional services, from needless financial injury. And it would protect juries and plaintiffs from themselves and their own misguided tendencies. Furthermore, excessive awards inhibit the freedom of others, particularly corporations, to freely pursue their business. Tort reform would lift that inhibition. And finally, tort reform would keep crooked players from ripping off everyone, and it would rescue true victims from the grip of voracious lowyers who fill victims' hearts and minds with fantasies of windfall wealth instead of the care and sympathy they truly deserve.

Every game needs rules. The question is, do we want to tilt the playing field to the advantage of a few individuals and turn them into millionaires because someone forgot to take a forceps out of a hysterectomy? Or do we want to be realistic about human error and keep the playing field level so everyone can benefit?

TRAVEL   As a major CEO, you will become a citizen of the world and international travel will become second nature to you. However, always remember that we live in perilous times and at any moment terrorists or kidnappers could target you. For this reason, always travel with an entourage, including bodyguards with Secret Service or FBI training. Try to stay in out of the way luxury hotels designed for diplomats and celebrities, places that are air tight with their own security staffs. Avoid the masses. Be sure your wife is equally protected when she does her humanitarian appearances and shopping. She could throw a wrench into your whole quarter by getting kidnapped.

TRIBALISM   Human beings are herd animals. Anthropologists call the herd a tribe when it is composed of closely related people who are pre-industrial in outlook and a society when it has banks, cathedrals, and mass-produced clothing. But whatever anthropologists call it, every human group is, or quickly becomes, a tribe, and whatever the level of its development, tribal loyalty is the bedrock of every human group.

In a company, for example, the natural instincts of competition and self-preservation lead members of one department to develop loyalty to their group and an identity slightly different from that developed by members of every other group. Each department believes that every other department is at least in part sub-human. At the same time, the company as a whole becomes a tribe and a center of true civilization, while other companies represent stupidity and barbarism. Try wearing a Pepsi logo in a Coke plant, or visa-versa. You'll be cannibalized.

You need to understand the dynamics of tribalism to successfully manage human resources, whether employees, competitors, investors, or consumers. In the consumer market and with investors, an appeal to the correct tribal values *du jour* can mean tremendous gains in sales and stock price, while violation of those values can spell disaster. Similarly, within your own company, you must design and maintain the tribal values you desire company wide, and at the same time, stimulate--yet limit--differing tribal values within. Internal tribal competition jump starts productivity, but only so long as departmental differences can be easily overcome to promote company-wide unity. Think of your company as a collection of families operating within sub-clans that operate within clans that make up a single tribe.

Competitors, on the other hand, are always evil, sub-human, and vile. You are "We," the Roman Empire, and they are "They," the Vandals, waiting at the gates to sack your civilization, rape your women, torture your sons, execute your warriors, pillage your villages, burn your homes, mutilate your goats, sell your daughters into slavery, and carry off your gold to foreign lands where godless shamen defile human corpses and drink their blood.

If that sounds a little over the edge, and therefore irrational, that's because it is. Greed and gut loyalty run successful corporations, not reason, and CEOs who understand that become winners. The purpose of reason is to build compelling myths to explain what has already occurred in order to reinforce your claim that you are more advanced than your adversaries. For instance, when you conquer someone else's tribe, you saved them from incompetent management, in the case of a corporation, or, in the case of a nation, your tribe rescued their tribe from brutal tyranny.

As chief of your tribe, whether your tribe is a nation, a political party, or a corporation, you have a grave responsibility to do whatever you must to ensure your tribe's survival using any means at your disposal, and then rationally dress up your actions so bystanders will admire you and hate your enemies.

TRICKLE DOWN   Remember the first time you bought a bank? Remember that warm, flushed feeling you got, as if someone had just walked up to you and given you a license to steal? That is how we all felt when President Reagan began to pursue his supply side economics and its cornerstone, the trickle down theory. According to this theory, if the administration rearranged the economy through tax breaks, de-regulation, union-busting, and other incentives to provide a massive transfer of wealth from ordinary citizens to those few of us who already controlled the majority of wealth and know how to manage it correctly, then we owners of capital would in turn invest in new businesses and the economy would grow and prosper and ordinary people would eventually reap more benefits than they lost as the new wealth trickled down in the form of high employment, higher wages and benefits, and more opportunities. It took only a few years to reap the benefits of President Reagan's policies. Many of us who were already millionaires became billionaires and a handful of *nouveau riche* was added to our ranks, including a few late adolescent high tech entrepreneurs and high performance athletes. Newcomers aside, the amount of capital transferred into the hands of those of us already accustomed to managing it was indeed massive, by far the largest such transfer in our nation's history, and the transfer continues at an accelerating pace today. More than anything, this Reagan Revolution gave us discretion, the discretion to decide what to do with all this capital.

Then came President Clinton, who, although a Democrat, was in fact a conservative economist who tended the economy better than any President in history. The American economy became so robust during the Clinton years, and so filled with opportunity, particularly in the high technology sector, and unemployment ran so low, that most of us saw no immediate need to expand the industrial base. There is a time to plant, and a time to harvest.

Similarly, the tax advantages, lack of environmental restrictions, and low wages available in Third World and developing nations, a situation aided by NAFTA and the WTO, became so attractive that many of us, if we decided to build new facilities at all, chose to build them in foreign countries. These businesses in turn became enormously profitable and for all intents and purposes, tax free, as if someone else had just walked up and offered us another license to steal. There is a time to plant new crops in new fields.

The net result of all this activity was that most of us were able to acquire assets several times greater than those we owned prior to President Reagan. We woke up and found ourselves in an era that makes the Gilded Age look paltry. We were able to add new automobiles, stretch limousines, new homes, new country club memberships, new beachfront mansions and ski lodges, new art collections, new jewelry, new jet airplanes, new sports teams, new racehorses, new yachts – the list could go on for several pages – to our holdings, in addition to considerable increases in our cash

flow and securities portfolios. It was a wonderful time to be rich. It solidi-
fied our position. And each one of us contributed to trickle down success
and our economy's expansion if by no other means than by our robust
personal spending.

Speaking just for myself and my wife, for instance, we added three
full time employees to one of our domestic staffs, a Mexican and two Gua-
temalans, one of whom speaks some English. We purchased an estate with
vineyards in Tuscany, a newer yacht to help us get there, and a small Lear
to help us get there quickly. We purchased our first stretch limo and hired a
chauffeur and a mechanic. Out West we provided employment for dozens
of workers and we purchased considerable raw materials, when we built
our new fourteen thousand square foot log cabin on a high ridge overlooking the neighboring Royal Teton Ranch, which had been carved out of the
wilderness of Paradise Valley, Montana decades before by Malcolm Forbes.
My wife purchased a herd of Angus cattle for decorative purposes so we
can watch them graze in their pasture next to those big round bales of
straw, so we also added a foreman, who doubles as our wine steward, and a
small staff of cowpersons as caretakers. We christened our place, "The Running 4-Bucks Ranch" and registered our own brand, personally designed
by Brootus Kingkitsch, the Painter of Blight. It features a winged number
four leaning forward as if racing toward a dollar sign. There is a time to feed
on what you have harvested, and a time to share some of the remaining
bounty by providing jobs to others less fortunate.

I think that there must be a photograph, a painting, or a bust of
President Ronald Reagan in nearly every home in America larger than ten
thousand square feet, and, albeit belatedly, I thank the American voters,
from every economic group, for their astute political wisdom. I can only
speak for myself, but rest assured, trickle down works.

As a CEO, whether you and your family are accustomed to managing
large quantities of capital or if you are one of the new ones, I admonish
you to do everything in your considerable power to advance or at least to
preserve this trend in the American economy before other elements wake
up and try to stimulate social unrest and discontent. I don't worry too
much about this happening, although restive signs are visible in the few
remaining bastions of so-called "progressive populist" thought. Always re-

member that it is important not to push ordinary people over their brink. Never take them for granted. They do vote, after all, and many of them own guns. Keep their wages in check, as always, but high enough so they can keep food on their tables and cars in their garages and can qualify for a modest mortgage. Use sports, talk shows, merchandise promotion, and information media to keep them entertained and properly focused. Let threats of international terror, pandemic disease, and catastrophic natural disasters exhaust their tolerance for social change and focus their loyalties on proven leaders. And above all else, give them credit and hope: Lots of credit to keep their dreams alive, and lots of hope that they too can still realize their American Dream and join the ranks of our nation's multi-millionaires. They need to be reminded that all they have to do is work harder, be more productive, acquire the right trappings, and keep their noses clean – or perhaps win a lottery -- then they too might find themselves in a position where they can spill a little surplus capital and watch the crowds below them scurry to grab it as it trickles down.

TRIP-N-ZIP BROWNIES

This wildly popular and privately held West Coast fast food company outsells MacChocolate, Brownie King, and Wicked Willy's in every community west of the Sierras. The American market for fast fast food brownies exemplifies fierce competition, yet decade after decade Trip-N-Zip emerges as the alpha dog in each of its markets. At the same time, it pays workers twice the industry norm and it does nothing to exploit its own success. After sixty years in business, its strategy for nationwide expansion is to open a new store in Arizona. It is an instructive case study of naïve capitalism at its best – and its worst.

Trip-n-Zip sells five products: The Double Doobie is their most popular item, followed by The Howler, Rama's Rocky Road, Maraschino Maya, and The Tantra Teaser. Its products give consumers a high you wouldn't believe, from all that caffeine and rich, dark chocolate. It also provides a homey setting and a Meaningful Experience, sit down or drive through. The company trips along in its quaint way, run by family members who like to shoot lead-based paintballs at each and print quotes from Jesus and the Upanishads on their straws. It rakes in enough profits to support better than upper middle class lifestyles for the handful of stockholders who own it, but the potential remains utterly on the shelf. They *close* on Christmas Day, Easter Sunday, and Allen Ginsberg's birthday (June 3). Every January 23 they give away Tantra Teasers, limit one per customer, to commemorate the first day of the Age of Aquarius.[34] Even worse, the company does not franchise and it coddles its employees.

If the company ever went public and was taken over by a real corporation, you can bet that two things would happen. First, there would be Trip-N-Zip Brownie joints from Peking to Istanbul feeding off the reputation of the original company. Revenues would jump a thousand fold. Second, wages and benefits would fall in line with brownie industry norms and this would increase net profits and return on invested capital two to five hundred percent. Investors would trip over themselves to get in on the action and would bid the stock to unprecedented highs. Those better than upper middle class homes the owners now enjoy would morph into playpens suitable for players in Abu Dhabi.

I get indigestion every time I think about some line worker in one of America's hottest brownie joints starting out at twelve dollars per hour, full benefits, plus a signed first edition of the *Gutenberg Bible*, dust jacket intact. And what about shift managers who rake in 100K per year and get a free Krugerrand for every forty thousand dollars in sales over projections? The owners are giving it away. And they don't need to. Their customers are loyal as lapdogs and their products taste good. I have actually eaten their Howler and I liked it as well as my favorite fast food, the Double-Double burger. But I had a hard time digesting it as I watched some thirty year old reincarnated Christian-Hindu hippie ex-pole dancer and Shiatsu masseuse with a high school GED and tattoos of Jesus and the Goddess Kali riding a Harley running the place as if it were her own, knowing that she is probably ready to buy a brand new BMW – and she can afford it. Sometimes I think that the world is going to hell in a hand basket.

---

34 The Age of Aquarius began at 17:35 GMT on January 23, 1997. It ended on Mount Shasta October 22, 2004 at 7:59 PM GMT, six thousand years after Creation. The next momentous cosmic event will be Rapture, though no one is sure exactly what day Rapture will occur or whether government offices and banks will be closed.

Hear this, brownie barons: It's time to change your karma. Take the company public! Grow it! Franchise it! Cut labor and operating costs! Get in step, for God's sake!

THE TROPHY HOUSE   From the perspective of keeping score, your whole career is preparation for that one shining moment when you can afford to build your first home that is large enough and magnificent enough to properly accommodate your accomplishments *and* the New York Philharmonic. Include thick eight foot tall rock walls, security gates, living quarters for the help, plenty of guest houses, swimming pools, tennis courts, stables, and enough acreage for a golf course. You may then refer to the property as, "The Compound," which will allow you to refer comfortably to future properties you buy or build, even though each of them might dwarf the Vatican, as "the apartment," "the cabin," "the getaway," and "the bungalow."

Whether you think of your compound as a permanent estate or a starter home, spare nothing. No accessory on earth will cause jaws to drop faster, for example, than a five-hundred pound hand faceted Czechoslovakian lead crystal bidet featuring solid gold washers, a diamond set platinum-palladium handle, and disposable cashmere tissues hand knit by Mongolian peasants. In addition to details of construction and decor, pay close attention to the setting. Choose an environment in which your home will outshine anything in view by a factor of at least three. You can then spend the odd Sunday afternoon overlooking the public road nearest to The Compound so you can watch the many passersby who drive near to pay homage.

Enjoy every moment. The greatest success a human can achieve is to become the object of universal envy.

TRUST   In North Dakota and in the diamond trade core populations are related to each other by background or by blood and they are stuck with each other. Consequently, in those two settings, square dealings are a tradition and trust means that a handshake will lead to anticipated results. Elsewhere it is assumed that those who trust most are most easily fleeced so most people use the term "trust" to refer to business arrangements that corner a market sector or to a legal setup that protects assets from relatives and associates their owner can't trust.

As a CEO, learn to trust others as you would expect them to trust you. The Golden Rule in all business is advantage, and the one who gains it will use it regardless of prior expectations. Like the second story of buildings on the old West frontier, trust in corporate business is the façade we erect to make the setting look more permanent, proper, and civilized. It has nothing to do with reality.

If they catch a farmer violating trust on the Northern Plains, he will thereafter have to buy with cash, sign contracts, and seek friends on the Internet. If they catch a broker violating trust in New York's diamond trade, he is out of business. If they catch a CEO violating trust in the rest of the world, it is not considered a catch.

TRUTH   Most of us have suffered through that dreadful moment, usually during the son's or daughter's sophomore year in college, when the student turns up for Christmas holiday sporting combat boots and a pierced eye brow, in the case of the daughter, or a Chullo hat and beard, in the case of the son. They want to search for truth.

Typically this phase doesn't last long. They have taken a group requirement in humanities or philosophy, or have fallen under the mesmerizing influence of their English professor, a failed writer in tweed with penchants for straight whisky, freshman girls, and profundity. Most of them quickly discover that truth is a slippery eel. Disillusionment sets in and they move on to feeding Africans or helping the college janitors achieve their endless desire for higher wages. Sooner or later, they begin to understand that they are jeopardizing their careers while others are advancing theirs. Another semester and they are back on track.

As a CEO, you too will quickly learn, if you don't already know it, that what fails isn't and what works is, and that is all that you will ever need to know about the truth.

THE TURNBUCKLE THING Was it bad breeding or too much influence from that Hollywood crowd he ran with? The nature/nurture argument will go on for many years.

Don't mistake my intent. Membership in The Club is secure for life for all members. But membership does not mean lack of scrutiny. Given his erratic behavior one is compelled to ask: What happened to Wild Bill Turnbuckle?

Billy showed promise and for a while he lived up to that promise. He was tough as nails, innovative as Edison, and acquisitive as a school of piranha. He flew to the ionosphere and back in a weather balloon. He owned teams, started networks, bought film studios, climbed the Himalayas, made a lot of money, and left his mark wherever he ventured. He could have gone on to live like Kublai Kahn. He could have owned Wall Street. He could have raised himself into an icon for generations of future CEO's to admire and emulate. And then, just when we all expected these truly great things from him, he began to throw his money away on international cooperation, endangered species, poverty, disease, hunger, sustainable ranching, problem pollutants, child mothers in poverty, and every other harebrained do-good scheme than happened along. Once he gave away a billion dollars after studying the idea for three minutes. Even more shocking, he declared that men should be banned from running the world for two centuries so women can set things right. This last gaffe we attribute to stress and too many divorces.

What kind of an example is this? Do not let the eccentric behavior of one maverick confuse you. You must understand that in every pack there is always one who thinks that he knows better than everyone else and who takes pride in acting like a lone wolf. There is nothing you can do but let him go his own way. Just take heart and know that your pack will always be there for you and no maverick will ever lead the majority astray.

To Billy I say: I salute you, sir, for your success. But you will forgive me if I turn my back and retire to another room where America's most promising individuals await guidance from someone who intends to stay the course. And, sir, I hope you know what you have given up. With our blessing, your resources, and some dental work, old boy, you could have been president. If not of The Club, at least of the country.

UNEMPLOYMENT When you see unemployment figures hovering between four and nine percent, know that the free market system is functioning as it should. Higher unemployment could trigger a consumer-driven recession. Lower unemployment might signal a labor shortage, higher wages, and inflation. Just the right unemployment shows that things are in balance. Let's take a closer look.

About a fourth of all out-of-work people are receiving unemployment or other benefits. They are disabled, injured, supposedly injured, or laid off. Their real job is to stay on the dole as long as possible, and they apply for work only when the system requires them to do so. Another fourth choose not to work. Some of these are just plain lazy. Some have figured out how to beat the system and they live in the underground work economy. Some are too disturbed to hold down a job. The rest are bums, hookers, thieves, con-artists, and drug dealers. Another fourth could work but won't because they refuse to work for less than they want or they won't take jobs they think are demeaning. They leave those for illegal immigrants. These are hold-outs and they have never asked themselves the question, "Who do you think can hold out longer, the worker who thinks he should be paid like a prince, or the employer who is?" These three groups ensure that a small percentage of people will always be unemployed. The remaining fourth are in transition and actually want work.

Anyone who wants work can find it. The only exceptions to this rule are periods of deep recession or depression, and today, economists know how to avert these aberrations. Nevertheless, keep a close eye on the statistics. High unemployment for people who want work is bad news. You might think that it will suppress your labor costs, but you can do that in other ways. The truth is that unproductive people suffer low self-esteem, lose good work habits, and have too much time on their hands. If they start to think of themselves as downtrodden, they will be vulnerable to radical ideas, union organizers, and other malcontents. Even worse, they can't hold up their end of consumer spending.

Try to keep these people working. You don't have to adopt them or offer them health care or any other benefits. You can offer minimum wage jobs for thirty or fewer hours a week and let welfare and charity organizations pick up the slack as needed. W*ALLMINE! has perfected this strategy for thousands of "permanent" workers and it adds millions to their bottom line. You can do the same for temporary part-time workers just to keep them in the system and motivate them. A little earned income will stimulate their natural greed. If they have any value at all they will either strive so they can get promoted to full time, or they will lose patience and find better work elsewhere. Either way we will all be better off keeping these people working. As long as they have jobs of some kind they will be able to buy more stuff to feel better about themselves and do their part to keep America strong.

UNIONS   A boxing match pits two fighters against each other and only one can win. Drop your guard or fail to exert your innate aggression, and you will lose. Your opponent wants to hurt you, beat you, and defeat you, and he will use any method at his disposal to do so. Would you allow an apposing boxer to use your personal gymnasium to train? Would you assist him? I think not. Then why would you tolerate even the barest hint of unionism in your workplace?

Unions are a scourge. Their leaders have too much power. They make alliances with other unions outside your business. Their rank and file are deluded by obsolete notions that workers should have a say in how much they are rewarded and how they are treated, as if they owned the company. At heart, they are power-hungry socialists. Destroy unions or they will destroy you. Crush every union movement. Tolerate no union organization, no union solicitation, and no union information in the workplace.

Use any means at your disposal to get rid of union sympathizers as soon as you identify them.

There was a time in our nation when corporations or political leaders could enlist Pinkertons, municipal police, or Hessian mercenaries to discourage ordinary people from organizing into radical groups to declare independence, promote self-determination, and undermine the authority of established leaders. That is somewhat more difficult today, so it is all the more important to stop any whiff of union activity before the union gains a foothold.

If you are unlucky enough to take a position in a company that is already union, then sharpen your negotiation skills, keep your community on edge with fears that you might shut down your plant, market your many virtues to the public, and do everything in your power to discredit local union leaders. For example, accuse them of forming alliances with organized crime or of hosting late night smokers where girl scouts are forced to perform unspeakable acts with badgers. Give up nothing without a life or death battle. Like any boxing match, only one contestant will emerge the winner. Be sure it is you. All the rest of us are counting on you.

There is no greater risk to business as usual than a highly organized majority of ordinary people determined to impose their will on those who hold power and own capital.

UPWARD MOBILITY
What keeps the masses of ordinary people from becoming a rebellious, unruly mob? The main factor is the promise of upward mobility, the central idea of The American Dream. As long as people don't believe that they are stuck in a bad situation forever, they will resist organization or mob rule and they will fend for themselves so they can scramble to improve their lot. As long as they believe that they too might become millionaires, they will not criticize those who are millionaires and they will not question the system that makes millionaires.

Think of all the kids in poor neighborhoods who dream of playing basketball in the NBA. They love the NBA and they idolize its players. Some of them spend their last dimes of lunch money on player endorsed paraphernalia, and they wear team colors like devoted soldiers, despite the fact that they have a better chance of flying to the moon under their own power than of making the NBA. Even though they are poor, do you ever hear them criticizing the league, the players, the players' salaries, or the system?

Hope is the key to a manageable public. As long as people hope that they can move out of that trailer, project, or tenement and into a suburban bungalow, or out of that bungalow into a four bedroom rancher with a swimming pool, or out of that nice rancher into a sprawling Tudor executive home on a few lots, or out of that Tudor masterpiece and into that custom built castle with the eight car garage and stables; as long as people believe that anything is possible, they will remain manageable as putty. Give them hope. Stimulate their fantasies. Encourage them to believe in the magic of upward mobility. And feed their appetites. Provide them with a taste of the good life, a ticket to a lottery, the promise of a lightning bolt of wealth, and stories about those who have made it. Do all that and they will serve you loyally and will not give you an ounce of real trouble.

USURY   Usury, or rates of interest deemed to be unreasonably or illegally high, is an antiquated concept. If borrowers are willing to pay thirty percent or three hundred percent for a loan then the market should provide. Market efficiency is the only force that should dictate interest rates. People with sterling credit get sparkling rates. People with atrocious credit pay high rates. That is their penalty for bringing added risk to the transaction. The greater the risk, the higher the rate should be. The point is that anyone can shop for the best interest rate lenders will provide, and nearly anyone can get a loan when needed if that person agrees to pay the rate provided. It's called supply and demand and it's the way things work.

In recent years, the loosening of usury laws in favor of these market forces has created opportunity. For example, pawn brokering, post-dated check cashing, and lending against car titles can be tremendously profitable, plus all three provide a valuable service to people who couldn't otherwise borrow a shovel from a chain gang. These little side businesses, under the umbrella of a limited liability corporation (LLC), can work like franchises not easily identified with you personally and they can provide a nice tidy workplace for some of your idle capital.

Thanks to deregulation and special exemptions from usury law, the idea of usury is almost dead, though Congressional Democrats will always attempt to resurrect the corpse. For the time being, you can still find ways to call your own shots if you pick the right venue. You will need good, stout collectors, though, because default rates are high and repossessions are common. Reserve deputies, over the hill prizefighters, out of work prison guards, bikers, and unemployed skinheads all work out well, plus they really like to scare people and will do it for next to nothing.

"Usury, or rates of interest deemed to be unreasonably or illegally high, is an antiquated concept." p. 392

VALUE   The value of all things must be quantified and translated into economic terms before we can make comparative sense of them. I am pleased to see, for example, that environmentalists have created a new academic field, environmental economics, which is now able to measure the value of pollutants, toxic emissions, sustainability, and other *causes celebres* of the environmental community in terms of dollars. Instead of having to spend millions to extract mercury from its emissions, a coal-fired generating plant can assign the emissions a dollar value, leave the mercury alone, and trade its value like stocks in a vital market.

Think about other possible applications. How much is a rookery of cranes worth, considering the attention it gets from bird watchers, versus the value of the drained wetland as a cluster community with box stores, a mini-mall, and apartments? How much is Yosemite National Park worth as a curiosity versus its worth as developed real estate? You might be astounded if you calculate value added real estate plus year-around boost to local economies plus increases in the tax base resulting from a Yosemite Pristine Parklands development. Think about a championship golf course in Yosemite Valley rimmed by the Merced River and a gated community of a few hundred six-thousand square foot getaway cabins plus peripheral communities for services and retail shops interspersed with a few thousand luxury condos, checkered in multi-story clusters, Phase One, Two, and Three, all with views of features like El Capitan, Ribbon Falls, and Yosemite Falls. And the tourists will still come, if for no other reason than to catch a glimpse of the good life. Don't even get me started on destination ski resorts for high altitude U.S. parks like Rocky Mountain, Glacier,

Teton, and Yellowstone and high latitude alpine parks in Alberta and British Columbia as global warming dries up traditional destinations.

While we might not agree with environmental economists' appraisals, at least now they are starting to bounce the ball in our court. It makes no sense whatsoever to evaluate the worth of natural commodities -- or even human resources -- in sentimental terms, or to associate that worth with values that are purely qualitative, subjective, and judgmental. For example, how can you apply cost-benefit analysis to a grassland when people think of it and describe it as "beautiful," "inspiring," and "tranquil," instead of "worth 1.3 million dollars as pasture?" As commercial real estate, it might be worth 13.72 million dollars. The quantification of value makes possible meaningful public discussion and it opens the door to useful negotiations over specific parcels of land and water that you might want to develop. It provides ammunition we need to fight our good fight and it restates the debate in terms that are practical and commercial.

Thank you, environmental economists. Keep talking value in dollars. It's our native language

VISION   *A vision* is a projection of an imagined future that looks better than the present. Visionaries, or people who continuously have visions, include philosophers, poets, prophets, and Amazon tribesmen who lick frogs.

Vision, on the other hand, as opposed to *a vision,* is a grasp of the big picture. It is a general state of mind, like Moore's Law, that allows us to formulate plans that will lead to profitable strategies that will accomplish worthwhile goals in the future. This difference between *a vision* and a plan spawned by vision is significant. For example, a dairy farmer with vision develops a plan. He buys land, puts up barns, breeds his stock, and works hard to build his herd for the future. Meanwhile, to feed his family, he milks the cows he has. Visionaries, on the other hand, have so much faith in *their vision* of the future that they think their livelihood will follow them wherever they go. In other words, visionaries think that cows fly because they want them to fly, or because, like Amazon tribesmen who suck on frogs, they see cows flapping magenta wings.

Every CEO must be able to plan. In other words, he must be able to envision a better future before he can build a strategy to achieve it. However, any plan worth mentioning must be grounded in rational cost-benefit analysis of the real world and it must assess the potential reward of the imagined future against the risks inherent in change and investment. It must also take into account human nature as it is, not as we might want it to be.

Look at the success of Microfang. Vision was on target. The plan became blueprints. The assessment was near-perfect. The strategies succeeded and they fit human nature like a glove. The final result is the ongoing transformation of civilization into a complex, delicately balanced, interdependent network that grafts the virtual into the tangible. That brave new world depends on electricity, not fantasy; on developing technologies, not dreams; on subtle mental movement in cyberspace, not crude physical motion in nature; and on specialized training, the profit motive, ergonomic chairs, really good firewalls, and power plants that don't malfunction. In other words, it depends on the real world. Microfang's success amassed huge concentrations of wealth for the best and the brightest and it created America's wealthiest man. Best of all, the Microfang vision provides failsafe procedures. If the new civilization crashes, just turn it off. Chances are when you turn it on again, everything will be fine.

On the other hand, *a vision* poses deadly risks because it is based on idealism. Look at what happened to Gandhi, one of history's most notable visionaries. The man believed that civilization could result from brotherhood, non-violence, humility, simplicity, truth, and love for God. He believed in complete self-determination for ordinary people. He thought that greed, wealth, property, and power were insignificant values and corrupting influences. And he believed in work that provided a kind of wealth he would not later need to give away because it already belonged to anyone who wanted it.

Who wins this competition?

Microfang's founder is today's alpha dog. His vision was a blueprint for success. Gandhi was assassinated. His *vision* was a sacred cow that couldn't fly. He died a pauper with nothing to show for his career. At the time of his death, his net worth consisted of one pair of glasses, two pairs of sandals, some eating utensils, a book, a pocket watch, and a set of three inch-high statuettes of monkeys that neither hear, see, nor speak any evil. Today, India is moving as we are moved by greed, the profit motive, techno-education, and competition.

Use the vision tool, but don't get caught in *the vision* trap. In other words, use vision to shape ideas that will energize your plan, but don't start believing in the ideals implicit in *the vision* itself.

WAGES   Wages for individual line workers should be kept as low as practical. Bid what you must in the labor marketplace for qualified workers, but not a dime more. Wages are a horrendous expense and a crushing burden on any corporation and therefore on its stockholders. Your only reward for wages paid is that part of them will come back to you, since wages translate into sales for the economy at large. Workers love to spend.

The best way to tell if your wages are in line is to measure them against productivity and against your industry's norms. As long as the spread between wages and productivity continues to widen, and your wages paid are slightly less than your industry mean, then you are on solid ground.

What about *your* wages? How should you set them and what is their relationship to wages paid to workers? Today, the average top level CEO makes between three and four hundred times what his company's average worker makes. That is up from thirty to forty times worker wages thirty years ago. I think you can do better. You should do better. Given the demands of the CEO's job in today's competitive world, you should definitely get an increase in your minimum wage. Forget about loans, deferred compensation, bonuses, potential profits from company stock and stock options, and other perks and benefits. Focus on your wages only and shoot for five to eight hundred times the wage paid to your average worker. You are one in a thousand, the top one percent of the top ten percent of the best and the brightest. Anything less than a thousand dollars paid to you for every dollar paid to the average worker is a bargain for your stockholders. Of course if most of your operations are in developing countries, you can up the ante.

In case you didn't know, *Rive Gauche,* the exclusive private men's club for world leaders to which I belong, offers a little prize every spring for the American CEO whose annual compensation represented the greatest percentage of total annual worker wages paid during the previous year, as determined by the club's board of directors. It is called "The Three Cheers Award," and it is a platinum cigar cutter that looks like a little megaphone. Had I not retired, I could easily have won the award in 2002 after my company simultaneously opened plants in Soweto, Bangladesh, Bolivia, the Marianas, and Shannon County, South Dakota.

WAR What ruler has not discussed business on the eve of war? And what businessman has not discussed war on the eve of recession? War can be many things, including a response to consumer demand, (aided, of course, by a little advertising), but, as far as business is concerned in an age equipped for unlimited destruction, and in a world economy built on mutual interdependence, a good war just isn't what it used to be. Is any war good for business? Of course it is, particularly if you are a part of the so-called Military-Industrial Complex. Provisioning a war machine is the most profitable and least scrutinized business on earth. Even rebuilding a nation in the aftermath of an invasion can provide extremely lucrative contracts if you and your corporation are high on the White House "A" list. I would be the last to miss such opportunities, particularly since wars occur outside North America.

However, I prefer to wage business free of the clutter, the bad public relations, the disruption to supply chains and markets, and the risk of wholesale destruction that a contemporary and widespread shooting war imposes. Precisely because its costs can exceed its benefits, war should be used as an engine of economic growth only as a next-to-last resort, government interference, like that imposed by Franklin Delano Roosevelt, being the last resort.

The fact is that in our modern era, business *is* war by safer means. As a group, CEOs represent a warrior class, only we do not spill blood. We spill dreams, money, careers, plans, and all the other resources that combine to make strategies, as companies compete against each other for the domination of markets. In this sense, then, let us celebrate war. It is the natural condition of *Homo sapiens* and those who rise to control empires ascend to their natural places of leadership over others because their abilities and their strategies have proved to be better than competing ones. When you walk into the board room of any major corporation you can have the confidence to know that those who come together in that room have been tested and proven and honed to a level of ability, even greatness, reserved for only a few. I would never presume to claim that we are war heroes. We claim only a rightful place, earned in the heat of commercial combat, comparable to that of history's conquerors, like Alexander the Great. To anyone who thinks I'm exaggerating, I say, defeat me in the marketplace or stand down.

WATER What fossil fuels are to the present economy, water will be to the future. Buy water. Don't wait. In a few years, hundreds of millions of people and millions of businesses will be clamoring for more water, and those who supply it will be gods.

WEALTH It goes without saying that I mean *real* wealth. After all, your wealth is the final judge of the toughness of your character. If you gain it and keep it, kudos. If you never obtain it or lose it, shame. Understand clearly the stakes: A few people whittle and play banjos and catch fish with worms. A vast number drink beer and bowl on Thursday nights. Somewhat fewer grill steaks, play Vivaldi, and drink the modest Merlots and blended Bordeaux they see featured in their upscale computing magazines and in their supermarkets. Very few drive Volvos and BMWs, dine on squid and pesto at fine Mediterranean restaurants, and drink Gattinara because they saw the name advertised with reverence in both *Sunset* and *Architectural Digest*. A tiny handful share a cocktail with their *Provençal* chef, vacation at "The Cabin" in Switzerland, drink cases of the golden Himmelreich Trockenbeerenauslese of the village Graach, and send their poodle to its stylist in the limo. And there are those occasional individuals who buy islands and cabinet ministers and visit them both on a yacht named after their wife's pet snow leopard. Relative wealth does not interest me. Absolute wealth does.

If you acquire wealth, it doesn't really matter how you acquired it because once you possess it, ninety-nine times out of a hundred, unless you are monumentally careless, no one will dare to touch you. No person, no court, no institution, no government, at least not for long. It's as though you had cast a magic spell on the entire world, from housewives to heads of state, a spell that makes you as close to immune as a man can be. On Wealth, my best advice is to obtain it; maintain it; hide it; increase it; buy whatever you want and whomever you must with it; flaunt it if you wish; pass it on without having to pay taxes if you can; and thoroughly wallow in its grandeur and in the immunity it provides.

There is no greater purpose than Wealth.

WHISTLEBLOWERS   Remember those kids in the fourth grade who couldn't wait to tell the headmaster what happened? They do become adults. Some of them become whistleblowers.

If you have one in your company, take him hunting. If you miss, make sure that no one in The Club will ever again have anything to do with him.

THE WIFE   With the possible exception of a Vacheron Constatin *Tour de l'Ile*, nothing looks better on a man's arm than a glamorous wife. If possible try to mix equal parts of Wellesley, Cover Girl, and Old Family. Give preference to women from New England, or from selected locations in the Deep South where finishing women for careers as prominent wives is taken as seriously as football. If you throw in some wit, humor, style, humility, charisma, unbendable loyalty, long legs, and a stupefying rack, you would have the perfect wife. Every associate or enemy you ever have will envy you. Nothing has changed since early adolescence. The guy who gets the hottest girl is still king of the playground.

However I strongly recommend careful scrutiny or outright dismissal for certain types. Women who come from an Old Family that has managed to hold on to its Old Money I tend to recommend enthusiastically, particularly since she will bring a solid financial base to the marriage. But scrutinize this type thoroughly because she could also be too independent, too spoiled, and impossible to impress. Avoid altogether strongly motivated career women. They always put themselves first. They belong in the boardroom, not in the bedroom. Fat women are fat for a reason, either a physical problem or a mental problem and you will not want to waste valuable time on someone else's problems. Outspoken feminists have issues. You don't need issues. Divorced women with children carry baggage and the prospect of inheriting two families, her relatives and her former husband and his relatives. One is sufficient. Baggage is meant for traveling. Plain or ugly women, whatever their other virtues, will always remain plain or ugly. Why drive an Edsel if you can own a Maserati? Women who have been sexually promiscuous will have just as hard a time saying "no" when they are married as when they were single. There are less complicated ways to experience humiliation and even to enjoy it. And there are cheaper ways to reward the pool guy. Finally, women raised on "the wrong side of the tracks" when thrown into affluence will spend the rest of their lives either in awe, and will therefore be boring, or in spite, and will therefore be annoying. The wrong wife can ruin a man's motivations and his career. The right wife can grease his wheels.

Now that I have stated the obvious, I need to add one more point often overlooked by busy men. Choose a wife who has real substance and depth. After all she must be able to entertain, always look her best, remember names, and hold amusing conversation with other women who belong to her clubs.

WINE It can take years, if not decades, to become an expert in fields such as opera, classical music, painting, gemstones, or even coins or stamps. Wine is the only field with deep snob appeal in which you can seem like an expert literally overnight. Read one good book on the world's wine, remember what you've read, and you'll have it. Plus, you can talk about wine in perfectly meaningless phrases and be meaningful. Like fine art critics, wine critics compare the properties of wines to other things that interest them, and those things are so subjective that no one else on earth has a clue what the critic intends, except that his impression is either good or bad.

That is all you need to know. Swirl, sniff, and taste then rhapsodize about the hint of teak or the suggestion of nutmeg or, if you feel truly imaginative, suggest an essence of power steering fluid blended subtly with orchids. Whatever you say will work so long as you act like the label is an old friend and you express clearly either disdain or guarded approval. Like a hand of poker or the hostile takeover of a company, wine just seems to invite a good snow job. Pithy comments, however meaningless, never disappoint.

WISDOM   Life's journey is long and varied and filled with snares. Those who survive have learned much along the way. It is incumbent upon each generation to pass on to the next the distillation of that experience in the form of wisdom. I remember my father offering me his deepest thoughts. Now it is my turn, in these very uncertain times, to offer you that same helping hand:

Keep twenty percent liquid regardless of higher returns in securities, properties, and ventures. It is too late to prepare for disaster when disaster strikes, and cash always talks.

WONDER   Never waste your time. If you are curious about something, hire people who know.

WORK   Work is what life is all about. To our credit, we American executives work more than other executives. That is why we are the best at work. Work long and prosper -- and do your part to win the work war.

WORK ETHIC   While climbing the corporate ladder to position yourself for promotion to CEO, count on working sixty to eighty hours or more every five-day work week plus all your weekends as needed. Work is the requisite endurance contest and the winner is often the one who spends the most time on the job. A reputation for tireless marathon working will elevate your reputation among your peers, will provide a role model for your subordinates, will help justify your compensation after you become a CEO, and will keep you from having to be too involved in the distracting trivia of your home and family life or other outside activities. After you solidify your position as a CEO, you can spend half your work time on vacation and call it work. Just remember that your laptop, satellite phone, and briefcase must travel wherever you travel if you want to maintain your proper image. Plus you will want to actually use them to keep an eye on things, make sure the mice don't play too savagely in your absence, and be ready to defuse the odd crisis.

A fanatical work ethic among CEOs goes without saying. Among workers, it is a constant battle to maintain even a minimal work ethic. The best work ethic in the world is now found in the poorer third world countries in which, for example, teenagers happy to have a job will gladly work ten to fourteen hours a day for two toilet breaks, a bowl of rice or a taco, and ten cents to a dollar an hour with no overtime pay or benefits. Our typical American worker wants a forty hour work week or less with two quarter hour breaks and a lunch hour daily, twenty dollars an hour with time and a half for overtime and double time for holidays or weekends, plus six or more paid holidays, plus five paid sick or personal days, plus two weeks or more vacation, plus comprehensive health, eye, and dental insurance, plus free psychological counseling, plus a 401-K or a company funded pension plan, plus a company paid parking place and on-site day-care, plus maternity leave, personal leave, family leave, and sick leave, plus free use of the computer, copy machine, and telephone, plus all the free coffee, tea, and spring water a person can drink. While our American workers have become spoiled, fat, lazy, disloyal, disobedient, and demanding, foreign workers from Third World and developing countries are enthusiastic to have a job, eager to please, and they make no demands. You tell me who will produce more for less?

Move your production and factoring facilities overseas, reap governmental incentives and lower taxes in the process, and watch your bottom line expand. With domestic workers, try to instill a proper work ethic. Crush unions before they get started. Reduce benefits incrementally at every opportunity, and hold the specter of massive layoffs and plant closings over their heads at all times. They will continue to damage your bottom line whatever you do so try to ignore their demands while reducing their wages and benefits. Follow the example of W*ALLMINE! Eventually you might be able to reduce workers' standard of expectations to that of Bangladesh. Meanwhile, however, be sure you do some domestic manufacturing or assembly, even if that means just sewing a collar button in L.A. onto a third world shirt. That way, you can push the "buy American" and "Made in America" campaigns. They are popular with consumers and the easiest way to score points for your patriotism.

WORKING CONDITIONS   In the modern world, there are two conditions required for work: A job that needs to be done, and a place to do it. Everything else is superfluous.

Today, the laws of supply and demand govern the employer-employee relationship just as they govern the product-consumer relationship. If an employee does not like the conditions of his or her workplace, then he or she is free to go work for someone else. If working conditions in a company are so atrocious as to be inhumane, then no one will work for that company and they will have to change their conditions to compete successfully for workers. Simple as that.

Still, there are a few OSHA-socialist-union types left who would have corporations adopt workers for life, pamper and protect them from every mishap, and provide them with food, clothing, shelter, medical care, dentistry, optometry, chiropractic service, holistic healers, psychological counselors, amusement on and off the job, transportation, day care, leave for child birthing and raising and for family illness, vacations, paid holidays, personal leave, pensions when they retire, and all the Twinkies they can eat. I think they would be happy to turn every workplace into a country club.

I think that Americans and good people everywhere prefer their independence and I have no desire to rob them of their independence by forcing a combination of country club/adult day-care service on them. Workers prefer to take care of themselves on their own terms, just as you and I do. So when these social engineers pay you a visit, either give them a boot to the seat of their pants, or fight them every inch of the way until they give up. Protect your workers from meddling do-gooders, and remember: The best working conditions in the world are in places so busy that no one has time to complain.

ZERO   The concept of zero, or nothingness, has always fascinated me. For decades I have listened with amusement to young MBAs discuss "Zero-Sum Games." What is a zero-sum game? Let's say that you and I play one hand of poker for all the stakes. What you lose, I win, and there is no change left on the table. That's a zero-sum game. Winnings minus losses equals zero. What could be simpler? When young Turks discuss zero-sum games, and applications of game theory to business and economics, however, they sound far more complicated, sophisticated, and abstruse. They remind me of stock traders who are technical analysts. They throw a lot of slick curves, sinkers, sliders, and knucklers, but their earned run averages are no better than those of pitchmen who stick to fast balls. Economics is one of those fields where jargon turns fools into experts.

Zero is a simple concept that people keep trying to make complicated. While we use the concept of zero to describe many phenomena, zero is merely an abstraction invented by the human mind and it exists only in the human mind. Even though we imagine zero, everything that appears to be nothing is, in reality, something that was transferred to or transformed into something else. No absolute zero exists. The universe itself cannot have exploded into existence from nothing, and when you die, you do not become a zero. You become disorganized and, after a small tithe to entropy, you become reorganized into other things. Similarly, when wealth is transferred from losers to winners, what has happened is a reorganization of capital, not a reduction to zero for the losers.

Yet the concept of zero always seems to take center stage. Why is that? I believe that there is a deep insecurity in the heart of every human being:

A fear of oblivion. A fear that nothingness dwells in the center of the universe; that all human efforts add up to zero; that there won't be enough to eat tomorrow; that death is always waiting just outside; that there is nothing after death; that nihilism is more powerful and more truthful than all human effort and all that results from human effort.

Without this fear, we would live a reactive existence like lower animals, which are incapable of imagining zero. Each day, we would hunt and gather and eat; dodge predators or not; arrange our dwellings; jockey for position in our clan; fuck, chatter, and sleep. We would have no economic motivation and no meaningful economic activity. We would react to stimuli forced upon us using our best instincts without reflection.

With this fear of oblivion, however, we are driven to insulate ourselves from zero. We accumulate food and clothing against days of shortage. We build arms to defend our territory and to make our hunt more efficient. We trade with other clans and tribes for useful goods we don't make. We plan invasions to take more productive land. In other words, our fear drives us to economic activity and that activity expands into politics, war, and society. In short, our fear of zero is the mother of greed; greed is the father of economics; and economics is the origin of all other human endeavors. So long as zero exists in human imagination people will fear it and they will be driven to want and to need and to acquire and to take. Fear forces a species, once willing merely to exist, to yearn and to strive and to adapt and survive.

Good business is not simply the facilitation of capital from one place to another. It is an implicit contract between those who are good at survival and those who are not so good to let winners organize capital for the benefit of the whole tribe. The chief benefit to losers, the vast majority, is the warding off of fear and the installation of security. The result of this contract is a non-zero-sum game with enough change dropped on the table by winners to feed the losers and keep them in the game. In this way, the losers become winners and the fear of oblivion is reduced to a tolerable level. Clearly, for the sake of the masses and for public order, you want to contain fear of zero; just as clearly, for your own benefit and to keep your needed place in society, you never want to reduce that fear of zero to zero.

This is the game we humans, and only we humans, play. The more wealth and power that leaders display, the more distant everyone else feels from zero. Thus great wealth, along with the power it brings, is the antidote to nihilism, whether one possesses great wealth one's self, or merely sees, by witnessing the rich, that it can be gained. This dynamic explains aristocracy and the awe it commands over ordinary people. Envy and resentment almost never overpower the need to emulate. Robespierre was an anomaly.

Fear of zero is the universal human imperative. Clearly, those of us who are best at insulating ourselves from the fear of oblivion should and do prevail. Like the leaders of the world's great religions, we stand for hope because we are the vision of salvation for all the rest.

I'm betting that you never understood until now just how much William Andrews Clark, Henry Ford, J. Paul Getty, and Howard Hughes had in common with Moses, Jesus, Mohammad, and Buddha.

ZERO POPULATION GROWTH
It is a widely held faith among environmentalists that all the resources of the natural and the human worlds combined cannot support a human population beyond a certain point. I agree. Resources are finite. However, I believe that technologies will arise to meet demand in such a way that the world will support populations much greater than the environmentalists believe.

Let's be realistic about this thing. People copulate to feel good and in doing so, they make babies. Nothing short of male infertility will ever stop that. Populations will continue to grow and to expand geometrically. I think that this can be a good thing. Technologies will develop to care for many of these people and growing populations will ensure strong economies and a vibrant, affordable workforce. Growth is the backbone of prosperity, and accelerating populations are the backbone of growth. The more people there are, the larger our markets. So I welcome population growth and I give a hearty Bronx cheer to the zero in "zero population growth," as it is presently defined. I also have some ideas about how we can redefine population and what we can do with the surplus.

Granted there will come a time, in the not too distant future, when populations exceed the world's ability to care for them and we will need to stop linear growth. What will happen then? Will there be massive starvation? Will populations continue to expand and will the species devolve and collapse as some so-called population experts predict? I think not. A curious fact of the business mind is that it always finds a way to turn a profit, whatever the circumstances. And I think I have a profitable solution to this future problem of overpopulation. What do you do with a surplus? The solution I have in mind is not entirely original. It has been suggested before by an important Anglo-Irish religious authority, though his presentation was merely satire and therefore frivolous. Mine means business.

Consider this: Recently, the United States achieved a new milestone in our history, the result of two decades of enlightened domestic policies aimed at enhancing opportunities for highly motivated, career-driven, business minded folks like us. This milestone is creating a new, valuable, *and* renewable resource that so far is unclaimed. Namely, the United States today boasts more children living in poverty than any other developed nation on earth. If this trend continues, even for only one generation, poor children in America could reach the number of those living in Brazil or Mexico. They already outnumber the world's population of beluga sturgeon.

What might you, the next generation of CEOs, do with such an abundance of poor children? What can you do to make sure that no child is left behind?

I think you should put them to maximum use. Now consider this: As an enterprising corporation, you could create clubs for children. Klub Kiddies, you might call them. Purchase hungry children from their parents. This arrangement would benefit millions of poor families by increasing their cash flow while reducing their overhead. And remember: Initially, you will be the only bidder so at first this will be a classic buyer's market. You'll get them cheap – and that means higher than average profit margins up front so you can build a capital base for expansion. But the best is yet to come. Think homeless and runaways. Feral children. They are a public nuisance and a drain on society. The solution? Harvest them. Round up these homeless waifs and runaway brats and do society and yourself a favor. After the initial domestic roundup and a quick spurt of growth, expand operations to a worldwide commodity base in third world and developing nations where birth rates are far greater than in developed nations and where the commodity is much more abundant. Think about the millions of foreign children currently forced to become sex slaves, indentured servants, or killers in rebel militias. You could rescue them from these tortures, provide them with a civilized life style, and bump your bottom line in the process. This is human commodity cheap and sometimes free for the taking. Round them up and mix them in with the domestic kids. This cost averaging will drop your unit price down to below wholesale levels. Talk about margins!

Now put all these kids into Kamps where they will be well fed and cared for and where they will not have to worry about school, militias, predators, gangs, or the law. Just let them play, exercise, run free, make shirts twelve hours a day, and even breed as they grow toward maturity. Of course, when they reach maturity, they will have lived longer and certainly better lives than they would have lived otherwise. And much better lives than most of them ever would have dared to dream, not unlike the poor of New Orleans after they received massive government assistance following Hurricane Katrina, a fact pointed out by a prominent former First Lady. So at that point, after the children have lived The Good Life, when they are taken to a peaceful slaughter, perhaps with Vivaldi's *Four Seasons* playing in the background, they will be able to look back on their lives with satisfaction. And the world will achieve a stable, sustainable population, and a vital new source of food.

Marketing the product will require all the finesse advertising geniuses are known for. I believe that they can meet the challenge. Once on the market, most likely blended with other sources of protein, such as soybeans, meal worms, and remainder parts of beef, chicken, pork, and fish, and sold under clever and enticing trademarks, these wholesome, protein-rich foods will feed millions of hungry adults and other children, and the leftover remains can be converted into animal feed and crop fertilizers. Harvest only at a level that maintains a sustainable world population. As soon as you launch a handful of Klub Kiddies, other multinational corporations will react to this idea the way miners reacted to the California gold rush. As ever, the trick will be to get there first. And don't forget the bonus. Klub Kiddies should be able to produce enough shirts at minimal cost to pay their own expenses and more, and their overhead will be slight since there will be no need for health insurance, retirement benefits, vacations, or wages. This will reduce your risk to near zero and shrink your cost-benefit ratio to levels unknown in other ventures.

One caveat. There will doubtless be moralists and religious extremists who advocate against eating children and young adults, and there won't be any practical way to silence them, though if they are invested in a retirement plan or mutual funds, and will therefore own stock in the venture, they are likely to grow quieter as they watch their portfolios, spurred on by Klub Kiddies, rise and rise. Nothing silences a malcontent like growing his net worth. If the market continues to offer resistance, however, zero in on the gourmet sectors. That is to say, if Americans aren't ready to eat their young, mix all the nationalities together and feed them to someone else. Someone with discriminating taste. There is always a market for high end products. For example, you could fatten the better specimens on beer and let them give each other massages several times daily to produce a particularly well-marbled, tender product comparable to Kobe beef. Test it on the Japanese and on gourmets everywhere. Chances are you would be able to charge a premium and expand margins. In addition, saturate supermarkets worldwide with production grade commodity, and introduce a line of reduced fat, low carbohydrate frankfurters made from remnants for the diet conscious. Dump your low end surplus along with any unsold inventories on foreign markets with growing but unmet demand for more nutrition, such as rural China. There is plenty of room for imagination in a market area so fraught with potential objections but so rich in potential profits. The trick will be to think outside the box. It will all come down to aggressive marketing.

I think the operative concept here is "potential." Human potential. How to get the most out of who and what we are through truly inspired, innovative marketing. If successful, the net result would be the achievement of zero population growth that keeps world population exactly at the threshold of the planet's carrying capacity, all based on a closed feedback loop strictly governed by supply and demand. Packaged correctly, as a kind of benign, Darwinian recycling system, this new industry could achieve all the appealing overtones of a worldwide humanitarian program, like those presented on late night television from sub-Saharan Africa, Central America, and South Asia. Push the recycling angle, but really magnify the human interest: Call it something simple and warm, like, "People Feeding People."

Consider this plan. It might just be the idea of the century. But then, that's why they pay us the big bucks, isn't it? My only regret is that I won't live long enough to see this idea become an integral part of a future American Dream. That future is in your hands.

End

David R. Montague is a native of Billings, Montana. He holds a Master's degree in English from Indiana University and a Bachelor's degree from the University of Montana. He lives with his wife, Mary Silkwood, in the Garnet Mountains of Western Montana.